MATHEMATICS FOR TECHNICAL STUDENTS

MATHEMATICS FOR TECHNICAL
STUDENTS. By A. GEARY, M.A., M.Sc.,
H V. LOWRY, M.A., and H. A. HAYDEN,
D.Sc., M.Sc.

Part I, with diagrams
Part II, with diagrams
Part III, with diagrams

MATHEMATICS FOR TECHNICAL STUDENTS

BY

A. GEARY, M.A., M.Sc.
Head of the Mathematics Department, Northampton Polytechnic

H. V. LOWRY, M.A.
Head of the Mathematics Department, Woolwich Polytechnic

AND

H. A. HAYDEN, D.Sc., M.Sc.
Head of the Mathematics Department, Battersea Polytechnic

PART III

WITH DIAGRAMS

LONGMANS, GREEN AND CO.
LONDON ◆ NEW YORK ◆ TORONTO

LONGMANS, GREEN AND CO LTD
6 & 7 CLIFFORD STREET LONDON W I

ALSO AT MELBOURNE AND CAPE TOWN

LONGMANS, GREEN AND CO INC
55 FIFTH AVENUE NEW YORK 3

LONGMANS, GREEN AND CO
215 VICTORIA STREET TORONTO I

ORIENT LONGMANS LTD
BOMBAY CALCUTTA MADRAS

NEW IMPRESSION 1952

Made and printed in Great Britain by
William Clowes and Sons, Limited, London and Beccles

PREFACE

THIS series is designed to provide the basic mathematical equipment for technical students. The range of work is that covered by national certificate courses in engineering, building and chemistry. Each of the three volumes includes one year's work, but the second and third contain sufficient revision to allow for variations in the syllabuses of different technical institutions. It is hoped that the series may also prove useful in junior technical schools, central schools and secondary schools with a technical side.

Short historical notes are included as they may help to develop in the student a further interest in the subject.

A. G.
H. V. L.
H. A. H.

v

AUTHORS' FOREWORD TO PART III

THIS volume is designed to cover the mathematics required during the third year of a three years' national certificate course in mechanical or electrical engineering. It therefore includes some topics which will mainly interest mechanical engineering students and others which will appeal more to students of electrical engineering.

It begins with a revision chapter on second year work, and students are advised to answer some of the questions in this chapter from time to time throughout the year's course. No previous knowledge of calculus is assumed, though there are simple exercises on differentiation and integration in Chapters XV and XVI of Part II.

The chapters are arranged in the order in which it is suggested they should be read, excepting that electrical students may read Chapter XII, pp. 280–295 after Chapter IV, and the remainder of Chapter XII after Chapter VIII.

Although alignment charts do not usually appear in national certificate examination papers, some knowledge of them is required by many technical students and we feel that this is a convenient stage at which to introduce them.

Three specimen examination papers are included at the end of this volume for use as revision tests on the whole of the course.

We wish to record our thanks to the Northern Counties Technical Examinations Council, the Union of Educational Institutions and the Union of Lancashire and Cheshire Institutes for permission to include their respective papers.

A. G.
H. V. L.
H. A. H.

CONTENTS

vii

CHAPTER I

MAINLY REVISION

This chapter consists mainly of revision examples. Before reading the subsequent chapters the student is advised to work through at least some of the questions from each exercise.

Simultaneous equations

The method of solution of two simultaneous equations was given in Part I, page 69. A similar method may be used to solve two or more simultaneous equations.

Example.—The currents x, y and z amp. respectively in three branches of a network are given by the following equations. Find the currents.

$$3x + 2y - 2z = 16 \quad . \quad . \quad . \quad . \quad . \quad (1)$$
$$4x + 3y + 3z = 2 \quad . \quad . \quad . \quad . \quad . \quad (2)$$
$$-2x + y - z = 1 \quad . \quad . \quad . \quad . \quad . \quad (3)$$

To eliminate z from (1) and (2), multiply (1) by 3 and (2) by 2, giving

$$9x + 6y - 6z = 48$$
$$8x + 6y + 6z = 4$$

By addition $\qquad 17x + 12y \quad = 52 \quad . \quad . \quad . \quad . \quad (4)$

To eliminate z from (2) and (3), multiply (3) by 3, giving

$$4x + 3y + 3z = 2$$
$$-6x + 3y - 3z = 3$$

1

By addition $-2x + 6y = 5$ . . . . . .   (5)

x and y may now be found from equations (4) and (5).

$$17x + 12y = 52$$

Multiply (5) by 2, $-4x + 12y = 10$

By subtraction $21x = 42$

$$\therefore x = 2$$

Substituting in (4), $34 + 12y = 52$

$$12y = 18$$

$$\therefore y = 1\tfrac{1}{2}$$

Substituting 2 for x and $1\tfrac{1}{2}$ for y in (1)

$$6 + 3 - 2z = 16$$

$$-2z = 7$$

$$\therefore z = -3\tfrac{1}{2}.$$

Hence the currents are 2, $1\tfrac{1}{2}$ and $-3\tfrac{1}{2}$ amp.

The negative sign in the last case shows that the current is in the opposite direction to that assumed in obtaining the equations.

Quadratic equations

Methods of solving quadratic equations were given in Part II, page 60.

Many equations, which in their original form are not quadratic equations, may be converted into quadratic equations by simple substitutions.

Example.—Solve the equation $2\sqrt{t} - 7 + \dfrac{4}{\sqrt{t}} = 0$.

Let $\sqrt{t} = x$.   The equation then becomes $2x - 7 + \dfrac{4}{x} = 0$.

Multiplying by x, $2x^2 - 7x + 4 = 0$.

Since the left-hand side has not simple factors, the equation may be solved by the formula in Part II, page 60.

$$x = \frac{7 \pm \sqrt{17}}{4} \simeq \frac{7 \pm 4 \cdot 123}{4} \simeq 2 \cdot 781 \text{ or } 0 \cdot 719$$

$$\therefore \quad \sqrt{t} \simeq 2 \cdot 781 \text{ or } 0 \cdot 719$$

$$t \simeq (2 \cdot 781)^2 \text{ or } (0 \cdot 719)^2$$

$$\simeq 7 \cdot 734 \text{ or } 0 \cdot 5170$$

$$t = 7 \cdot 73 \text{ or } 0 \cdot 517 \text{ to 3 sig. fig.}$$

When it has been necessary to square at some stage in solving an equation, the results obtained must be checked to see if they are all solutions of the original equation.

Example.—Solve the equation $\dfrac{3}{x-2} - \dfrac{2x}{x+1} = 1\frac{1}{2}$

$$\frac{3}{x-2} - \frac{2x}{x+1} = \frac{3}{2}$$

Simplifying the left-hand side, $\dfrac{3(x+1) - 2x(x-2)}{(x-2)(x+1)} = \dfrac{3}{2}$

$$\frac{-2x^2 + 7x + 3}{(x-2)(x+1)} = \frac{3}{2}$$

Multiplying both sides by $2(x-2)(x+1)$,

$$2(-2x^2 + 7x + 3) = 3(x^2 - x - 2)$$

$$-4x^2 + 14x + 6 = 3x^2 - 3x - 6$$

$$7x^2 - 17x - 12 = 0$$

$$(x-3)(7x+4) = 0$$

$$\therefore \quad x = 3 \text{ or } -\frac{4}{7}.$$

Properties of roots of quadratic equations

A quadratic equation whose roots are 2 and 3 is

$$(x-2)(x-3) = 0 \text{ or, if we expand, } x^2 - 5x + 6 = 0.$$

Similarly a quadratic equation whose roots are α and β is $(x - \alpha)(x - \beta) = 0$. If we expand by multiplying $x - \alpha$ by $x - \beta$ we obtain $x^2 - (\alpha + \beta)x + \alpha\beta = 0$.

It will be seen from these examples that, when the coefficient of x^2 in a quadratic equation is unity, the coefficient of x with its sign changed gives the sum of the roots, and the constant term gives the product of the roots.

Consider the quadratic equation $7x^2 - 4x - 3 = 0$. Dividing by 7, this may be written $x^2 - \frac{4}{7}x - \frac{3}{7} = 0$.

Hence the sum of the roots is $\frac{4}{7}$ and the product $-\frac{3}{7}$.

Exercise I

1. When a rectangular lamina is immersed vertically in a liquid with the lower edge at a depth p and the upper edge at a depth q below the surface, the depth of the centre of pressure is $\frac{2}{3} \cdot \frac{p^3 - q^3}{p^2 - q^2}$. Show that this is equal to $\frac{2}{3} \cdot \frac{p^2 + pq + q^2}{p + q}$.

2. Show that the volume of a thin spherical shell of thickness t and radius R is approximately $4\pi R^2 t$.

The volume of a thin spherical shell of radius 8·5 cm. is 1·36 cu. cm. Find the thickness in mm.

Express in factors the H.C.F. and L.C.M. of :

3. $15m^2 - 13mn + 2n^2$, $10m^2 + 33mn - 7n^2$, $25m^2 - 10mn + n^2$.

4. $10x^2 - 9x - 7$, $2xy^2 + y^2$, $6xy + 4x + 3y + 2$.

5. $6p^2 - 16p + 8$, $9p^2 - 4$, $27p^3 - 8$.

6. $b^3 + 125c^3$, $ab^2 - 5abc + 25ac^2$, $(b + 5c)^2 - 15bc$

7. The currents x, y and z amp. respectively in three branches of a network are given by $2x + y + z = 0$, $3x - y + 2z = -1$, $4x + 2y - 3z = -15$. Find the currents.

Solve the equations :

8. $2p + q + 3r = -4$, $-3p + 4q + 7r = 29$, $4p + 3q - 2r = -24$.

9. $y + z = a$, $z + x = b$, $x + y = c$ for x, y, z in terms of a, b, c.

10. $\dfrac{1}{x} + \dfrac{1}{y} + \dfrac{3}{z} = 2$, $\dfrac{2}{x} - \dfrac{3}{y} + \dfrac{2}{z} = 1$, $\dfrac{3}{x} - \dfrac{4}{y} + \dfrac{4}{z} = 3$ for $\dfrac{1}{x}, \dfrac{1}{y}, \dfrac{1}{z}$ and hence find x, y, z.

11. A current i enters a network consisting of three wires in parallel of known resistances R_1, R_2, R_3 respectively. If i_1, i_2, i_3 be the corresponding currents, $i_1 + i_2 + i_3 = i$ and $i_1 R_1 = i_2 R_2 = i_3 R_3$. Find i_3 in terms of i, R_1, R_2, R_3.

12. R, r_1, r_2 are known resistances and e_1, e_2 known E.M.F.'s in the equations $i = i_1 + i_2$, $Ri + r_1 i_1 = e_1$, $Ri + r_2 i_2 = e_2$. Find the current i. Evaluate it when $R = 2 \cdot 4$ ohms, $r_1 = 0 \cdot 25$ ohm, $r_2 = 0 \cdot 3$ ohm, $e_1 = 1 \cdot 9$ volts, $e_2 = 1 \cdot 8$ volts.

13. If f tons per sq. in. is the tenacity of copper at $t°$ F., $f = a - b(t - 60)^2$ where a and b are constants; $f = 15 \cdot 2$ at 50° F. and $f = 13 \cdot 4$ at 400° F. Find a and b and hence the tenacity at 250° F. Also find the temperature when $f = 14$.

14. It is required to draw a parabola whose equation is $y = a + bx + cx^2$ through the points $(-1, 0)$, $(1, 4)$, $(2, 3)$. Substitute these corresponding values of x and y in the given equation and hence find the values of a, b, c and draw the parabola on graph paper.

15. In a platinum resistance thermometer, the resistance R ohms and the temperature $t°$ are connected by the relation $R = a + bt + ct^2$ where a, b, c are constants. When $t = 0$, $R = 3 \cdot 110$; when $t = 10$, $R = 3 \cdot 216$, and when $t = 100$, $R = 4 \cdot 146$. Find a, b, c and express your results in the form $m10^n$ where $1 < m < 10$; give each value of m to three significant figures.

16. The relation between the grid potential V volts and the anode current I milliamp. of a thermionic tube for a certain constant anode potential is $I = a + bV + cV^2$. When $V = -6$, $I = 0 \cdot 56$; when $V = -4$, $I = 1 \cdot 55$; and when $V = -2$, $I = 3 \cdot 05$. Find I when $V = -5$.

Solve the equations :

17. $\dfrac{2}{x - 3} - \dfrac{1}{x - 2} = \dfrac{1}{x}$.

18. $\dfrac{2x}{x - 1} - \dfrac{3}{x + 4} = 2$.

19. $\dfrac{5x}{x + 2} - \dfrac{x}{4} = 2$.

20. $\dfrac{3}{x - 3} - \dfrac{2}{x - 4} + \dfrac{1}{2} = 0$.

21. $3y - 5\sqrt{y + 1} = 0$.

22. $x - \dfrac{5}{x} + \dfrac{4}{x^3} = 0$.

23. $z - 5\sqrt{z - 1} - 15 = 0$ by substituting $\sqrt{z - 1} = x$.

24. The following equation arose in connection with aeroplane structure : $1 \cdot 03m^2 + 12 \cdot 2m + 12 = 0$. Find the values of m, each correct to three significant figures.

25. A coil of 50 ohms is adjusted to take a current of 1 ampère by tapping from one end of a coil of 150 ohms across 125 volts to an appropriate point on the coil. If x ohms is the required resistance x is given by $\left(\dfrac{50}{x} + 1\right)(150 - x) = 75$. Find the necessary resistance.

26. If $V_1 = \dfrac{RrI_1}{R + r}$, $V_2 = (R - a)I_2$ and $\dfrac{V_1}{I_1} = \dfrac{V_2}{I_2}$, find a quadratic equation giving R in terms of a and r and hence find R.

27. A battery of 20 volts and internal resistance 5 ohms supplies current through a resistance x ohms. If, when the resistance is shorted by a 6-ohm coil the power in the circuit external to the battery is unchanged, x is given by

$$\frac{400x}{(5 + x)^2} = \frac{2400x}{\left(5 + \dfrac{6x}{6 + x}\right)^2 (6 + x)}.$$

Find the resistance.

28. In graduating the potentiometer, Fig. 1, to give a desired

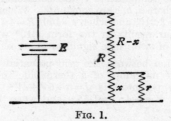

Fig. 1.

P.D. e across the resistance r, x is given by $\dfrac{E}{R - x} = \dfrac{e}{x} + \dfrac{e}{r}$. Express x in terms of the other symbols. If the current is to be reduced from I to i, $\dfrac{E}{e} = \dfrac{I}{i}$. Find the resistance x when $R = 36$ ohms, $r = 12 \cdot 4$ ohms and the current is to be reduced from $8 \cdot 75$ amp. to $4 \cdot 7$ amp.

29. An electromagnet has internal radius a in. and external radius b in. If, when a distance x in. is unwound, the current is increased in the ratio $n : 1$, x is given by the equation $\frac{1}{2}x(2b-x)=(n-1)\frac{1}{2}(b+a)(b-a)$. Solve this equation for x.

Find the distance unwound when the internal and external diameters are 8 in. and 15 in. respectively and the current is increased from 180 amp. to 200 amp.

30. Solve the equation $3x^2-7x-5=0$ and hence verify that the sum of the roots is $\frac{7}{3}$ and the product is $-\frac{5}{3}$.

31. If a compound pendulum be oscillated about a horizontal axis at a distance h from its centre of gravity, the period t is given by $t=2\pi\sqrt{\dfrac{h^2+k^2}{gh}}$ where k (the radius of gyration about a parallel axis through the centre of gravity) is constant. Write this equation as a quadratic in h and hence show that for each value of t there are two values of h. If h_1 and h_2 be these values, prove that $k=\sqrt{h_1 h_2}$.

If l be the length of the equivalent simple pendulum, $l=h+\dfrac{k^2}{h}$. Deduce that $h_1+h_2=l=\dfrac{gt^2}{4\pi^2}$.

32. In Fig. 2, A is the point $(0, 1)$ and B the point (p, q). The

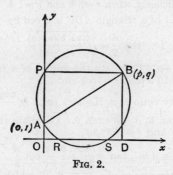

Fig. 2.

circle on AB as diameter intersects Ox in R and S. Prove that $OR+OS=p$ and $OR . OS=q$ and hence that OR and OS are the roots of the equation $x^2-px+q=0$. [Hint. If the circle intersects Oy in P and BD is perpendicular to Ox, prove that $OPBD$ is a rectangle.]

Solve the equation $2x^2-9x+4=0$ by the above method.

33. Solve the equation $2x^2 + 3x - 8 = 0$ (i) graphically as in Question **32**, (ii) by formula, (iii) by drawing the graph of $y = 2x^2 + 3x - 8$, (iv) by drawing the graphs of $y = x^2$ and $2y + 3x - 8 = 0$.

Exercise II

1. The following formulæ have been used to calculate the horse-power of an engine (i) $0.195d(d-1)(r+2)n$, (ii) $0.25(d-\frac{1}{2})^2 ns^{\frac{1}{2}}$, where d in. is the cylinder diameter, r is the ratio of stroke to diameter, n is the number of cylinders and s in. is the stroke. Use each formula to calculate the horse-power of a 4-cylinder engine with cylinders 9 cm. in diameter and 13·5 cm. stroke.

2. The stress f lb. per sq. in. in a plate is given by

$$f = \frac{P}{\pi t^2}\left(\frac{4}{3}\log_e \frac{d}{d_1} + 1\right).$$

Calculate the stress when $P = 1500$, $t = 0.55$, $d_1 = 1.3$, $d = 6.7$.

3. The efficiency of a compressor is given by

$$\frac{\log_e r}{\frac{2n}{n-1}\left\{r^{\frac{n-1}{2n}} - 1\right\}}.$$

Calculate the efficiency when $r = 6.5$ and $n = 1.4$.

4. The angle A of a triangle ABC is given by

$$\tan \frac{A}{2} = \sqrt{\frac{(s-b)(s-c)}{s(s-a)}}$$

where $2s = a + b + c$. Calculate the angles of a triangle in which $a = 27.2$ cm., $b = 16.9$ cm., $c = 15.3$ cm.

5. The velocity ratio in a Hooke's joint is $\dfrac{\cos \phi \sec^2 \theta_1}{\sec^2 \theta}$ where θ_1 is given by $\tan \theta_1 \cos \phi = \tan \theta$. Calculate the velocity ratio when $\phi = 15° 20'$ and $\theta = 108° 30'$.

6. In a triangle ABC, $\tan \dfrac{B-C}{2} = \dfrac{b-c}{b+c}\cot \dfrac{A}{2}$. Calculate $\dfrac{B-C}{2}$ and hence find the angles of a triangle in which $b = 17.8$, $c = 15.4$ and $A = 73° 20'$.

7. When the ratio of connecting rod to crank in an engine is $4:1$ and the crank makes an angle θ with the centre line, the velocity of the end of the connecting rod is $\sin \theta\left(1 - \dfrac{\cos \theta}{\sqrt{15 + \cos^2 \theta}}\right)\omega$ ft. per sec. Find the velocity when $\omega = 3$ and $\theta = 57\frac{1}{2}°$.

8. By taking logarithms, solve the equation $3^x \cdot 5^{3x} = 1 \cdot 936$.

9. Solve the equations $2^{3x} \cdot 4^y = 2 \cdot 83$, $4^x \cdot 5^{2y} = 3 \cdot 55$.

10. Find the values of p and v common to the isothermal $pv = 540$ and the adiabatic $pv^{1 \cdot 4} = 1600$.

11. A machine depreciates each year by 8% of its value at the beginning of the year. After how many years will its value be first less than half of its original value ?

12. The deflection at the centre of a girder l feet long of given material, under a uniformly distributed load W tons varies as $\frac{Wl^3}{I}$. If the load is increased by 40% and I by 20%, calculate the percentage decrease in the length of the beam in order that the deflection at the centre may be unaltered.

13. In the case of solid screwed stays the working pressure W lb. per sq. in. varies as the square of $d - c$ where d in. is the diameter of stay over threads and c is a constant depending on the material and coarseness of the threads. Find d if $W = 9000$ when $c = 0 \cdot 34$ and $W = 11,000$ when $c = 0 \cdot 267$.

14. The square of the time of pneumatic transmission through a tube under constant pressure varies as the cube of the length when the diameter is constant and inversely as the diameter when the length is constant. If the time is $0 \cdot 06$ sec. for a tube of length $32 \cdot 5$ ft. and diameter $0 \cdot 3$ ft., find the time for a tube of length 38 ft. and diameter $0 \cdot 35$ ft.

15. A law used for determining fusing current is based on the assumption that the fusing current I amp. varies as d^n where d in. is the diameter of the wire. For a copper wire of $0 \cdot 0108$ in. diameter the fusing current is $11 \cdot 5$ amp. and for diameter $0 \cdot 028$ in. the fusing current is 48 amp. Find n and the fusing current for a diameter of $0 \cdot 036$ in.

16. The horse-power absorbed in drilling cast-iron varies partly as the square root of the diameter of the drill and partly inversely as the square root of the diameter. For a diameter of $\frac{1}{4}$ in. the horse-power is $1 \cdot 58$ and for a diameter of $\frac{3}{4}$ in. the horse-power is $1 \cdot 27$. Find the horse-power for 2 in. diameter.

17. Ground rents for plots of land on a site vary partly as the frontage and partly as the frontage and depth jointly. The ground rent for a plot with 30 ft. frontage and 100 ft. depth is £38, and for a plot with 36 ft. frontage and 140 ft. depth is £60. What is the ground rent for a plot of frontage 24 ft. and depth 90 ft. ?

1*

Graphs

The graphs of algebraic functions previously considered have been continuous curves, but there are many cases in which the curve is not continuous.

Example.—Draw the graph of $\dfrac{x^2 + 5}{x - 2}$ and hence find the maximum and minimum values of the function.

The graph is shown in Fig. 3.

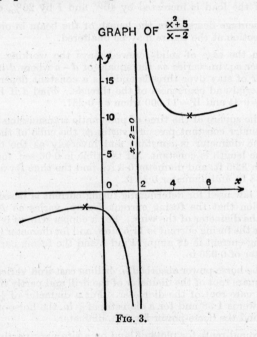

GRAPH OF $\dfrac{x^2 + 5}{x - 2}$

Fig. 3.

In considering the curve $y = \dfrac{x^2 + 5}{x - 2}$ it is advisable to find where it intersects the axes.

To find where it intersects the x-axis we put $y = 0$ which gives $x^2 + 5 = 0$. From this equation there are no real values of x and hence the curve does not intersect the x-axis.

To find where it intersects the y-axis we put $x = 0$. This gives $y = -2.5$. The curve therefore intersects the y-axis at the point $(0, -2.5)$.

It is important to note that as $x \rightarrow 2$, $y \rightarrow \pm \infty$. From the graph it can be seen that when x is a little less than 2, y has a large negative value and that when x is a little greater than 2, y has a large positive value and hence that as $x \rightarrow 2$, the curve approaches the line $x - 2 = 0$ on either side.

The line $x - 2 = 0$ in this case is called an *asymptote*.

It is a great help in drawing the graph to know how it approaches the line $x - 2 = 0$, and this we may find as follows.

In the equation, substitute $2 - h$ for x where h is small and positive. Then $y = \dfrac{(2-h)^2 + 5}{2 - h - 2} \simeq \dfrac{9}{-h}$, a large negative number which $\rightarrow -\infty$ as $h \rightarrow 0$. Hence if x is a little less than 2, y is a large negative number, and as x approaches nearer and nearer to 2, y remains negative but increases numerically.

Substituting $2 + h$ for x, $y = \dfrac{(2+h)^2 + 5}{2 + h - 2} \simeq \dfrac{9}{h}$, a large positive number which increases as h decreases, i.e. as x approaches nearer to 2.

In drawing these graphs it is also useful to know the values which y approaches as $x \rightarrow \infty$ and $-\infty$.

In this case, if x is large $y \simeq \dfrac{x^2}{x} = x$. Hence as $x \rightarrow \infty$, $y \rightarrow \infty$ and as $x \rightarrow -\infty$, $y \rightarrow -\infty$.

A table of values of x with the corresponding values of y will now make it possible to draw the graph.

From the graph we see that the function has a maximum value -2 (when $x = -1$) and a minimum value 10 (when $x = 5$).

In this case the maximum value is less than the minimum value, illustrating that a maximum value of a function is not necessarily a greatest value but a value which is greater than the values near to it on either side.

Dividing $x^2 + 5$ by $x - 2$, we see that $\dfrac{x^2 + 5}{x - 2} = x + 2 + \dfrac{9}{x - 2}$. The discussion of the function in this form would have been slightly easier.

Example.—Draw the graphs of tan $2x$ and $1 - x$ for values of x between $-\dfrac{\pi}{2}$ and $\dfrac{\pi}{2}$, and hence find approximate values of x between $-\dfrac{\pi}{2}$ and $\dfrac{\pi}{2}$ satisfying the equation tan $2x = 1 - x$.

The graphs are shown in Fig. 4.

GRAPHS OF tan 2x and 1−x

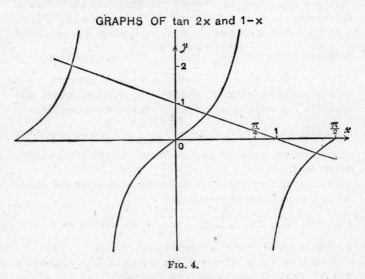

Fig. 4.

The limits for x are given as $-\dfrac{\pi}{2}$ and $\dfrac{\pi}{2}$, indicating that angles are expressed in radians.

The line $y = 1 - x$ is drawn in the usual way, but when the point (1, 0) is taken on the x-axis, it must be remembered that the corresponding ordinate of the graph of tan $2x$ will be tan 2^c (and not tan 2°). A scale will therefore be chosen on the x-axis so that fractions of π can be easily marked.

The solution of the equation will be the values of x where the graphs intersect. It will probably be advisable in the first place to read them off as fractions of π; they will then be converted into decimals, but the answers must not be given to a greater degree of accuracy than it is possible to read from the scale of the graph.

Solutions are $-1 \cdot 0$, $0 \cdot 3$ and $1 \cdot 4$ to one decimal place.

Exercise III

1. Draw the graph of $x + \dfrac{4}{x-1}$ and find the maximum and minimum values of the function.

2. Draw the curve $y = 1 + \dfrac{3}{x-2}$ and hence solve the equations $(x-2)(y-1) = 3$, $3x - 4y - 4 = 0$.

3. Draw the graph of $\dfrac{x(x-5)}{(x-1)(x-4)}$ and hence find the minimum value of the function.

4. The inner surface area of an open tank with square base is 36 sq. ft. If the side of the base is x ft. show that the volume is $9x - \dfrac{x^3}{4}$ cu. ft. Draw a graph of this function and hence find the dimensions of the tank for maximum volume. What is the side of the base when the volume is 18 cu. ft. ?

5. Draw a graph showing the values of 5^x for values of x from 0 to 1. From your graph find the value of $\log_5 2$ and deduce the value of $\log_\frac{1}{5} 2$.

6. Draw the graphs of $\dfrac{10-x}{1+x}$ and 2^x for values of x from -3 to 3. Show that the value of x where the curves intersect is a root of the equation $x = \log_2(10-x) - \log_2(1+x)$ and hence solve this equation.

7. At time t sec. a current is $50\left(1 - e^{-\frac{Rt}{L}}\right)$ amp. Draw a graph showing the change of the current with time for values of

t from 0 to 0·05 when $\frac{R}{L} = 25$. After what time will the current be 20 amp. ?

8. When a sphere of diameter 3 in. and of specific gravity 0·75 floats in water. its centre is at a depth x in. below the surface where x is a root of $8x^3 - 54x + 27 = 0$. Find x by drawing the curve $y = x^3$ and a further suitable graph.

9. When a uniform beam of length l ft. is fixed horizontally at one end and freely supported at the same level at the other end, the downward deflection at a distance x ft. from the free end is proportional to $2r^4 - 3r^3 + r$ where $r = x/l$. Draw the shape of the beam and hence find the distance from the free end at which the deflection is a maximum.

The deflection is a maximum at x ft. from the free end where r is a root of $8r^3 - 9r^2 + 1 = 0$. Show that 1 is a root of this equation and hence solve the equation and verify your previous work.

10. Find the values of x between 0 and 2π satisfying the equation $\tan x = 2 - x$.

11. Draw a graph of $\cos x$ for values of x from 0 to 2π. By drawing also the graph of $0·1x + 0·25$, find the range of values of x within the limits 0 and 2π for which $0·1x + 0·25 > \cos x$.

12. One arc of a corrugated sheet is 2·25 in. long and the distance between the ends of the arc is 1·75 in. If the arc subtends an angle 2θ radians at the centre of the circle of which it is part, show that $\sin \theta = \frac{7}{9}\theta$. Draw a graph of $\sin \theta$ and find the angle at the centre in degrees.

13. Draw the graph of $2 \cos 2x + \sin x$ for values of x from 0 to 360°. Hence solve the equation $4 \cos 2x + 2 \sin x = 3$.

14. The displacement s in. of a slide-piece in a mechanism at time t sec. is given by $s = 6 \sin (3t + 0·8)$. Show graphically the displacement for values of t from 0 to $\frac{2\pi}{3}$. For what values of t in this range is the displacement (i) 3·5 in., (ii) $-2·5$ in. ? What is the maximum displacement ?

15. The area of a segment of a circle of radius r subtending an angle θ at the centre is $\frac{1}{2}r^2(\theta - \sin \theta)$. Draw a graph of $\theta - \sin \theta$ for values of θ from 0 to 2π and hence find θ when the area of the segment is a quarter that of the circle. What is the distance from the centre of a chord of a circle of radius 2 in. if the area of the minor segment is a quarter that of the circle ?

16. In Fig. 5, C is the centre of the circle PAQ of radius 1 in. A is the centre of the arc PBQ. If the area enclosed by the arcs PAQ and PBQ is half that of the circle centre C, θ is given by $\sin \theta - \theta \cos \theta = \dfrac{\pi}{2}$. Draw the graph of $\sin \theta - \theta \cos \theta$ for values of θ between $\dfrac{\pi}{0}$ and π and hence find θ.

17. When a square lamina $ABCD$ is immersed vertically in liquid with A in the surface and AB inclined at an angle θ to the surface, the centre of pressure is distant $\dfrac{4+3 \tan \theta}{1+\tan \theta} \cdot \dfrac{a}{6}$ from AB and $\dfrac{3+4 \tan \theta}{1+\tan \theta} \cdot \dfrac{a}{6}$ from AD where a is the side of the square. On a square $ABCD$ show the curve traced by the centre of pressure as θ varies from 0 to 90°.

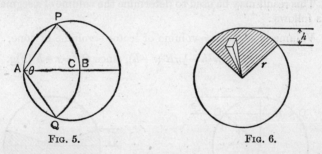

FIG. 5.   FIG. 6.

Sector of a sphere

A sector of a sphere (shaded part in Fig. 6) is the solid subtended at the centre of a sphere by the curved surface of a segment.

Suppose the sector to be divided into a large number of pyramids with small bases, one of which is shown in Fig. 6.

If we make the bases of the pyramids very small, the sum of the areas of the bases is approximately equal to the area of the curved surface of the segment. Making the bases smaller and smaller we see that ultimately—

sum of areas of bases = area of curved surface of segment
$$= 2\pi rh \text{ (Page art II, p 188).}$$

As the base of each pyramid becomes smaller and smaller, its height becomes more and more nearly equal to r and the volume of the sector becomes more and more nearly the sum of the volumes of the pyramids. Thus the volume of the sector

= sum of volumes of pyramids,

= $\frac{1}{3}$ (sum of bases) × radius, since volume of pyramid
$$= \tfrac{1}{3} \text{ base} \times \text{height,}$$

= $\frac{1}{3}$ (area of curved surface of segment) × radius.

= $\frac{1}{3} \times 2\pi r h \times r$.

$\therefore$ volume of sector = $\frac{2}{3}\pi r^2 h$.

This result may be used to determine the volume of a segment as follows :

Volume of segment = volume of sector − volume of cone,
$$= \tfrac{2}{3}\pi r^2 h - \tfrac{1}{3}\pi R^2(r-h), \text{ since } OP = r - h \text{ (Fig. 7).}$$

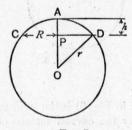

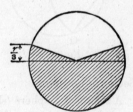

Fig. 7.   Fig. 8.

From the right-angled triangle OPD,
$$PD^2 = OD^2 - OP^2,$$
i.e. $R^2 = r^2 - (r-h)^2 = 2rh - h^2$ . . . . (i)

$\therefore$ volume of segment = $\frac{2}{3}\pi r^2 h - \frac{1}{3}\pi(2rh - h^2)(r-h)$
$$= \tfrac{1}{3}\pi(3rh^2 - h^3)$$
$$= \tfrac{1}{3}\pi h^2(3r - h).$$

The formula $\frac{1}{6}\pi h(3R^2 + h^2)$ was given for the volume of a segment in Part II, page 188. By substituting the value of R^2 obtained in (i) above, the student should show that the two formulæ are equivalent.

Example.—From a segment of height $\frac{4r}{3}$ of a sphere of radius r a conical portion is removed. The vertex of the cone is at the centre of the sphere and its base coincides with the base of the segment. Show that the volume remaining is two-thirds that of the sphere.

Volume remaining = volume of sphere – volume of sector (Fig. 8).

Volume of sector $= \frac{2}{3}\pi r^2 \cdot \frac{2}{3}r = \frac{4}{9}\pi r^3$,

$\qquad\qquad\qquad = \frac{1}{3} \cdot \frac{4}{3}\pi r^3 = \frac{1}{3}$ (volume of sphere).

∴ volume remaining $= \frac{2}{3}$ (volume of sphere).

Definition

Solid Angle.—When a surface diverges from a vertex as in Fig. 9 the solid angle enclosed is defined as the number of

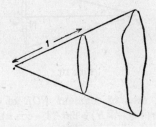

FIG. 9.

units of area cut off on a sphere of unit radius with the vertex as centre

From the properties of similar figures we see that the solid angle is the area cut off on any sphere with the vertex as centre divided by the square of the radius.

Thus the solid angle of a sector of a sphere which cuts off one-sixth of the area of the sphere $= \dfrac{1}{6} \cdot \dfrac{4\pi r^2}{r^2} = \dfrac{2\pi}{3}$.

The solid angle is used to solve many problems in illuminating engineering in which the unit solid angle is called a "steradian."

The candle-power of a source in a given direction is defined as the luminous flux in "lumens" emitted per unit solid angle in that direction. Thus, if F lumens is the flux radiated by a point source throughout a solid angle ω, the average candle-power throughout ω is $\dfrac{F}{\omega}$.

Since the total solid angle about a point is 4π, the "mean spherical candle-power" of a source F lumens is $\dfrac{F}{4\pi}$ candles.

Solid angle of a cone

Referring to Fig. 10, if V be the vertex of the cone of semi-

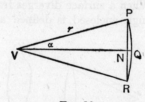

FIG. 10.

vertical angle α, area of segment PQR of sphere of radius r is $2\pi r \cdot NQ = 2\pi r (VQ - VN) = 2\pi r^2 (1 - \cos \alpha)$.

$$\therefore \text{ solid angle} = \frac{2\pi r^2 (1 - \cos \alpha)}{r^2} = 2\pi (1 - \cos \alpha).$$

Example.—A projector having an efficiency of 40 per cent. and utilizing a lamp which emits 20,000 lumens concentrates the beam into a cone of semi-vertical angle 5°. What is the mean candle-power of the beam ?

Effective flux $= \dfrac{40}{100} \times 20{,}000 = 8000$ lumens.

Solid angle of cone $= 2\pi(1 - \cos 5°)$.

$\therefore$ mean candle-power

$= \dfrac{8000}{2\pi(1 - \cos 5°)} = \dfrac{4000}{\pi \times 0\cdot0038}$

$\simeq 335{,}000$ candles.

No.	Log.
4000	3·6021
3·142	0·4972
0·0038	$\bar{3}$·5798
	$\bar{2}$·0770
$3\cdot351 \times 10^5$	5·5251

Exercise IV

1. In Fig. 11, TP and TQ are tangents to the circle, centre C. Use the intersecting chords theorem to find the radius of the circle. Prove that the triangles DCQ and QCT are similar and hence find the height of the minor segment cut off by PQ.

2. A scale drawing of a template has the dimensions shown in Fig. 12. AB and CD are equal quadrants of circles and BED is

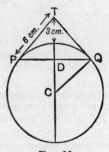

FIG. 11.

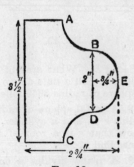

FIG. 12.

a semi-ellipse. Find the area of the drawing. If it be drawn to a quarter scale, what is the true area ?

3. A tube in the flue of a boiler is in the shape of a frustum of a cone. The diameters of the ends are 6 in. and 11 in. respectively and the distance between them is 2 ft. 6 in. Calculate the area of the heating surface.

4. The dome shown in Fig. 13 is bounded by the caps of two concentric spheres. Calculate the number of square feet of sheet lead necessary to cover the outer curved surface.

5. A cylindrical drum containing 2 gallons of oil stands with its base on an inclined surface. If the diameter of the base is 10 in. find the area of the oiled surface, assuming 1 gal. = 277 cu. in.

6. The base of a spire 20 ft. high is a regular hexagon of side 3 ft. Find the area of the sheet lead covering the sloping faces. To what vertical height would half this area of sheet lead cover the faces ?

7. In Fig. 14 OA and OB are tangents to the circle, centre C. Show that if OP is small compared with the radius of the sphere

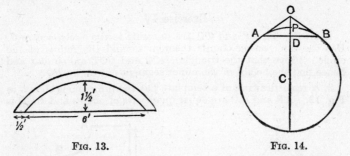

FIG. 13.   FIG. 14.

$OP \simeq PD$. What area of the earth's surface is visible from a height of half a mile above the earth. [Assume the earth to be a sphere of radius 3960 miles.]

8. A metal sphere of radius 3 ft. is cast into a hemisphere of radius r ft. and a cylinder of base radius r ft. and height 5 ft. Show that r is a root of the equation $2r^3 + 15r^2 - 108 = 0$ and hence find r.

9. A plane divides a sphere into two parts whose curved surface areas are in the ratio 4 : 1. Find the ratio of the volumes of the two segments into which the sphere is divided.

10. From a sphere of radius 2 in. a segment is cut of height h in. If the volume of the segment is one-quarter that of the sphere, show that $h^3 - 6h^2 + 8 = 0$. Hence find the height of the segment.

11. A zone of a sphere is formed by a plane through the centre of a sphere of radius 2 ft. and a parallel plane at a distance of 1 ft. from the centre. From the zone a cone is removed with its vertex at the centre and its base coincident with the smaller plane end of the zone. Calculate the volume of the remaining part of the zone.

12. Fig. 15 shows the top of a hopper. The bottom is a similar trapezium with sides one-third those of the top. If it is 3 ft. deep, find the volume it contains.

13. A cylindrical hole is drilled through a sphere, the axis of the cylinder passing through the centre of the sphere. If the hole is of length $2h$, show that the volume of the remaining solid is $\frac{4}{3}\pi h^3$.

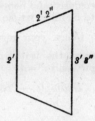

14. Two concentric circles, centre C and of radii a and b respectively $(a > b)$ are drawn on a plane. VC is perpendicular to the plane and $VC = h$. What is the solid angle between the two cones, vertex V with the circles as bases ?

Fig. 15.

15. Draw a graph showing the variation of solid angle included between two co-axial cones with the same vertex and of semi-vertical angles θ and $\theta + 5°$, as θ varies from 0° to 175°.

16. A reflector is so designed that all the luminous flux above the horizontal, where the average candle-power is 100 candles, is concentrated within a cone with axis vertical and semi-vertical angle 30°. What is the average candle-power within this cone if 20% of the light is lost at reflection ?

17. An incandescent lamp having a small filament is placed at a distance of 10 in. from a converging lens and an image of the filament is formed at a distance 50 in. beyond the lens. The candle-power of the lamp in the direction of the lens is 100 candles. Find the candle-power of the image, assuming 20% loss of light due to reflection and absorption at the lens, if the diameter of the lens is 1 in.

18. A lamp is placed 5 ft. above the centre of a circular table of radius 2 ft. 6 in. If the average candle-power of the lamp in the direction of the table is 200, what is the average value of the illumination on the table in ft. candles ? [1 ft. candle = 1 lumen per sq. ft.]

19. The table gives the pressures in lb. wt. per sq. in. at ten equal intervals as recorded on an indicator diagram :

	38	28	22	15	10	6	4	2	0	
72										18
	220	144	104	88	80	73	65	56	44	

Draw the indicator diagram. Use Simpson's rule to find the area of the closed figure and hence find the mean pressure.

20. Draw the isothermals $pv = 180$, $pv = 540$ and the adiabatics $pv^{1.4} = 1600$, $pv^{1.4} = 2000$. Use Simpson's rule to find the area enclosed and hence the work done in the cycle, assuming pressure to be in lb. wt./sq. in. and volume in cu. in.

Check your result by using the formula $\dfrac{b-a}{n-1} \log_e \dfrac{d}{c}$ for the area, the isothermals being $pv = a$, $pv = b$ and the adiabatics $pv^n = c$, $pv^n = d$.

Example.—Prove that in a triangle ABC,

$$\cot B = \frac{c}{b} \operatorname{cosec} A - \cot A.$$

Calculate the remaining angles of a triangle in which $b = 17.4$ cm., $c = 14.5$ cm., $A = 72° 34'$.

Let CP be the perpendicular from C to AB in the triangle ABC (Fig. 16).

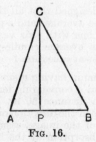

FIG. 16.

$$CP = b \sin A.$$
$$AP = b \cos A \; ; \; \therefore \; BP = c - b \cos A.$$
$$\cot B = \frac{BP}{CP} = \frac{c - b \cos A}{b \sin A} = \frac{c}{b} \operatorname{cosec} A - \cot A.$$

When $b = 17 \cdot 4$ cm., $c = 14 \cdot 5$ cm. and $A = 72° \, 34'$,

$$\cot B = \frac{14 \cdot 5}{17 \cdot 4 \sin 72° \, 34'} - \cot 72° \, 34'$$

$$= \frac{14 \cdot 5}{17 \cdot 4 \sin 72° \, 34'} - \tan (90° - 72° \, 34')$$

$= 0 \cdot 8736 - \tan 17° \, 26'$

$= 0 \cdot 8736 - 0 \cdot 3140$

$= 0 \cdot 5596$

$\therefore \tan B = 1 \cdot 787$

$\therefore B = 60° \, 46'$

$\therefore C = 46° \, 40'$ since $A + B + C = 180°$.

	No.	Log.
	$14 \cdot 5$	$1 \cdot 1614$
Num.		$1 \cdot 1614$
	$17 \cdot 4$	$1 \cdot 2405$
$\sin 72° \, 34'$		$\bar{1} \cdot 9796$
Den.	$1 \cdot 2201$	$1 \cdot 2201$
	$0 \cdot 8736$	$\bar{1} \cdot 9413$

NOTE. This example has been worked on the assumption that cosec and cot tables are not available.

Example.—Solve the triangle ABC in which $a = 14 \cdot 6$ in., $b = 12 \cdot 8$ in. and $c = 9 \cdot 5$ in.

Let ABC, Fig. 17, be the triangle and AP the perpendicular

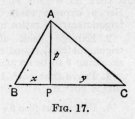

Fig. 17.

from A to BC; let $AP = p$ in., $BP = x$ in. and $CP = y$ in.

$$p^2 = 9 \cdot 5^2 - x^2 = 12 \cdot 8^2 - y^2 \text{ (Pythagoras)}.$$

$$\therefore y^2 - x^2 = 12 \cdot 8^2 - 9 \cdot 5^2 = 163 \cdot 8 - 90 \cdot 25$$

$$y^2 - x^2 = 73 \cdot 55 \quad \ldots \ldots \quad (1)$$

$$y + x = 14 \cdot 6 \quad \ldots \ldots \quad (2)$$

	No.	*Log.*
Dividing (1) by (2) $y - x = \dfrac{73 \cdot 55}{14 \cdot 6}$	73·55	1·8666
	14·6	1·1644
$= 5 \cdot 037$		
$\therefore y = \dfrac{19 \cdot 637}{2} = 9 \cdot 818\,(5)$	5·037	0·7022
$x = \dfrac{9 \cdot 563}{2} = 4 \cdot 781\,(5)$		
$\cos B = \dfrac{4 \cdot 781}{9 \cdot 5}$	4·781	0·6795
	9·5	0·9777
$B = 59° \, 47'$		
		$\overline{1} \cdot 7018$
$\cos C = \dfrac{9 \cdot 818}{12 \cdot 8}$		
	9·818	0·9921
$C = 39° \, 54'$	12·8	1·1072
$\therefore A = 80° \, 19'$		
		$\overline{1} \cdot 8849$

Angles are 80° 19′, 59° 47′, 39° 54′.

Exercise V

1. In Fig. 18 ABC is a right-angled triangle with hypotenuse unity. If $A = \theta$, show that $AB = \cos \theta$ and $BC = \sqrt{1 - \cos^2 \theta}$. Hence express each of the other five trigonometrical ratios in terms of $\cos \theta$.

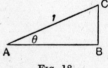

FIG. 18.

2. Express each of the other five trigonometrical ratios in terms of $\tan \theta$, assuming θ to be an acute angle.

3. Prove that $\cot^2 A - \cos^2 A \equiv \cot^2 A \cos^2 A$.

4. Prove that $(\sec \theta + \tan \theta)^2 \equiv \dfrac{1 + \sin \theta}{1 - \sin \theta}$.

5. If $\sec x + \tan x = k$, show that $\sec x - \tan x = \dfrac{1}{k}$. Hence solve the equation $\sec x + \tan x = 2 \cdot 5$.

6. If $a \sin \theta + b \cos \theta = p$ and $a \cos \theta - b \sin \theta = q$, prove that $a^2 + b^2 = p^2 + q^2$.

7. If $\sin \theta = \cos \phi + \sin \phi$ and $2 \cos \theta = \cos \phi - \sin \phi$, prove that $3 \cos^2 \theta = 1$ and $3 \sin 2\phi + 1 = 0$.

8. The velocity ratio in a Hooke's joint is $\dfrac{\cos \phi \sec^2 \theta_1}{\sec^2 \theta}$ where θ_1 is given by $\tan \theta_1 \cos \phi = \tan \theta$. Prove that the velocity ratio is $\dfrac{1 - \sin^2 \phi \cos^2 \theta}{\cos \phi}$ and hence that as θ varies, the velocity ratio varies between $\cos \phi$ and $\dfrac{1}{\cos \phi}$.

9. If a force P, making an angle θ with an inclined plane, is required to prevent a body of weight W from sliding down the plane, $P \cos \theta + \mu(P \sin \theta + W \cos \alpha) = W \sin \alpha$ where α is the inclination of the plane and μ is the coefficient of friction. Prove that if $\mu = \tan \lambda$, $P = \dfrac{W \sin (\alpha - \lambda)}{\cos (\theta - \lambda)}$ and deduce that as θ varies, the least force required is $W \sin (\alpha - \lambda)$.

10. If a rod subtends an angle 2α at the centre of a rough bowl when resting inside it in equilibrium, its inclination θ to the vertical is given by $2 \cot \theta = \tan (\alpha + \lambda) - \tan (\alpha - \lambda)$ where λ is the angle of friction. Show that its inclination to the vertical is $\tan^{-1} \dfrac{\cos 2\alpha + \cos 2\lambda}{\sin 2\lambda}$.

11. When a projectile is fired up a hill with velocity v in a direction making an angle θ with the hill, the time of flight t is given by $t = \dfrac{2v \sin \theta}{g \cos \alpha}$ where α is the inclination of the hill. If the projectile hits the hill horizontally $t = \dfrac{v \sin (\theta +)\alpha}{g}$. Prove that $\tan \theta = \dfrac{\sin \alpha \cos \alpha}{1 + \sin^2 \alpha}$.

12. $\sin A = \tfrac{3}{5}$ and $\cos B = \tfrac{5}{13}$, and A and B are acute angles. Without using tables calculate $\sin 2A$, $\cos 2B$, $\sin (A + B)$ and $\tan (A + B)$.

13. If $\cos \theta = \tfrac{7}{9}$, find without using tables, the possible values of $\sin \dfrac{\theta}{2}$, $\cos \dfrac{\theta}{2}$, $\tan \dfrac{\theta}{2}$.

14. Find the values of x between $0°$ and $360°$ satisfying (i) $\sin 4x = \tfrac{1}{2}$, (ii) $\cos 6x = -\tfrac{1}{2}$, (iii) $\tan 3x = -1$.

15. Find the two values between $0°$ and $360°$ of (i) $\sin^{-1} 0 \cdot 25$ and (ii) $\cos^{-1} 0 \cdot 25$. Prove for acute angles that $\sin^{-1} k + \cos^{-1} k = 90°$.

16. If $\cos (A+B)=0{\cdot}525$ and $A-B=38°\ 14'$, find the values of A and B between $0°$ and $180°$.

17. Solve the equation $4 \cos 2x - 2 \sin x - 1 = 0$.

18. The acceleration f of a piston rod is given by

$$f = c\,(\cos \theta + k \cos 2\theta).$$

Find θ when $c=120$, $k=\frac{1}{8}$ and $f=100$.

19. Solve the equation $\sec\left(\theta + \dfrac{\pi}{4}\right) + \dfrac{1}{\sec\left(\theta + \dfrac{\pi}{4}\right)} = \dfrac{5}{2}$. Give the

general solution and the solutions between $-\pi$ and π.

20. Prove that $\tan (45° - x) = \dfrac{1 - \tan x}{1 + \tan x}$ and solve the equation $\tan x + \tan (45° - x) = \frac{5}{6}$.

21. A wheel is mounted on a horizontal axle and weights of 3 lb., 4 lb. and 5 lb. are attached to points on its rim which form the vertices of an equilateral triangle. If θ is the angle the radius to the 3 lb. weight makes with the horizontal,

$$3 \cos \theta + 4 \cos\left(\theta + \frac{2\pi}{3}\right) + 5 \cos\left(\theta + \frac{4\pi}{3}\right) = 0.$$

Find θ.

22. If r is positive and α is between $0°$ and $360°$, find values of r and α which satisfy (i) $r \sin \alpha = 4$, $r \cos \alpha = -3$, (ii) $r \sin \alpha = -4$, $r \cos \alpha = 3$.

Express $3 \sin \theta - 4 \cos \theta$ in the form $r \sin (\theta - \alpha)$ and hence solve the equation $3 \sin \theta - 4 \cos \theta = 2$.

23. Express $5 \cos \omega t + 12 \sin \omega t$ in the form $r \cos (\omega t - \phi)$ giving ϕ in radians, and hence find the smallest value of t for which $5 \cos \omega t + 12 \sin \omega t$ is a maximum when $\omega = 100\pi$.

24. The displacement of a particle due to two oscillations is given by $x = 3 \sin\left(4t + \dfrac{\pi}{8}\right) + 5 \sin\left(4t - \dfrac{\pi}{4}\right)$. Express x in the form $r \sin (4t + \phi)$, and hence find the maximum and minimum values of x and the smallest value of t for which $x = 4$.

25. The alternating current in a circuit is $E \cdot \dfrac{R \sin pt - Lp \cos pt}{R^2 + L^2 p^2}$.

Show that this is equal to $\dfrac{E}{\sqrt{R^2 + L^2 p^2}} \sin\left(pt - \tan^{-1}\dfrac{Lp}{R}\right)$.

26. A force of 3 lb. wt. acts in a given direction and the resultant of this force and a force of 5 lb. wt. makes an angle α with the given direction. If the angle between the resultant and the 5 lb. wt. is θ, prove that $\sin \theta = \frac{3}{5} \sin \alpha$; prove also that the resultant is $3 \cos \alpha + \sqrt{16 + 9 \cos^2 \alpha}$ Calculate θ and the resultant when $\alpha = 35° 20'$.

27. A ship S observes an object P on the shore to be in a direction N. α W.   It sails m miles in a direction N. θ W. ($\theta > \alpha$) and then a further n miles in a direction N. ϕ W. ($\phi > \alpha$).   The bearing of P is now N. β W. and the ship is d miles from P.   Show, by projecting on a line perpendicular to SP, that

$$d \sin (\alpha - \beta) = m \sin (\theta - \alpha) + n \sin (\phi - \alpha).$$

If $SP = l$ miles, show that

$$l = m \cos (\theta - \alpha) + n \cos (\phi - \alpha) + d \cos (\alpha - \beta).$$

Calculate SP when $\alpha = 30° 12'$, $\theta = 44° 15'$, $\phi = 58° 20'$, $\beta = 12° 32'$, $m = 12$, $n = 15$.

28. $ABCDE$ is a regular pentagon.   Vectors of equal magnitude are represented by the sides taken in order. AX makes an angle θ with AB.   Show by resolving along AX that

$$\cos \theta + \cos \left(\theta + \frac{2\pi}{5} \right) + \cos \left(\theta + \frac{4\pi}{5} \right) + \cos \left(\theta + \frac{6\pi}{5} \right) + \cos \left(\theta + \frac{8\pi}{5} \right) \equiv 0.$$

Show also that

$$\sin \theta + \sin \left(\theta + \frac{2\pi}{5} \right) + \sin \left(\theta + \frac{4\pi}{5} \right) + \sin \left(\theta + \frac{6\pi}{5} \right) + \sin \left(\theta + \frac{8\pi}{5} \right) \equiv 0.$$

Deduce two similar identities by starting with a regular hexagon.

29. To check the angle A, Fig. 19, a cylinder was placed in

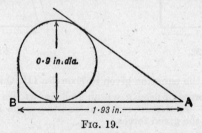

FIG. 19.

contact as shown and the distance AB measured.   Calculate the angle A.

30. To test the taper of the wedge a cylinder was placed as shown in Fig. 20. Calculate the angle θ.

31. The section of a tunnel is of shape as shown in Fig. 21, the top being an arc of a circle. Calculate the area of the cross-section.

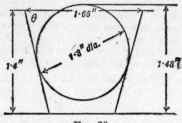

FIG. 20.

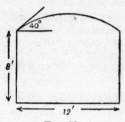

FIG. 21.

32. Fig. 22 shows an oblique frustum of a cylinder. Calculate the total surface area and the volume.

33. Find the volume of the solid whose section is shown in Fig. 23. It consists of a frustum of a cone surmounted by a segment of a sphere, the two meeting tangentially.

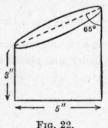

FIG. 22.

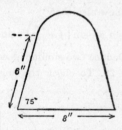

FIG. 23.

34. Prove the equation given in Exercise III, Question 16.

35. Two forces of 6·7 Kg. wt. and 5·8 Kg. wt. are inclined at an angle of 42°. Find their resultant and the angle it makes with the larger of the given forces.

36. OA is the crank and AP the connecting rod of a mechanism, Fig. 24. Show that $OP = \sqrt{l^2 - r^2 \sin^2 \theta} - r \cos \theta$. Calculate OP if $r = \frac{3}{4}'$, $l = 12'$ and $\theta = 127°$.

37. Solve the two possible triangles in which $a = 12$ in., $b = 14$ in., $A = 52°$. Verify that your two values of c are correct by solving the quadratic equation $a^2 = b^2 + c^2 - 2bc \cos A$ when the given values are substituted.

38. Show in the triangle ABC in Fig. 25 that $p^2 = (c + x)(c - x)$, $x = \dfrac{c^2 + a^2 - b^2}{2a}$ and hence that $a^2 p^2 = 4s(s - a)(s - b)(s - c)$. Deduce the formula for the area of a triangle in terms of its sides.

Find the angles and the area of a triangle whose sides are 12·1, 14·2 and 16·5 in. respectively.

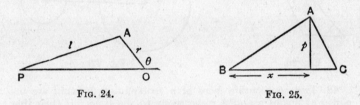

FIG. 24. FIG. 25.

39. Show that there are two possible triangles of area 62 sq. cm. with sides 11·5 and 14 cm. Calculate their angles.

40. The bearing of an aerodrome A from a pilot is S. 57° W. and that of B is S. 10° W. If A is 25 miles N.W. of B, how far is the pilot from the nearer aerodrome ?

41. A is on one side of a hill and three-quarters of a mile from the summit S ; B is on the other side and half a mile from S. The slope of AS is 1 in 5 (measured on the incline) and that of B is 1 in 3. Find the length of a straight tunnel from A to B and its inclination in the form 1 in n.

42. From the formulæ $\triangle = \frac{1}{2}bc \sin A$ and $\dfrac{a}{\sin A} = \dfrac{b}{\sin B} = \dfrac{c}{\sin C}$, deduce that $\triangle = \dfrac{a^2 \sin B \sin C}{2 \sin A}$.

From a base-line BC, 150 yards long, bearings are taken of a point A. $A\widehat{B}C = 54°\ 25'$ and $A\widehat{C}B$ is 61° 12′. Find the area of ABC.

43. From the vector diagram in Fig. 26 find the lag λ when $V_2 = 130$, $V_3 = 106$, $V_1 = 38$.

44. A factory is built on a hill inclined at 5° to the horizontal. From a point *A* on the hillside the elevation of the top of the chimney is 45°, and from a point *B* 60 ft. farther up the hill the elevation of the top is 57°. Calculate the height of the chimney.

45. In the two-crank mechanism shown in Fig. 27 calculate the angle *θ*.

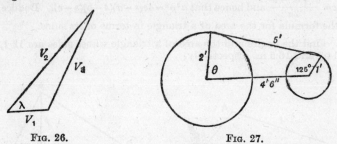

FIG. 26.   FIG. 27.

46. Two consecutive faces of a rectangular pyramid are inclined at angles α and β respectively to the base. If their line of intersection makes an angle θ with the base, show that $\cot^2 \theta = \cot^2 \alpha + \cot^2 \beta$. Calculate θ when α = 50° 16′, β = 45° 32′.

47. An aeroplane flying due N. at constant height is seen from an observation post to be S. α E. at an elevation θ. A second observation *t* sec. later, gives the direction as N. β E. and the elevation φ. Prove that sin α tan φ = sin β tan θ.

Find the speed of the plane in m.p.h. if its height is 6000 ft. α = 47°, β = 35°, θ = 80° 10′ and *t* = 6.

48. A hillside slopes in a southerly direction. When walking obliquely across it in a direction N.W. the gradient, i.e. tan (inclination), is 1 in 3; when walking in a direction N.E. the gradient is 1 in 5. Find the gradient of a path of greatest slope.

49. Using approximations for cos θ and sin θ where θ is a small angle expressed in radians, show that cos 30° 12″ is less than cos 30° by approximately $2\cdot9 \times 10^{-5}$

50. A machine part is to be in the shape of a right-angled triangle of sides 5, 12 and 13 cm. respectively. When it is made it is found that the longest side is 13·01 cm. By how many minutes does the greatest angle exceed a right angle ?

51. Find the small root of the equation cos θ + θ sin θ = 1·0008

52. An aeroplane travelling at 200 m.p.h. at a height of 20,000 ft. is sighted directly overhead. Find to the nearest minute, without using tables, through what angle the sights must be turned to have them on the aeroplane 5 sec. later.

53. A bar of length $2b$ is suspended in a horizontal position by two vertical strings each of length c attached to its ends. The bar is turned through an angle α so that it is still horizontal and the strings are taut. Prove that it has risen a distance $c - \sqrt{c^2 - 4b^2 \sin^2 \frac{\alpha}{2}}$ and that, if each string has turned through an angle θ, $c \sin \theta = 2b \sin \frac{\alpha}{2}$. If α and θ are small and expressed in radians, deduce that $\theta = \frac{b\alpha}{c}$.

CHAPTER II

SERIES

If a man's salary starts at £150 a year and increases £10 a year, he receives £150, £160, £170, etc., in successive years. In the tenth year he receives £$(150 + 9 \times 10)$ = £240, so that in ten years the number of pounds he has received is

$$150 + 160 + 170 + 180 + 190 + 200 + 210 + 220 + 230 + 240 \quad \text{(A)}$$

A sequence of numbers or symbols like this, in which each one is related to the one before it by some law, is called a series. The numbers or symbols are called the terms of the series. In the series above the law of the series is that each term is 10 more than the one before it. Other examples of series are :

$$5 + 5 \times 0.9 + 5 \times 0.9^2 + 5 \times 0.9^3 + \cdots + 5 \times 0.9^{20} \quad \text{(B)}$$

$$1 + \frac{1}{2} + \frac{1}{2^2} + \frac{1}{2^3} + \frac{1}{2^4} + \cdots \cdots \cdots \quad \text{(C)}$$

$$a^6 - 6a^5b + 15a^4b^2 - 20a^3b^3 + 15a^2b^4 - 6ab^5 + b^6 \quad \text{(D)}$$

In the series (B) the dots indicate that further terms up to 5×0.9^{20} are formed by the same law, which is that each term is 0.9 times the one before it. In the series (C) the dots are not ended by a term as in the series (B) ; this indicates that the series is unending ; such a series is called an infinite series.

It is frequently necessary to sum a given number of terms of a series and in some cases a simple formula can be found for the sum. We shall consider below how to find such formulæ for certain types of series.

Arithmetical progression

A series like (A) on page 32, in which each term differs from the one before it by the same amount, is called an Arithmetical Progression. The sum of any number of terms is found by reversing their order and adding the series so formed to the original series. Thus, if the sum of the series (A) is S,

$$S = 150 + 160 + 170 + 180 + 190 + 200 + 210 + 220 + 230 + 240,$$

and

$$S = 240 + 230 + 220 + 210 + 200 + 190 + 180 + 170 + 160 + 150.$$

Therefore

$$2S = 390 + 390 + 390 + 390 + 390 + 390 + 390 + 390 + 390 + 390.$$

(ten equal terms)

$$\therefore \ 2S = 3900$$

$$\therefore \ S = 1950.$$

Now suppose the first term of an arithmetical progression of n terms is a, the last term is l and the difference between successive terms is d. Then the second term is $a + d$, the third $a + 2d$ and so on. Hence the nth term, $l = a + (n-1)d$. Working from the other end the last term but one is $l - d$, the last but two $l - 2d$ and so on. Hence the sum S of the n terms is given by

$$S = a + (a + d) + (a + 2d) + \ \ldots \ + (l - 2d) + (l - d) + l.$$

Reversing

$$S = l + (l - d) + (l - 2d) + \ \ldots \ + (a + 2d) + (a + d) + l.$$

Adding

$$2S = (a + l) + (a + l) + (a + l) + \ \ldots \ + (a + l) + (a + l) + (a + l)$$

$$\{n \text{ terms each equal to } (a + l)\}.$$

$$\therefore \ 2S = n(a + l)$$

$$\therefore \ S = \tfrac{1}{2}n(a + l).$$

2

This is illustrated very clearly by Fig. 28. The height of each of the steps is the common difference d, so that, if the base

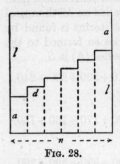

of each rectangle is unity, the area under each step is equal to a term of the series. Hence the total area under the set of steps equals the sum of the arithmetical progression. If an equal set is placed upside down on top of the first set we get a rectangle of area $n(a + l)$. Hence $S = \frac{1}{2}n(a + l)$.

Fig. 28.

Geometrical progression

A series like (B) or (C) on page 32, in which every term bears the same ratio to the one before it, is called a Geometrical Progression, and the ratio is called the common ratio of the terms. If a is the first term and r is the common ratio, the 2nd term is ar, the 3rd is ar^2 and so on. In each of these the index of r is one less than the number of the term and hence the nth term is ar^{n-1}. Therefore, if S is the sum of n terms starting from a,

$$S = a + ar + ar^2 + \ldots + ar^{n-2} + ar^{n-1}.$$

Multiplying by r

$$rS = ar + ar^2 + \ldots + ar^{n-2} + ar^{n-1} + ar^n.$$

Subtracting this line from the one above,

$$(1 - r)S = a - ar^n = a(1 - r^n).$$

$$\therefore S = \frac{a(1 - r^n)}{1 - r}.$$

This may also be written $S = \dfrac{a(r^n - 1)}{r - 1}$, which is more convenient if $r > 1$.

Example.—Find the sum of the series (B), namely,

$$5 + 5 \times 0 \cdot 9 + 5 \times 0 \cdot 9^2 + \ldots + 5 \times 0 \cdot 9^{20}.$$

Here the first term is 5, the common ratio is 0·9 and there are 21 terms.

$$\therefore \text{ sum} = \frac{5(1 - 0.9^{21})}{1 - 0.9} = 50(1 - 0.9^{21})$$

$$\log 0.9^{21} = 21 \times \log 0.9 = 21 \times \bar{1}.9542 = \bar{1}.0382.$$

$$\therefore 0.9^{21} \simeq 0.1091$$

$$\therefore \text{ sum} \simeq 50(1 - 0.1091) = 50 \times 0.8909 = 44.55.$$

Example.—A machine which cost £800 depreciates $7\frac{1}{2}$ % of its value each year. Show that the values at the ends of successive years are in geometrical progression, and find the value after 15 years.

Since the machine depreciates $7\frac{1}{2}$ % per annum, its value at the end of any year is $92\frac{1}{2}$ % of its value at the beginning of the year. Hence, working in pounds,

$$\text{value after one year} \quad = \frac{92\frac{1}{2}}{100} \cdot 800 = 800 \times 0.925,$$

$$\text{,, \quad two years} = \frac{92\frac{1}{2}}{100}(800 \times 0.925) = 800 \times 0.925^2,$$

$$\text{,, \quad three years} = \frac{92\frac{1}{2}}{100}(800 \times 0.925^2) = 800 \times 0.925^3,$$

and so on.

Hence the values at the ends of successive years form a geometrical progression with common ratio 0·925.

Since the index of 0·925 is the same as the number of years, the value after n years is 800×0.925^n. In particular, after 15 years it is 800×0.925^{15}. Evaluating this by logarithms,

800	2·9031
0·925^15	$15 \times \bar{1}.9661 = \bar{1}.4915$
248	2·3946

Hence the value after 15 years is £248.

Example.—In designing the gearing for a machine it is required to arrange for 18 speeds from 12 r.p.m. to 300 r.p.m. inclusive, so that the speeds shall be in geometrical progression throughout the range. Find the common ratio of the progression. The speeds are arranged in three groups of six speeds each. Calculate the lowest speed of each group.

If the ratio of the speeds is r, the successive speeds are 12, $12r$, $12r^2$, $12r^3$. . . . There are to be 18 speeds in all and hence the highest speed must be $12r^{17}$, but this speed is 300.

$$\therefore 12r^{17} = 300, \text{ i.e. } r^{17} = 25$$

$$\therefore 17 \log r = \log 25$$

$$\therefore \log r = \frac{\log 25}{17} = \frac{1 \cdot 3979}{17} = 0 \cdot 08223$$

$$\therefore r \fallingdotseq 1 \cdot 209.$$

The lowest speed of the second group is the seventh speed, which is $12r^6$.

$$\log 12r^6 = \log 12 + 6 \log r = 1 \cdot 0792 + 0 \cdot 4934 = 1 \cdot 5726$$

$$\therefore 12r^6 = 37 \cdot 38.$$

The lowest speed of the third group is the thirteenth speed, which is $12r^{12}$.

$$\log 12r^{12} = \log 12 + 12 \log r = 1 \cdot 0792 + 0 \cdot 9868 = 2 \cdot 0660$$

$$\therefore 12r^{12} = 116 \cdot 4.$$

Therefore the lowest speeds of the three groups are 12, 37·38, 116·4 r.p.m. respectively.

Example.—Find the sum of ten terms of the series (C), namely, $1 + \frac{1}{2} + \frac{1}{2^2} + \frac{1}{2^3} + $ . . ., and find also how the sum of the series behaves as the number of terms is made larger and larger.

The first term of the series is 1 and the common ratio is $\frac{1}{2}$.

$\therefore$ the sum of ten terms $= \dfrac{1\{1 - (\frac{1}{2})^{10}\}}{1 - \frac{1}{2}}$

$$= 2\left(1 - \frac{1}{2^{10}}\right)$$

$$= 2 - \frac{1}{2^9}$$

$$\fallingdotseq 2 - 0.00195$$

$$= 1.99805.$$

The sum of n terms $\quad = \dfrac{1 - (\frac{1}{2})^n}{1 - \frac{1}{2}}$

$$= 2\left(1 - \frac{1}{2^n}\right)$$

$$= 2 - \frac{1}{2^{n-1}}.$$

Now, as n becomes larger and larger 2^{n-1} becomes larger and larger and $\dfrac{1}{2^{n-1}}$ becomes smaller and smaller. In fact, by taking n large enough we can make the sum as near to 2 as we like. For this reason 2 is called the sum to infinity of the infinite or unending series. This number 2, to which the sum approaches closer and closer but never actually reaches, is called the limiting value of the sum to n terms as n is made infinitely large and we write this statement shortly as

$$\lim_{n \to \infty} \left(2 - \frac{1}{2^{n-1}}\right) = 2.$$

We therefore write

$$1 + \frac{1}{2} + \frac{1}{2^2} + \frac{1}{2^3} + \ldots \text{ to infinity} = 2.$$

Formula for the sum to infinity

The formula $S = \dfrac{a(1 - r^n)}{1 - r}$ may be written

$$S = \frac{a}{1 - r} - \frac{ar^n}{1 - r}$$

Now, if r is numerically less than 1, r^n and hence also the term $\dfrac{ar^n}{1 - r}$ become nearer and nearer to 0 as n becomes larger and larger.

$$\therefore \text{ sum to infinity} = \frac{a}{1 - r}.$$

Example.—Find the sum to infinity of the series

$$1 - \tfrac{1}{3} + \tfrac{1}{9} - \tfrac{1}{27} + \ldots$$

The common ratio is $-\tfrac{1}{3}$ and the first term is 1.

$$\therefore \text{ sum to infinity} = \frac{1}{1 - (-\tfrac{1}{3})} = \tfrac{3}{4}.$$

Example.—A ball is thrown up with a velocity of 20 ft./sec. Each time it bounces its velocity is reduced 25 %. Assuming $g = 32$ ft./sec.^{2}, find how long it will be before it comes to rest on the ground.

Since the velocity is reduced 32 ft./sec. every second, the ball comes to rest instantaneously after $\tfrac{20}{32}$ sec. Hence it hits the ground again after $\tfrac{40}{32} = \tfrac{5}{4}$ sec. It then rebounds with a velocity $\tfrac{3}{4} \times 20$ ft./sec. and so the time from the first to the second bounce is $\tfrac{5}{4} \times \tfrac{3}{4}$ sec. Similarly, the time from the second to the third bounce is $\tfrac{5}{4} \times (\tfrac{3}{4})^2$ sec., and so on. Hence the number of seconds the ball is in motion is the sum of the unending series.

$$\tfrac{5}{4} + \tfrac{5}{4} \times \tfrac{3}{4} + \tfrac{5}{4} \times (\tfrac{3}{4})^2 + \tfrac{5}{4} \times (\tfrac{3}{4})^3 + \ldots$$

Here $a = \tfrac{5}{4}$ and $r = \tfrac{3}{4}$ and so the sum to infinity is

$$\frac{\tfrac{5}{4}}{1 - \tfrac{3}{4}} = \frac{\tfrac{5}{4}}{\tfrac{1}{4}} = 5 \text{ secs.}$$

Exercise VI.

Find the sums of the following arithmetical progressions :

1. $1 + 5 + 9 + 13 + \ldots$ to 50 terms.

2. $3\cdot4 + 3\cdot7 + 4\cdot0 + 4\cdot3 + \ldots$ to 13 terms.

3. $1 + 2 + 3 + \ldots + (n-2) + (n-1)$.

4. $2\frac{1}{4} + 2\frac{3}{4} + 3\frac{1}{4} + \ldots$ to 20 terms.

5. What is the 20th term of the progression $1 + 4 + 7 + 10 + \ldots$? Find the sum of the first 20 terms and also of the next 20 terms.

6. How many odd numbers are there less than 100 ? Find their sum.

7. How many terms has the progression $4 + 4\frac{2}{3} + 5\frac{1}{3} + \ldots + 13\frac{1}{3} + 14$? Find its sum.

8. Find the 12th term of the progression $30 + 27 + 24 + 21 + \ldots$ and find the sum of the first twelve terms.

9. Show that the number of circles in Fig. 29 is $1 + 2 + 3 + \ldots + 12$. Find the total number.

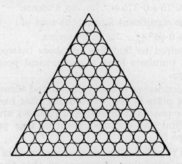

Fig. 29.

10. It is required to cut 17 lengths of wood so that the longest is 12 ft. long and the shortest 8 ft. long, and there are 15 intermediate lengths with an equal difference between consecutive lengths. Find the intermediate lengths and the total length used.

11. In addition to interest a householder has to repay a capital sum to a building society by paying £20 the first year and 10s. less each year. If he makes 25 payments in all, find how much he repays altogether.

12. Prove that $(n+1)^3 - (n-1)^3 \equiv 6n^2 + 2$. Write out this identity with $n = 1, 2, 3, 4, \ldots,$ etc., and hence by addition show that $(n+1)^3 + n^3 - 1 = 6(1^2 + 2^2 + 3^2 \ldots + n^2) + 2n$. Hence prove that $1^2 + 2^2 + 3^2 + \ldots + n^2 = \frac{1}{6}n(n+1)(2n+1)$.

13. By writing $1.2 + 2.3 + \ldots + n(n+1)$ in the form $(1 + 2 + 3 + \ldots + n) + (1^2 + 2^2 + \ldots + n^2)$ and using the result in Question 12, show that the sum of the given series is $\frac{1}{3}n(n+1)(n+2)$.

A number of balls are piled in a pyramid so that the bottom layer forms an equilateral triangle with n balls in a side, the next layer forms an equilateral triangle with $n-1$ balls in a side and so on. Show that there are $\frac{1}{2}n(n+1)$ balls in the bottom layer and $\frac{1}{6}n(n+1)(n+2)$ balls in the pyramid.

Find the sums of the following geometrical progressions :

14. $2 + 6 + 18 + \ldots$ to 6 terms.

15. $3 + 6 + 12 + 24 + \ldots$ to 10 terms.

16. $3 - 6 + 12 - 24 + \ldots$ to 10 terms.

17. $1 - \frac{1}{2} + \frac{1}{2^2} - \frac{1}{2^3} + \ldots$ to 9 terms.

18. $3 + 1 \cdot 5 + 0 \cdot 75 + 0 \cdot 375 + \ldots$ to 8 terms.

Find, to three significant figures the sum of :

19. $1 + 0 \cdot 95 + 0 \cdot 95^2 + \ldots$ to 20 terms.

20. It is required to find five numbers between 8 and 64 so that the seven numbers form a geometrical progression. Find the five numbers.

21. When a condenser is being discharged through a resistance the charge on a plate is $10e^{-2t}$ coulombs after t sec. Show that the values of the charge at intervals of $\frac{1}{10}$th sec. are in geometrical progression. Find the common ratio of this progression. Cf. example on page 58.

22. Owing to the air resistance the amplitude of the oscillations of the bob of a pendulum decreases so that the amplitudes of successive swings (on the same side) form a geometrical progression. It is observed that the amplitude of the first swing is 8 in. and of the second is 7 in. Calculate the amplitude of the fifth and tenth swings.

23. A rope with a tension T at one end is passed round a capstan so that it touches it through an angle θ^c. The other end is then held with a force t which is given by $t = Te^{-\mu\theta}$. Show that the values of t required when the rope is passed once, twice, three times, etc., right round the capstan form a geometrical progression. Find its common ratio. If the rope is passed three times round, with what force will it have to be held when, $T = 500$ lb. wt. and $\mu = 0 \cdot 2$?

24. There are 120,000 people in a town to-day. If the population increases by $2\frac{1}{2}\%$ every year, what will it be at the end of eleven years from now ?

25. The value of a machine which cost £500 depreciates by 5% per annum. What is its value after n years ? Calculate its value after 8 years.

26. If the cost of repairs to a machine is £2 in the first year, and if it is estimated that the cost will increase 30% per annum, find the probable cost of repairs in the tenth year and the total amount that is likely to be spent on repairs in the first ten years.

27. The speeds of a drilling machine are to be eight in number, varying from 20 r.p.m. to 200 r.p.m. If the speeds are to be in geometrical progression, find the common ratio and make a table showing the eight speeds.

Find the sums to infinity of the series :

28. $1 \cdot 728 + 1 \cdot 44 + 1 \cdot 2 + 1 + \ldots$

29. $1 + \frac{1}{3} + \frac{1}{9} + \frac{1}{27} + \ldots$

30. $100\{1 - (\frac{3}{4}) + (\frac{3}{4})^2 - (\frac{3}{4})^3 + \ldots \}$

31. Find the sum to infinity of $0 \cdot 1 + 0 \cdot 01 + 0 \cdot 001 + \ldots$ Hence express the recurring decimal $0 \cdot \dot{1}$ as a fraction. Express $0 \cdot \dot{1}\dot{2}$ as a fraction by the same method.

32. Show by division that $\frac{1}{7} = 0 \cdot \dot{1}4285\dot{7}$ and then verify this by summing the geometrical progression $0 \cdot 142857 + 0 \cdot 000000142857 + \ldots$ to infinity.

33. A ball is dropped under gravity from a height of 4 ft. Find its velocity when it reaches the ground. [Take $g = 32$ ft./sec.²] If it loses $\frac{1}{10}$th of its velocity at each bounce, show that the total time from when it is dropped till it comes to rest is

$$\tfrac{1}{2} + \{\tfrac{9}{10} + (\tfrac{9}{10})^2 + \ldots \text{ to } \infty\} \text{ sec.}$$

Find this time.

34. When a certain electrical machine is switched on for 2 hours and then off for $1\frac{1}{2}$ hours its temperature rises to $40°$ C. and then drops to $15°$ C. If it is then switched on again the temperature rises again from $15°$ C. by the same amount, namely, $40°$ C., to $55°$ C. and then drops the same percentage as before, $62\frac{1}{2}\%$. If this process is repeated continuously, show that the maximum temperature it reaches when it is switched on the sixth time is $40[1 + \frac{3}{8} + (\frac{3}{8})^2 + \ldots + (\frac{3}{8})^5]$ degrees.

2*

Calculate this temperature.   Show also that if the machine were switched on and off an infinite number of times its highest temperature would be 64°.

The Binomial series

The series (D) on page 32 is called a binomial series because its sum is $(a-b)^6$, which is the sixth power of the binomial or two term expression $a-b$. The series (D) is called the expansion of $(a-b)^6$ in powers of a and b. We will consider below the expansion of $(1+x)^n$ in powers of x when n is a positive whole number.

Expansion of $(1+x)^n$

The expansions of low powers of $1+x$ can be found by direct multiplication as follows :

$$(1+x)^1 = 1+1 \cdot x$$

$$x(1+x)^1 = \quad 1 \cdot x + 1 \cdot x^2$$

$$\therefore (1+x)^1(1+x) = 1+(1+1)x+1 \cdot x^2$$

$$\therefore (1+x)^2 = 1+2 \cdot x + 1 \cdot x^2$$

$$x(1+x)^2 = \quad 1 \cdot x + 2 \cdot x^2 + 1 \cdot x^3$$

$$\therefore (1+x)^2(1+x) = 1+(1+2)x+(2+1)x^2+1 \cdot x^3$$

$$\therefore (1+x)^3 = 1+3 \cdot x + 3 \cdot x^2 + 1 \cdot x^3$$

$$x(1+x)^3 = \quad 1 \cdot x + 3 \cdot x^2 + 3 \cdot x^3 + 1 \cdot x^4$$

$$\therefore (1+x)^3(1+x) = 1+(1+3)x+(3+3)x^2+(3+1)x^3+1 \cdot x^4$$

$$\therefore (1+x)^4 = 1+4 \cdot x + 6 \cdot x^2 + 4 \cdot x^3 + 1 \cdot x^4$$

From the above it is clear that when we multiply $(1+x)^3$ by x in the process of forming $(1+x)^4$ each coefficient is moved one place to the right as shown by the arrowheads so that, for instance, the coefficient of x^3 in $(1+x)^4$ is formed by adding 3, which is the coefficient of x^2 in $(1+x)^3$, to 1 the

coefficient of x^3 in $(1+x)^3$. Hence, if we set out the coefficients of the powers of x in successive powers of $1+x$ in a
triangle as below, each coefficient is formed by adding the
two numbers to its right and left in the line above it, as
indicated by the arrowheads. This triangle is called Pascal's
triangle after its discoverer, who lived in France (1623–1662),
i.e. in the time of Cromwell.

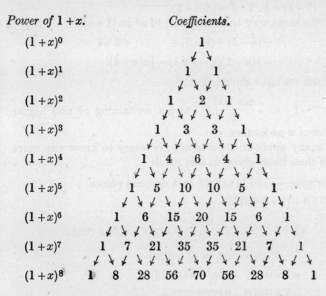

Power of $1+x$.						*Coefficients.*							
$(1+x)^0$						1							
$(1+x)^1$					1		1						
$(1+x)^2$				1		2		1					
$(1+x)^3$			1		3		3		1				
$(1+x)^4$		1		4		6		4		1			
$(1+x)^5$	1		5		10		10		5		1		
$(1+x)^6$		1	6		15		20		15		6	1	
$(1+x)^7$	1	7		21		35		35		21		7	1
$(1+x)^8$	1	8	28		56		70		56		28	8	1

The coefficients of the various powers of x in any higher
power of $1+x$ can be found by continuing the triangle downwards forming each new row from the one above it in the
same way. The last row in the triangle above shows that

$$(1+x)^8 = 1 + 8x + 28x^2 + 56x^3 + 70x^4 + 56x^5 + 28x^6 + 8x^7 + x^8.$$

It is clear from the triangle that the coefficient of x in
$(1+x)^n$ is always n. It is easy to find an expression for the
coefficient of x^2. Consider, for example, the coefficient of

x^2 in $(1+x)^8$. Working backwards from the bottom to the top row we find

$$28 = 7 + 21 = 7 + 6 + 15 = 7 + 6 + 5 + 10 = 7 + 6 + 5 + 4 + 6$$
$$= 7 + 6 + 5 + 4 + 3 + 3 = 7 + 6 + 5 + 4 + 3 + 2 + 1.$$

This is an arithmetical progression of seven terms, the first and last terms being 7 and 1 respectively. Hence its sum is $\frac{1}{2} \cdot 7 \cdot (7+1) = \frac{1}{2} \cdot 7 \cdot 8 = \frac{1}{2}8(8-1)$.

In the same way the coefficient of x^2 in $(1+x)^n$

$$= (n-1) + (n-2) + \ldots + 2 + 1$$
$$= \tfrac{1}{2}(n-1)(n-1+1) = \tfrac{1}{2}n(n-1).$$

Hence we have shown that

$$(1+x)^n = 1 + nx + \frac{n(n-1)}{2}x^2 + \text{terms containing } x^3 \text{ and higher}$$

powers of x as factors.

In many applications it is not necessary to know any more terms than those given in this result.

Example.—Find $(1 \cdot 0015)^6$ to 4 decimal places.

$(1 \cdot 0015)^6 = (1 + 0 \cdot 0015)^6$

$$= 1 + 6 \times 0 \cdot 0015 + \frac{6 \cdot 5}{2}(0 \cdot 0015)^2 + \text{terms containing}$$

higher powers of $0 \cdot 0015$

$= 1 + 0 \cdot 009 + 15(0 \cdot 00000225) + \ldots$

$= 1 + 0 \cdot 009 + 0 \cdot 00003375 + \ldots$

$= 1 \cdot 0090$ to 4 decimal places.

We are, of course, assuming here that the sum of the remaining terms is not large enough to alter the number in the fourth decimal place.

One of the most important of the discoveries made by Sir Isaac Newton (1642–1727), who did his main work during the reign of Charles II, was that the coefficients of the various powers of x in the expansion of $(1+x)^n$ are given by the following formula, even in cases when n is not a positive integer.

$$(1+x)^n = 1 + nx + \frac{n(n-1)}{1 \cdot 2}x^2 + \frac{n(n-1)(n-2)}{1 \cdot 2 \cdot 3}x^3$$
$$+ \frac{n(n-1)(n-2)(n-3)}{1 \cdot 2 \cdot 3 \cdot 4}x^4$$
$$+ \ldots$$

This series is called the binomial series.

If n is a positive integer the series ends at x^n because ultimately there is a zero factor in the numerator. If n is not a positive integer the series is an unending or infinite series, and it can be shown that the series is equal to $(1+x)^n$ provided that x is numerically less than 1. The complete proof of this formula is beyond the scope of this book.

Example.—Find the coefficients of the powers of x in $(1+x)^8$ and verify that they agree with those found by Pascal's triangle.

Coefficient of $x = 8$

Coefficient of $x^2 = \dfrac{8 \cdot 7}{1 \cdot 2} = 28$

Coefficient of $x^3 = \dfrac{8 \cdot 7 \cdot 6}{1 \cdot 2 \cdot 3} = 56$

Coefficient of $x^4 = \dfrac{8 \cdot 7 \cdot 6 \cdot 5}{1 \cdot 2 \cdot 3 \cdot 4} = 70$

Coefficient of $x^5 = \dfrac{8 \cdot 7 \cdot 6 \cdot 5 \cdot 4}{1 \cdot 2 \cdot 3 \cdot 4 \cdot 5} = \dfrac{8 \cdot 7 \cdot 6}{1 \cdot 2 \cdot 3}$

$= $ coefficient of $x^3 = 56$.

After this the coefficients are clearly repeated in the reverse order. These numbers are the same as those in the Pascal's triangle.

Example.—From the series for $(1+x)^n$ find the series for $(a+b)^n$ when n is a positive integer.

$$(a+b)^n = \left\{ a\left(1 + \frac{b}{a}\right) \right\}^n$$

$$= a^n\left(1 + \frac{b}{a}\right)^n$$

$$= a^n\left\{ 1 + \frac{n}{1}\cdot\frac{b}{a} + \frac{n(n-1)}{1\cdot 2}\left(\frac{b}{a}\right)^2 + \frac{n(n-1)(n-2)}{1\cdot 2\cdot 3}\left(\frac{b}{a}\right)^3 \right.$$

$$\left. + \ldots + \left(\frac{b}{a}\right)^n \right\}.$$

$$= a^n + na^{n-1}b + \frac{n(n-1)}{1\cdot 2}a^{n-2}b^2 + \ldots + b^n.$$

Example.—Find the series for $\sqrt{1+x}$ in powers of x (if x is numerically less than 1) and show that when x is small enough for x^3 to be neglected $\sqrt{1+x} \backsimeq 1 + \frac{1}{2}x - \frac{1}{8}x^2$.

$$\sqrt{1+x} = (1+x)^{\frac{1}{2}}$$

$$= 1 + \frac{1}{2}x + \frac{\frac{1}{2}(\frac{1}{2}-1)}{1\cdot 2}x^2 + \frac{\frac{1}{2}(\frac{1}{2}-1)(\frac{1}{2}-2)}{1\cdot 2\cdot 3}x^3 + \ldots$$

$$= 1 + \frac{1}{2}x + \frac{\frac{1}{2}(-\frac{1}{2})}{1\cdot 2}x^2 + \frac{\frac{1}{2}(-\frac{1}{2})(-\frac{3}{2})}{1\cdot 2\cdot 3}x^3 + \ldots$$

$$= 1 + \frac{1}{2}x - \frac{1}{2\cdot 4}x^2 + \frac{1\cdot 3}{2\cdot 4\cdot 6}x^3 - \frac{1\cdot 3\cdot 5}{2\cdot 4\cdot 6\cdot 8}x^4 + \ldots$$

If x^3 and higher powers can be neglected

$$\sqrt{1+x} = 1 + \frac{1}{2}x - \frac{1}{8}x^2$$

Example.—Use the series in the example above to find $\sqrt{1\cdot 1}$ to four decimal places.

Putting $x = 0 \cdot 1$,

$$\sqrt{1 \cdot 1} = (1 + 0 \cdot 1)^{\frac{1}{2}}$$

$$= 1 + \tfrac{1}{2}0 \cdot 1 - \tfrac{1}{8}(0 \cdot 1)^2 + \tfrac{1}{16}(0 \cdot 1)^3 - \tfrac{5}{128}(0 \cdot 1)^4 - \quad \cdots$$

$$= 1 + 0 \cdot 05 - 0 \cdot 00125 + 0 \cdot 00006 - \cdots \text{ to five decimal}$$
$$\text{places}$$

$$= 1 \cdot 05006 - 0 \cdot 00125$$

$$= 1 \cdot 04881$$

$$= 1 \cdot 0488 \text{ to four decimal places.}$$

Example.—If a simple pendulum has a length l and a period of oscillation T the acceleration g due to gravity is given by $g = \dfrac{4\pi^2 l}{T^2}$. If in an experiment l is measured 1% too large and T 2% too small, find the percentage error in the calculated value of g approximately.

Let l, T and g be the true values ; then the measured value of l is $\frac{101}{100}l = 1 \cdot 01l$ and the measured value of T is $\frac{98}{100}T = (1 - 0 \cdot 02)T$. Hence the calculated value of the acceleration due to gravity is

$$\frac{4\pi^2(1 + 0 \cdot 01)l}{(1 - 0 \cdot 02)^2 T^2} = \frac{1 + 0 \cdot 01}{(1 - 0 \cdot 02)^2}g, \text{ since } g = \frac{4\pi^2 l}{T^2}.$$

This value equals $(1 + 0 \cdot 01)(1 - 0 \cdot 02)^{-2}g$

$$\eqsim (1 + 0 \cdot 01)\{1 + (-2)(-0 \cdot 02)\}g, \text{ neglecting } 0 \cdot 02^2$$

$$= (1 + 0 \cdot 01)(1 + 0 \cdot 04)g$$

$$= (1 + 0 \cdot 01 + 0 \cdot 04)g, \text{ neglecting } 0 \cdot 01 \times 0 \cdot 04$$

$$= 1 \cdot 05g$$

$$= \frac{105}{100}g.$$

Therefore the calculated value of the acceleration is nearly 5% too large.

Factorial notation

The product $1 \times 2 \times 3 \times 4 \times \ldots n$ is usually denoted by $n!$ (or $\underline{|n}$), which is read as "factorial n."

Summation of series by direct addition

Sometimes it is not easy to find a formula for the sum of an infinite series and then we have to find an approximation to the sum, to the degree of accuracy required, by direct addition. The calculation should be set out as in the example below.

Example.—Find the sum of the series

$$1 + \frac{x}{2 \cdot 5} + \frac{x^2}{2 \cdot 4 \cdot 5 \cdot 7} + \frac{x^3}{2 \cdot 4 \cdot 6 \cdot 5 \cdot 7 \cdot 9} + \cdots$$

when $x = \frac{2}{3}$ to four places of decimals.

To obtain accuracy to four places of decimals we have to work to five places.

Number of Term		*Value*
1		1
2	$\dfrac{\frac{2}{3}}{2 \cdot 5} = \dfrac{1}{15}$	$= 0 \cdot 06667$
3	$\dfrac{(\frac{2}{3})^2}{2 \cdot 4 \cdot 5 \cdot 7} = \dfrac{\frac{2}{3}}{4 \cdot 7} \dfrac{\frac{2}{3}}{2 \cdot 5} = \dfrac{1}{42} \times$ 2nd term	$= 0 \cdot 00159$
4	$\dfrac{(\frac{2}{3})^3}{2 \cdot 4 \cdot 6 \cdot 5 \cdot 7 \cdot 9} = \dfrac{1}{81} \times$ 3rd term	$= 0 \cdot 00002$
5	$\dfrac{(\frac{2}{3})^5}{2 \cdot 4 \cdot 6 \cdot 8 \cdot 5 \cdot 7 \cdot 9 \cdot 11} = \dfrac{1}{156} \times$ 4th term ; negligible.	
		Sum $= 1 \cdot 06828$

Therefore the sum is $1 \cdot 0683$ to four places of decimals.

The fifth term and the terms after it are too small to affect even the number in the fifth decimal place.

We now give an example of the summation of a series which has positive and negative terms.

Example.—Tables of natural sines can be calculated by using the following series :

$$\sin (x \text{ radians}) = x - \frac{x^3}{3!} + \frac{x^5}{5!} - \frac{x^7}{7!} + \ldots \text{ to infinity.}$$

Use this series to find sin 20° to four places of decimals.

$$20° = \frac{20\pi^c}{180} = \frac{3 \cdot 14159^c}{9} = 0 \cdot 34907^c$$

$$\therefore \sin 20° = 0 \cdot 34907 - \frac{0 \cdot 34907^3}{3!} + \frac{0 \cdot 34907^5}{5!} - \ldots$$

	Positive Terms		*Negative Terms*	
Term		*Value*	*Term*	*Value*
1		0·34907		
3	$\dfrac{0 \cdot 34907^5}{5!}$		2 $\dfrac{0 \cdot 34907^3}{3!}$	
	$= \dfrac{0 \cdot 122 \times 0 \cdot 00709}{20} = 0 \cdot 00004$		$= \dfrac{0 \cdot 04255}{6} = 0 \cdot 00709$	

Sum of positive terms 0·34911
Sum of negative terms 0·00709

Sum of series   0·34202

$\therefore$ sin 20° = 0·3420 to four decimal places.

The student will find that this agrees with the value given in tables.

Exercise VII

Write out the binomial series in powers of x as far as x^4 for the following expressions :

1. $(1+x)^{12}$. 2. $(1-x)^{\frac{1}{3}}$. 3. $(1+x)^{-2}$.
4. $(1-x)^7$. 5. $(1+x)^{-\frac{1}{2}}$. 6. $(1-x)^{-3}$.

7. Write out the first five terms of the series for $(1-x)^n$ in powers of x. [Replace x by $-x$ in the series for $(1+x)^n$.]

8. Show that, if x is numerically less than 1,

$$\frac{1}{\sqrt{1-x}} \simeq 1 + \tfrac{1}{2}x + \frac{1\cdot 3}{2\cdot 4}x^2 + \frac{1\cdot 3\cdot 5}{2\cdot 4\cdot 6}x^3.$$

9. Show that if $x = \tfrac{1}{50}$, $\dfrac{1}{\sqrt{1-x}} = \tfrac{5}{7}\sqrt{2}$ and hence, by putting $x = \tfrac{1}{50}$ in the series in Question 8, find the value of $\sqrt{2}$ to six decimal places.

10. Use Pascal's triangle to write out the expansions of (i) $(1+x)^5$, (ii) $(a-b)^6$.

11. By continuing the Pascal triangle on page 43, find the coefficients of the terms in the expansion of $(1+x)^{11}$.

Expand the following expressions in powers of x as far as x^3 and state for what values of x each expansion is true:

12. $(1+2x)^7$.   **13.** $\dfrac{1}{(1-x)^2}\{=(1-x)^{-2}\}$.   **14.** $\sqrt{4-x}$.

15. By putting $x = 0\cdot 02$ in the series for $\sqrt{1+x}$, find the value of $\sqrt{1\cdot 02}$ to seven decimal places.

16. Calculate the value of $(1\cdot 01)^8$ to four decimal places.

17. Calculate the approximate value of $\dfrac{(0\cdot 996)^3}{1\cdot 005}$ by writing it as $(1-0\cdot 004)^3(1+0\cdot 005)^{-1}$ and using the binomial theorem.

18. Calculate the approximate values of (a) $0\cdot 988 \times \sqrt{1\cdot 01}$; (b) $\dfrac{1\cdot 04^2 \times 1\cdot 001^8}{1\cdot 005^4}$ by the method indicated in Question 17.

19. An error of $\tfrac{1}{2}\%$ is made in measuring the diameter of a sphere. What is the approximate percentage error in its volume?

20. The period of the oscillations in an electrical aerial containing an inductance L and a capacity C is $2\pi\sqrt{LC}$. If L is measured 3% too large and C 1% too small what is the approximate percentage error in the period?

21. If x is small prove that $1 - \dfrac{1}{\sqrt{1+x}} \simeq \tfrac{1}{2}x$. What is the percentage error in taking $1 - \dfrac{1}{\sqrt{1\cdot 06}} = 0\cdot 03$?

22. Calculate the value of $1 + x + \dfrac{x^2}{2!} + \dfrac{x^3}{3!} + \ldots$ when $x = \tfrac{1}{2}$ giving the answer to three decimal places.

23. It can be shown that $\cos x^c = 1 - \dfrac{x^2}{2!} + \dfrac{x^4}{4!} - \dfrac{x^6}{6!} + \; \ldots$ to infinity. Verify that this is correct to four places of decimals when $x = 1$ and when $x = \frac{1}{2}$. Also use the series to calculate the value of $\cos 25°$ to four decimal places.

24. The following series is used in the construction of tables :

$$\log_e \frac{1+x}{1-x} = 2\left\{ x + \frac{x^3}{3} + \frac{x^5}{5} + \; \ldots \text{ to infinity} \right\}.$$

By putting $x = \frac{1}{2}$ in this series, calculate the value of $\log_e 3$ to four decimal places.

25. A function $J_0(x)$, called Bessel's function of order zero, is given by

$$J_0(x) = 1 - \frac{x^2}{2^2} + \frac{x^4}{2^2 \cdot 4^2} - \frac{x^6}{2^2 \cdot 4^2 \cdot 6^2} + \; \ldots \text{ to infinity}.$$

Calculate the values of $J_0(x)$ when $x = 0$, $\frac{1}{2}$, 1, $1\frac{1}{2}$, 2, $2\frac{1}{2}$, each to four decimal places. Hence plot a graph of $J_0(x)$ from $x = 0$ to $x = 2 \cdot 5$. Does $J_0(x) = 0$ in this range ; if so, for what value of x ?

CHAPTER III

GRAPHS

Graph of 10ˣ

$$10^{\frac{1}{2}} = \sqrt{10} = 3 \cdot 162$$

$$10^{\frac{1}{4}} = \sqrt{10^{\frac{1}{2}}} = \sqrt{3 \cdot 162} = 1 \cdot 778$$

$$10^{\frac{1}{8}} = \sqrt{10^{\frac{1}{4}}} = \sqrt{1 \cdot 778} = 1 \cdot 334$$

$$10^{\frac{1}{16}} = \sqrt{10^{\frac{1}{8}}} = \sqrt{1 \cdot 334} = 1 \cdot 155$$

$$10^{\frac{1}{32}} = \sqrt{10^{\frac{1}{16}}} = \sqrt{1 \cdot 155} = 1 \cdot 075, \text{ etc.}$$

Values of 10^x at successively smaller intervals of x can be found by using the above values. Thus, to find the values at intervals for x of $\frac{1}{8}$ unit, we proceed as follows :

$$10^{\frac{3}{8}} = 10^{\frac{1}{4}} \times 10^{\frac{1}{8}} = 1 \cdot 778 \times 1 \cdot 334 = 2 \cdot 371$$

$$10^{\frac{5}{8}} = 10^{\frac{1}{2}} \times 10^{\frac{1}{8}} = 3 \cdot 162 \times 1 \cdot 334 = 4 \cdot 217$$

$$10^{\frac{3}{4}} = 10^{\frac{1}{2}} \times 10^{\frac{1}{4}} = 3 \cdot 162 \times 1 \cdot 778 = 5 \cdot 623$$

$$10^{\frac{7}{8}} = 10^{\frac{3}{4}} \times 10^{\frac{1}{8}} = 5 \cdot 623 \times 1 \cdot 334 = 7 \cdot 499$$

Then
$$10^{1\frac{1}{8}} = 10 \times 10^{\frac{1}{8}} = 13 \cdot 34$$

$$10^{1\frac{1}{4}} = 10 \times 10^{\frac{1}{4}} = 17 \cdot 78$$

$$10^{1\frac{3}{8}} = 10 \times 10^{\frac{3}{8}} = 23 \cdot 71, \text{ and so on.}$$

Also
$$10^{2\frac{1}{8}} = 10^2 \times 10^{\frac{1}{8}} = 100 \times 10^{\frac{1}{8}} = 133 \cdot 4,$$

and so for higher powers.

Further
$$10^{-\frac{1}{8}} = 10^{-1} \times 10^{\frac{7}{8}} = \tfrac{1}{10} \times 10^{\frac{7}{8}} = 0 \cdot 7499$$

$$10^{-\frac{1}{4}} = 10^{-1} \times 10^{\frac{3}{4}} = \tfrac{1}{10} \times 10^{\frac{3}{4}} = 0 \cdot 5623,$$

and so on for negative powers.

The student will see for himself how to calculate the values of 10^x for values of x at intervals of $\frac{1}{16}$, $\frac{1}{32}$, etc. In this way the graph of $y = 10^x$ may be drawn with as high a degree of accuracy as may be required. The graph is shown, for values of x between -1 and 1, in Fig. 30.

GRAPH OF $y = 10^x$

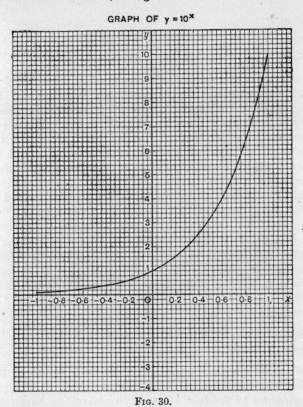

Fig. 30.

The value of 10^x for any value of x may be read off from the graph. For example, when $x = 0.4$ we find that $y \simeq 2.5$; hence $10^{0.4} \simeq 2.5$.

When $y = 10^x$ then $x = \log_{10} y$, and so the graph can also be used to read off values of logarithms to the base 10. Thus we find from the graph that when $y = 6$, $x \simeq 0.78$; hence $\log_{10} 6 \simeq 0.78$. Also when $y = 0.5$, $x \simeq -0.30$; hence $\log_{10} 0.5 \simeq -0.30 = \bar{1}.70$.

Graph of e^x

Since
$$3 = 10^{0.4771}$$
$$3^x = (10^{0.4771})^x = 10^{0.4771x}.$$

The ordinate of the graph of 3^x for any value of x is therefore equal to the ordinate of the graph of 10^x for the value $0.4771x$. For example, $3^{1.2} = 10^{0.4771 \times 1.2} = 10^{0.5725}$; hence the ordinate of the graph of $y = 3^x$ when $x = 1.2$ is equal to the ordinate of the graph of $y = 10^x$ when $x = 0.5725$. In other words, the graph of $y = 3^x$ can be obtained from the graph of $y = 10^x$ by merely altering the scale of x. The two graphs have the same general shape.

Similarly, any other positive number a can be expressed as a power of 10; for, by the definition of a logarithm, $a = 10^{\log_{10} a}$. Hence $a^x = 10^{x \log_{10} a}$. Thus the graph of a^x can be obtained from that of 10^x by merely altering the scale of x. [If $a < 1$, the scale factor $\log_{10} a$ is negative and the curve falls from left to right instead of rising.]

There is an important number which is discussed in Chapter X. It is usually denoted by e and its value is approximately 2.7183.

$\log_{10} e = 0.4343$, to four places of decimals, and $e = 10^{0.4343}$.

Hence
$$e^x = 10^{0.4343x}.$$

The graph of $y = e^x$ from $x = -3$ to $x = 3$ is one of the graphs shown in Fig. 31.

Logarithms to the base e are called *natural*, or *Napierian*, *logarithms*. The reason for using this number e as a base of logarithms is explained in Chapter X. We can easily convert from logarithms to the base 10 to logarithms to the base e and vice versa. For

$$\log_e x = \frac{\log_{10} x}{\log_{10} e} = \frac{\log_{10} x}{0 \cdot 4343} = 2 \cdot 3026 \log_{10} x$$

and
$$\log_{10} x = 0 \cdot 4343 \log_e x.$$

Natural logarithms can also be read off from the graph of e^x.

GRAPHS OF $y = e^x$, $y = e^{1 \cdot 5x}$ and $y = e^{-x}$

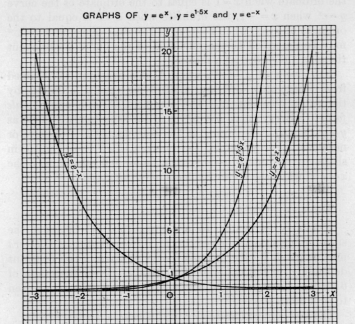

Fig. 31.

Graph of Ce^{kx}

The graph of $y = e^{kx}$ where k is any constant can be obtained from that of $y = e^x$ by altering the scale of x. The graph of $y = e^{1 \cdot 5x}$ is shown in Fig. 31.

The ordinate of the curve $y = e^{1\cdot5x}$ when $x = 2$ is equal to that of the curve $y = e^x$ when $x = 1\cdot5 \times 2 = 3$, and similarly for other values of x.

If k is negative the direction of slope of the curve is reversed. For example, in the case of the curve $y = e^{-x}$ (shown in Fig. 31), the ordinate when $x = 1$ is equal to the ordinate of the curve $y = e^x$ when $x = -1$, the ordinate when $x = 2$ is equal to the ordinate of $y = e^x$ when $x = -2$, and so on. The curve $y = e^{-x}$ may be described as the reflection of the curve $y = e^x$ about the y-axis regarded as a mirror.

The graph of $y = Ce^{kx}$, where C is a constant, is obtained from that of $y = e^{kx}$ by multiplying every ordinate by the same constant C. The numbers C and k are *scale factors*. Every curve $y = Ce^{kx}$ is of the same general shape as $y = e^x$ or $y = e^{-x}$ according as the scale factor k is positive or negative. For example, the curve $y = 8e^{-0\cdot6x}$ is similar in shape to the curve $y = e^{-x}$; the factor $0\cdot6$ affects only the x-scale, while the factor 8 affects only the y-scale.

Example.—Cooling Curve

If a body is heated to a temperature $\theta_1°$ C. above the surrounding air and allowed to cool, its temperature $\theta°$ C. after t min. is given by the formula $\theta = \theta_1 e^{-kt}$ where k is a constant depending on the material of the body. Draw the graph of θ against t if $\theta_1 = 42$ and $k = 0\cdot0721$, and find the time taken to cool down to 25° C.

The law connecting θ and t in this case is $\theta = 42e^{-0\cdot0721t}$.

The table below gives values of θ from $t = 0$ to $t = 40$.

To calculate θ we take logs. (to the base 10)

$$\log \theta = \log 42 - 0\cdot0721t \log e$$
$$= 1\cdot6232 - 0\cdot0721 \times 0\cdot4343t$$
$$= 1\cdot6232 - 0\cdot0313t.$$

t	0	5	10	15	20	25	30	35	40
$0\cdot0313t$		0·1565	0·3130	0·4695	0·6260	0·7825	0·9390	1·0955	1·2520
$\log \theta$		1·4667	1·3102	1·1537	0·9972	0·8407	0·6842	0·5277	0·3712
θ	42	29·29	20·43	14·25	9·94	6·93	4·83	3·37	2·35

The graph of θ against t is shown in Fig. 32. From the graph we find that $\theta = 25$ when $t \fallingdotseq 7\cdot2$. Hence the time taken to cool down to 25° C. is 7·2 min. (approx.).

Curves of the type $y = Ce^{kx}$, where C and k are constants, are called *exponential curves* and the law connecting y and x is called an *exponential law*. If k is negative the curve is often called a " negative exponential curve."

Since any number a can be expressed as a power of e, viz. $a = e^{\log_e a}$ (this being the definition of $\log_e a$), it follows that $a^x = e^{x \log_e a}$, and hence every curve of the type $y = Ca^x$ is an

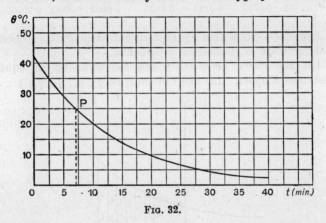

FIG. 32.

exponential curve. For example, since $2 = e^{0\cdot69315}$ and $10 = e^{2\cdot3026}$, the equation $y = 2^x$ can be written in the form $y = e^{0\cdot69315x}$ and $y = 10^x$ can be written in the form $y = e^{2\cdot3026x}$.

The exponential law occurs very frequently in physics, chemistry, engineering and other sciences, and numerous examples of it are given in Chapter X, as well as in Exercise VIII.

The student should observe the following general features from the graphs of e^x and e^{-x}.

(1) e^x and e^{-x} are positive for all values of x.

(2) When x is positive, $e^x > 1$ and $e^{-x} < 1$.

(3) As x increases, e^x increases more and more rapidly, and hence e^{-x}, which is equal to $\dfrac{1}{e^x}$, decreases more and more rapidly.

(4) As x tends to infinity, e^x tends to infinity and e^{-x} tends to zero.

Some idea of the rate at which e^x increases, and e^{-x} decreases, is obtained from the following table :

x	0	2	4	6	8	10	12
e^x	1	7·3891	54·598	403·43	2980·7	22,027	1,627,500
e^{-x}	1	0·1353	0·0183	0·0025	0·0003	0·00005	0·0000006

Example.—Show that equidistant ordinates of an exponential curve are in geometrical progression.

Let the curve be $y = Ce^{kx}$ and the ordinates at equal distances h apart. Let the ordinates be y_1, y_2, y_3, y_4, . . .,

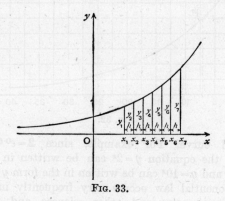

Fig. 33.

and their abscissæ x_1, x_2, x_3, x_4, . . ., so that $x_2 - x_1 = x_3 - x_2 = x_4 - x_3 = \ldots = h$.

Then $y_1 = Ce^{kx_1}$, $y_2 = Ce^{kx_2}$, $y_3 = Ce^{kx_3}$, etc.

$$\therefore \frac{y_2}{y_1} = \frac{Ce^{kx_2}}{Ce^{kx_1}} = e^{k(x_2 - x_1)} = e^{kh},$$

$$\frac{y_3}{y_2} = \frac{Ce^{kx_3}}{Ce^{kx_2}} = e^{k(x_3-x_2)} = e^{kh},$$

$$\frac{y_4}{y_3} = \frac{Ce^{kx_4}}{Ce^{kx_3}} = e^{k(x_4-x_3)} = e^{kh}, \text{ etc.}$$

Hence the ratio of any two consecutive ordinates is the same, viz. e^{kh}. Thus y_1, y_2, y_3, ... form a geometrical progression of common ratio e^{kh}.

Graph of $Ae^{-kt} \sin(\omega t + \alpha)$. Damped oscillations

The graph $y = A \sin(\omega t + \alpha)$ where t is a variable, usually denoting time, is a pure sine wave and represents a simple harmonic oscillation, such as, for example, the displacement of a weight vibrating at the end of a spring or the swing of a pendulum or of a galvanometer needle.

A pure sine wave has a constant amplitude, but in actual practice we find that mechanical oscillations gradually die away, the amplitude decreasing at each swing. This may be due to air resistance or friction at the bearing of a pendulum or to the stiffness of the spring or, as in the case of most galvanometers, it may be deliberately effected. Oscillations of gradually diminishing amplitudes are called *damped oscillations*. We shall see that the equation $y = Ae^{-kt} \sin(\omega t + \alpha)$ represents damped oscillations.

Fig. 34 shows the graph of $y = 10e^{-0.4t} \sin(3t + 0.75)$ for positive values of t, the angle being measured in radians.

The ordinates are calculated as follows. Taking logarithms,

$$\log y = \log 10 - 0.4t \log e + \log \sin(3t + 0.75)$$
$$= 1 - 0.4t \times 0.4343 + \log \sin(3t + 0.75)$$
$$= 1 - 0.1737t + \log \sin(3t + 0.75).$$

The calculation of y is shown on page 61. There is one slight difficulty in this calculation. If the angle $(3t + 0.75)$ radians is in the third or fourth quadrant its sine is negative and so we cannot find its logarithm. One example (taken from the table on page 61) will show how to deal with such cases.

When $t=1$, $y=10e^{-0.4}\sin 3.75 = 10e^{-0.4}\sin 214° 52'$

$$= 10e^{-0.4}(-\sin 34° 52') = -10e^{-0.4}\sin 34° 52'.$$

We therefore calculate $10e^{-0.4}\sin 34° 52'$, which is obtained by ignoring the negative sign in the fourth row of the table, and then insert the negative sign for y in the final result. The table on page 61 gives values of y from $t=0$ to $t=4$. For convenience we denote the angle $3t+0.75$ radians by θ.

The curve may also be obtained by drawing the sine-curve $y=10\sin(3t+0.75)$, shown dotted in Fig. 34, and multiplying its ordinates by the values of $e^{-0.4t}$ for the corresponding values of t. Since $e^{-0.4t}$ is less than 1 for all positive values

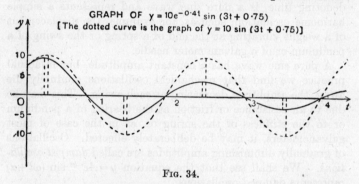

GRAPH OF $y=10e^{-0.4t}\sin(3t+0.75)$

[The dotted curve is the graph of $y=10\sin(3t+0.75)$]

FIG. 34.

of t, the ordinates of the resulting curve are all less than the corresponding ordinates of the sine-curve. Also, since $e^{-0.4t}$ decreases as t increases, the reduction in the heights of the ordinates becomes more pronounced as t increases. As t increases indefinitely, $e^{-0.4t}$ tends to zero and hence y also tends to zero.

The two curves shown in Fig. 34 both cross the axis of t at the same points, namely, when $\sin(3t+0.75)$ is zero, i.e. when $3t+0.75$ is a multiple of π.

The maximum and minimum ordinates of both curves are shown and it will be noticed that they do not coincide; those of the damped curve occur slightly before those of

t	0	0.5	1	1.5	2	2.5	3	3.5	4
$3t+0.75$ (i.e. θ in radians)	0.75	2.25	3.75	5.25	6.75	8.25	9.75	11.25	12.75
θ in degrees	42° 58'	128° 55'	214° 52'	300° 49'	386° 46'	472° 43'	558° 40'	644° 37'	730° 34'
$\sin \theta$	sin 42° 58'	sin 51° 5'	−sin 34° 52'	−sin 59° 11'	sin 26° 46'	sin 67° 17'	−sin 18° 40'	−sin 75° 23'	sin 10° 34'
$\log \sin \theta$ (except for sign)	$\bar{1}.8336$	$\bar{1}.8910$	$\bar{1}.7571$	$\bar{1}.9339$	$\bar{1}.6536$	$\bar{1}.9649$	$\bar{1}.5052$	$\bar{1}.9857$	$\bar{1}.2633$
-0.17371	0	$-0.0868 = \bar{1}.9132$	$-0.1737 = \bar{1}.8263$	$-0.2605 = \bar{1}.7395$	$-0.3474 = \bar{1}.6526$	$-0.4342 = \bar{1}.5658$	$-0.5211 = \bar{1}.4789$	$-0.6079 = \bar{1}.3921$	$-0.6948 = \bar{1}.3052$
1	1	1	1	1	1	1	1	1	1
$\log y$ (except for sign)	0.8336	0.8042	0.5834	0.6734	0.3062	0.5307	$\bar{1}.0841$	0.3778	$\bar{1}.5685$
y	6.817	6.371	−3.832	−4.714	2.024	3.394	−0.964	−2.387	0.870

the sine-curve, the time-difference being constant. namely, 0·044.

In the same way the graph of $y = Ae^{-kt} \sin(\omega t + \alpha)$, for any values of k, ω and α, may be obtained by drawing the sine-curve $y = A \sin(\omega t + \alpha)$ and multiplying the ordinates by the factor e^{-kt} which decreases as t increases and tends to zero as t tends to infinity.

Since $\sin(\omega t + \alpha)$ is numerically less than, or equal to, 1 for

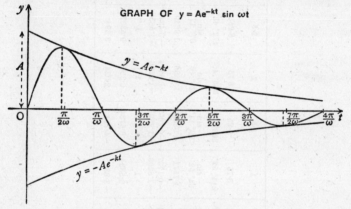

GRAPH OF $y = Ae^{-kt} \sin \omega t$

FIG. 35.

all values of t, $Ae^{-kt} \sin(\omega t + \alpha)$ is numerically less than, or equal to, Ae^{-kt} for all values of t. It follows that the curve $y = Ae^{-kt} \sin(\omega t + \alpha)$ lies entirely between the curves $y = Ae^{-kt}$ and $y = -Ae^{-kt}$, as shown in Fig. 35 (where α is taken to be 0). It touches one or other of those curves when $\sin(\omega t + \alpha) = \pm 1$, i.e. when $\omega t + \alpha$ is an odd multiple of $\pi/2$.

Determination of laws from experimental data

If two variable quantities x and y are thought to be connected by a linear relation $y = ax + b$, where a and b are constants, this can easily be tested by plotting the values of

y against the corresponding values of x and seeing whether the points lie on a straight line. Experimental error must be allowed for, so that if the points lie *nearly* on a straight line we may conclude that there is probably a theoretical law of the type $y = ax + b$ connecting x and y.

The constants a and b can be found by drawing the straight line which most nearly fits the points, and substituting in the equation the values of x and y at two points on the line. Alternatively we may make use of the fact that a is the gradient of the line (assuming x is plotted horizontally and y vertically as is usually done) and that b is the value of y when $x = 0$.

Other types of laws may also be tested by converting them into linear laws as explained in the examples below. (Some examples are also given in Part II, pages 112–119.)

Law of type $y = Cx^n$ (i.e. y varying as a power of x).

If $y = Cx^n$, where C and n are constants,

$$\log y = \log C + n \log x.$$

If we write X for $\log x$ and Y for $\log y$, then

$$Y = nX + \log C,$$

and hence the graph of Y against X is a straight line whose gradient is n, making an intercept $\log C$ on the Y-axis.

Thus to test whether y varies as some (unknown) power of x, i.e. whether x and y are connected by a relation of the type $y = Cx^n$, we plot values of $\log y$ against $\log x$. If the points lie approximately on a straight line we conclude that such a relation is satisfied, and the power n is the gradient of the line which most nearly fits the points.

Example.—The following table gives the volume v cu. ft. of 1 lb. of saturated steam at various pressures p lb.wt./in². Show that p varies as a power of v, and find the law connecting p and v.

p			25	30	35	40	50	60
v			16·29	13·72	11·86	10·48	8·500	7·162

If $p = Cv^n$, then $\log p = \log C + n \log v$ and the graph of $\log p$ against $\log v$ should be a straight line. Tabulating $\log p$ and $\log v$ for the values given in the question we have :

| $\log p$ | .. | 1·3979 | 1·4771 | 1·5441 | 1·6021 | 1·6990 | 1·7782 |
| $\log v$ | .. | 1·2119 | 1·1373 | 1·0740 | 1·0204 | 0·9294 | 0·8550 |

These numbers are plotted in Fig. 36. The points lie almost exactly on a straight line, and hence there is a law of the type $p = Cv^n$.

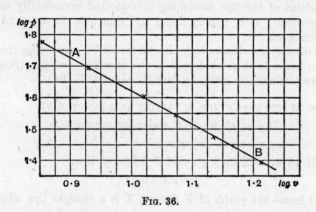

FIG. 36.

To find the constants in the equation we take two points on the line with convenient abscissæ, say A and B, which are not too close together.

At A, $\log v = 0·9$, $\log p = 1·728$;

at B, $\log v = 1·2$, $\log p = 1·409$.

Substituting these values in the equation

$$\log p = \log C + n \log v,$$

we have $\qquad 1·728 = \log C + 0·9n$

$$1·409 = \log C + 1·2n.$$

Subtracting,

$$-0.319 = 0.3n$$

$$\therefore n = -\frac{0.319}{0.3} \backsimeq -1.063$$

$$\therefore \log C = 1.728 - 0.9n = 1.728 + 0.957$$

$$= 2.685$$

$$\therefore C \backsimeq 484$$

Hence the law connecting p and v is, approximately,

$$p = 484v^{-1.063}$$

[Note that since n is negative in this example, the gradient of the line is negative as is seen in Fig. 36.]

Law of type $y = Ce^{kx}$ (i.e. an exponential law).

If $y = Ce^{kx}$, where C and k are constants,

$$\log y = \log C + kx \log e$$

$$= \log C + (k \log e)x.$$

If we write Y for $\log y$, then

$$Y = (k \log e)x + \log C.$$

Since $k \log e$ is a constant, the graph of Y against x is a straight line. Its gradient is $k \log e$ and its intercept on the Y-axis is $\log C$.

Thus to test for a law of the type $y = Ce^{kx}$ we plot values of $\log y$ against x (*not* against $\log x$), and see whether the points lie on a straight line.

Example.—If a rope passes over a rough cylinder and carries a weight W lb. at one end, the force P lb. wt. which must be applied at the other end in order to move the weight is, according to theory (see page 252, later), $P = We^{\mu\theta}$, where μ is the coefficient of friction and θ radians is the angle of lap. In an experiment to test the truth of this law the following results were obtained : $W = 5$.

θ ..	..	$\pi/6$	$\pi/3$	$\pi/2$	$2\pi/3$	$5\pi/6$	π
P ..	..	5.8	6.6	7.75	8.9	10.5	12

3

Verify that these values satisfy the theoretical **law** very approximately, and find the coefficient of friction.

If $P = We^{\mu\theta}$, then $\log P = \log W + \mu\theta \log e$, i.e.

$$\log P = \log W + (\mu \log e)\theta,$$

and the graph of $\log P$ against θ should be a straight line. Tabulating the values of $\log P$ we have :

θ	$\pi/6$	$\pi/3$	$\pi/2$	$2\pi/3$	$5\pi/6$	π
$\log P$ ..	0·7634	0·8195	0·8893	0·9494	1·0212	1·0792

These numbers are plotted in Fig. 37, and since the points

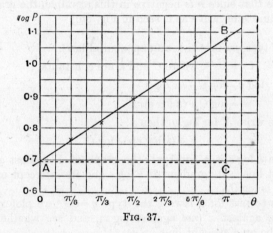

Fig. 37.

lie very nearly on a straight line we conclude that there is an exponential law, of the type $P = We^{\mu\theta}$, connecting P and θ.

Since $\log P = \log W + (\mu \log e)\theta$, $\log W$ is the value of $\log P$ when $\theta = 0$, i.e. at the point A on the line. Hence, from the graph, $\log W = 0·697$. Therefore $W \simeq 4·98$.

This agrees as well as we should expect with the value required by the theoretical law, viz. $W = 5$.

The gradient of the line is $\mu \log e$. Hence, taking the two points A and B on the line,

$$\mu \log e = \frac{CB}{AC} \text{ (each measured on its own scale)}$$

$$= \frac{1 \cdot 081 - 0 \cdot 697}{\pi}$$

$$= \frac{0 \cdot 384}{\pi}$$

$$\therefore \quad \mu = \frac{0 \cdot 384}{\pi \log e} = \frac{0 \cdot 384}{3 \cdot 1416 \times 0 \cdot 4343} \backsimeq 0 \cdot 28.$$

Specially printed graph paper is obtainable which reduces the work involved in examples of these types. In *logarithmic paper* the scales along both axes are not uniform scales but logarithmic scales, so that in testing for a law of the type $y = Cx^n$ the numbers x and y can be plotted directly, without tabulating $\log x$ and $\log y$. In *semi-logarithmic* paper one axis only is marked according to a logarithmic scale, the other axis having a uniform scale ; this can be used for testing exponential laws. (Non-uniform scales are discussed in Chapter XIII.)

Graphs in polar co-ordinates

The position of a point in a plane may be determined in various ways. The commonest way is by means of its distances x and y from two fixed lines at right angles ; these numbers x and y are called Cartesian co-ordinates (in honour of the French mathematician and philosopher Descartes, who lived in the first half of the seventeenth century and was the founder of co-ordinate geometry). An equation between x and y represents a curve and we have already had numerous examples of plotting a curve from its equation in Cartesian co-ordinates.

Another very useful way of specifying the position of a point P is by means of its distance r from a fixed point O (the *origin* or *pole*) and the angle θ between OP and a fixed straight line OX (called the *initial line* or axis). The quantities r, θ are called the *polar co-ordinates* of the point P with reference to the origin O and initial line OX. We call r the radius and θ the vectorial angle. The usual convention for positive and negative angles is observed, the positive direction of rotation being taken as anti-clockwise.

If pairs of corresponding values of r and θ are given, by plotting the points whose polar co-ordinates are r, θ and joining up these points we get a curve, which is the polar graph of r against θ.

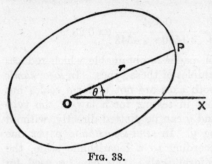

FIG. 38.

Polar co-ordinates are especially useful for describing the shape of a closed curve, like an oval; by choosing a point inside the curve as origin and measuring the radii in different directions, we can make a table of values of θ and r, from which the curve could be drawn.

If I candle-power is the intensity of illumination of a lamp in a direction making an angle θ with the vertical, then if radii are drawn proportional to the values of I we obtain the polar graph of I against θ. This curve is called the *distribution curve* for the lamp, and it gives us a picture of the way in which the light is distributed in different directions.

Example.—The intensity of illumination in different directions for a certain lamp is given by the following table :

θ (degrees) ..	0	5	10	15	20	25	30	35	40	
I (candle-power) ..	580	620	600	565	550	560	585	620	600	
θ (degrees) ..	45	50	55	60	65	70	75	80	85	
I (candle-power) ..	480	280	180	140	130	125	120	100	70	
θ (degrees)	90–310	315	320	325	330	335	340	345	350	355
I (candle-power)	0	65	95	100	115	125	130	145	200	430

Draw the distribution curve for the lamp.

Taking a scale of 1 cm. = 100 candle-power, radii are drawn from the origin O (which in this case represents the lamp) whose lengths represent I on that scale. When the points are joined the distribution curve shown in Fig. 39 is obtained.

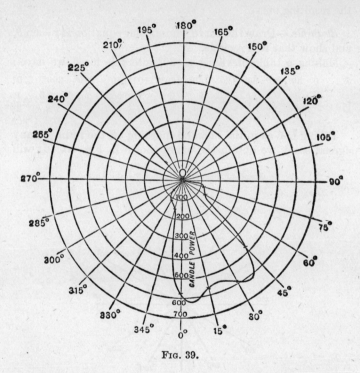

Fig. 39.

[In order to make the figure clearer some of the radii are not shown here.]

The circles in Fig. 39 are of radii representing 100, 200, 300 candle-power, etc., and form a radial scale by which the figure can be read.

Polar equations

Given an equation connecting r and θ, we can make up a table of pairs of values by giving θ special numerical values and calculating the corresponding values of r from the equation. The given equation is called the *polar equation* of the resulting curve.

Example.—Draw the curve whose polar equation is $r = \sin \theta$, and show that it is a circle.

Making a table of values at 30° intervals for θ, we have:

θ ..	0°	30°	60°	90°	120°	150°	180°	210°	240°	270°	300°	330°
r ..	0	$\frac{1}{2}$	$\frac{\sqrt{3}}{2}$	1	$\frac{\sqrt{3}}{2}$	$\frac{1}{2}$	0	$-\frac{1}{2}$	$-\frac{\sqrt{3}}{2}$	-1	$-\frac{\sqrt{3}}{2}$	$-\frac{1}{2}$

Taking OX as initial line and marking off the radii, on any agreed scale, we obtain the curve shown in Fig. 40. It will

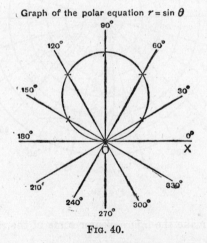

Graph of the polar equation $r = \sin \theta$

Fig. 40.

be noticed that when θ lies between 180° and 360°, r is negative. This means that the radial distance must be measured backwards. If the student marks out the points he will see that as θ varies from 0° to 360° the tracing point describes the curve twice.

Draw a circle of diameter $OA = 1$ unit at right angles to OX (Fig. 41). If P is any point on the circumference, $O\widehat{P}A$ is a right angle, since it is an angle in a semi-circle.

$$\therefore\ O\widehat{A}P = 90° - A\widehat{O}P = \theta$$
$$\therefore\ OP = OA \sin \theta$$
$$\therefore\ r = \sin \theta$$

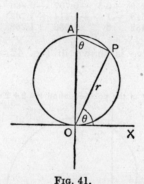

Fig. 41.

The effect of adding a constant α to θ in this equation is merely to turn each radius through the same angle α; also the effect of multiplying each radius by a constant A is merely to alter the scale of the figure and not to alter the shape of the curve. Hence it is seen that an equation of the type $r = A \sin (\theta + \alpha)$, where r and θ are *polar* co-ordinates, represents a circle of diameter A.

Example.—The profile of a cam is a curve whose polar equation is $r = 3 + 2 \cos \theta$, the origin being at the axis of the cam. Draw the curve.

Since $\cos (-\alpha) = \cos \alpha$ for any angle α, the radius r has the same value when $\theta = -\alpha$ as when $\theta = \alpha$. Hence the curve is symmetrical about the line XOX'. We need therefore plot only one-half of the curve, say that corresponding to values of θ between 0° and 180°; the other half can then be obtained by reflecting the part which has been drawn about the line XOX'. Tabulating at 15° intervals for θ we get :

θ			0°	15°	30°	45°	60°	75°	90°
$\cos \theta$			1	0·966	0·866	0·707	0·5	0·259	0
$2 \cos \theta$			2	1·932	1·732	1·414	1	0·518	0
r			5	4·932	4·732	4·414	4	3·518	3

θ			105°	120°	135°	150°	165°	180°
$\cos \theta$			−0·259	−0·5	−0·707	−0·866	−0·966	−1
$2 \cos \theta$			−0·518	−1	−1·414	−1·732	−1·932	−2
r			2·482	2	1·586	1·268	1·068	1

The complete curve is shown in Fig. 42. Such a curve is called a *limaçon*.

Graph of the polar equation $r = 3 + 2 \cos \theta$

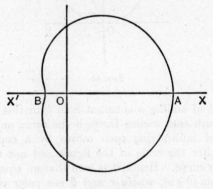

Fig. 42.

It is easily seen that if a cam of this shape rotates about O with constant angular velocity, a follower, moving in a vertical line through O, will execute simple harmonic oscillations. For suppose the cam rotates with angular velocity ω, starting with the longest radius OA vertically above O. Let

P be the point of contact of the end of the follower with the cam after time t (Fig. 43) and let x be its height above the fixed point O. Then $\theta = \omega t$, and

$$x = OP = 3 + 2 \cos \theta = 3 + 2 \cos \omega t = 3 + 2 \sin \left(\omega t + \frac{\pi}{2} \right).$$

As the cam rotates the follower moves vertically up and down and the form of the equation connecting x and t shows

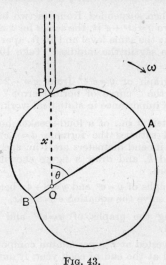

FIG. 43.

that its motion is simple harmonic. The centre of the oscillations (of the end) is 3 units of length above O, and the amplitude is 2 units. The follower is at the end of its travel when OA or OB is vertical.

By choosing different constants a and b in the equation for the cam profile $r = a + b \cos \theta$, the amplitude and centre of the oscillations can be varied; while by altering the speed of rotation of the cam the period of the oscillations can be altered at will.

3*

Exercise VIII.

1. Draw the graph of e^x from $x = -2$ to $x = 2$, and from it read off the values of $\log_e 4$ and $\log_e 0.6$.

2. Draw the graph of $y = e^x + \dfrac{1}{x}$ for positive values of x and hence find the minimum value of y.

3. Draw the graph of $y = e^{-2x} - e^{-3x}$ for positive values of x and find the value of x for which y is a maximum.

4. A chain when suspended from its two ends hangs in the form of the curve $y = e^{\frac{1}{2}x} + e^{-\frac{1}{2}x}$, the scales for x and y being equal. If the ends are at the same level and 20 ft. apart, draw the curve and measure the sag in the middle. [Take 10 ft. as your unit for x and y.]

5. Plot the graph of $y = e^{-x^2}$ from $x = -2$ to $x = 2$. [This curve is called the " curve of normal error " or " probability curve " and is of importance in statistical work.]

6. The diameter, d in., of a loud-speaker horn at x in. from the narrow end satisfies the formula $d = d_0 e^{kx}$. The horn is 12 in. long, and its end diameters are 1 in. and 10 in. Find the values of d_0 and k, and draw a figure showing a longitudinal section of the horn.

7. Plot the graphs of $y = e^x$ and $y = 8 - 4x$ between $x = -2$ and $x = 2$, and hence solve the equation $e^x = 8 - 4x$.

8. By drawing the graphs of $y = e^{-x}$ and $y = x^2$ solve the equation $x^2 e^x = 1$.

9. If £P is invested at $r\%$ per annum compound interest, and interest is added at the end of each year, it amounts at the end of n years to £A where $A = P\left(1 + \dfrac{r}{100}\right)^n$. Plot the graph of A against n from $n = 0$ to $n = 10$ when $P = 5000$ and $r = 3$.

[The law connecting A and n is an exponential law, since it is of the type $A = Pa^n$ where $a = 1 + \dfrac{r}{100}$.]

10. The temperature θ of a coil which is being heated is related to the time t by the law $\theta = \theta_m (1 - e^{-t/\tau})$, where θ_m is the maximum (i.e. final) temperature and τ is a constant—called the " time constant." Draw the graph of θ (in degrees Centigrade) against t (in minutes) if $\theta_m = 39°$ C. and $\tau = 21.5$ min., and find the time taken to reach a temperature $25°$ C.

11. The angular displacement $\theta°$ of the needle of a ballistic galvanometer at time t sec. is given by $\theta = 24e^{-0.06t} \cos \frac{1}{2}\pi t$. Draw the graph of θ against t between $t = 0$ and $t = 10$.

12. Read off the maximum and minimum ordinates of the curve in Question 11 and verify that they are in geometrical progression.

Show that the variables in the following questions are related by a law of the form stated and find approximately the values of the constants in the law:

13. Q cu. ft./sec. is the flow over a weir when the head is H in. Law: $Q = aH^n$.

H	..	..	6	9	12	15	18
Q	..	..	214	381	596	830	1080

14. i amp. is the current which melts a copper wire of diameter d in. Law: $i = ad^n$.

$d \times 10^3$..	36	28	20	14·8	11·6	10·0	7·6	6·8	6·0
i ..	70·0	48·0	29·0	18·4	12·8	10·2	6·79	5·74	4·76

Find also the diameter of the thinnest copper wire which will take a current of 15 amp.

15. p in. is the reading of a mercury barometer at a height h ft. above the ground. Law: $p = Ce^{kh}$.

h	..	1,000	2,000	4,000	7,000	10,000	15,000
p..	..	28·75	27·66	25·58	22·78	20·26	16·65

Find also the height of an aeroplane in which the barometer registers 21·4 in.

16. L microhenrys is the inductance of a choking coil of N turns. Law: $L = cN^k$.

N	..	15	24	30	40	48	65	72
L	..	38	96	155	272	380	700	890

17. $T°$ is the absolute temperature of a gas, which is being compressed adiabatically, when its pressure is p lb. wt./sq. in. Law: $T = kp^n$.

p	..	..	12	16	22	35	50	64
T	..	..	351	380	407	464	509	540

18. i amp. is the current in an inductive circuit after t sec. Law: $i = ae^{kt}$.

t	..	..	0	1	2	3	4
i	..	..	75	31	14	6	2·4

19. The following table gives the coefficient of viscosity η (in c.g.s. units) of glycerine at temperature $\theta°$ C. Find a formula of the type $\eta = Ce^{k\theta}$ which approximately fits the data.

θ	..	..	0	10	20	30
η	..	..	46·0	21·0	8·5	3·5

20. In the formation of p-chloracetanilide from the isomeric N-chloroamine the titration figures y (ml. of sodium thiosulphate) measure the amount of unchanged material at time t min.

t	..	..	0	60	120	180	240	360
y	..	..	49·3	35·6	25·75	18·5	13·8	7·3

Verify that there is a law of the type $y = ae^{-kt}$ and find the constants a and k.

21. In an experiment on the hydrolysis of phenyl acetate, in which the initial concentration a was 0·1815 mols per litre, the amount, x mols per litre, of phenol liberated in t min. was given by :

t	..	175	240	300	360	480	500	535
x	..	0·0261	0·0351	0·0418	0·0493	0·0620	0·0644	0·0683

Verify that there is a law of the type $x = a(1 - e^{-kt})$ connecting x and t, and find the value of the constant k. [Hint. Graph $\log(a - x)$ against t.]

22. Plot the polar curve given by the following table :

θ ..	0°	30°	60°	90°	120°	150°	165°	180°	195°	210°	240°	270°	300°	330°
r ..	1·3	1·4	1·55	1·7	1·9	2·25	2·6	4·0	2·6	2·25	1·9	1·7	1·55	1·4

23. The intensity of illumination, I candle-power, due to a lamp mounted above a circular opal-glass disc in the ceiling of a room is given by $I = 100 \cos \theta$, where θ is measured from the vertical. Draw the distribution curve (i.e. the polar graph of I against θ) and show that it is a circle.

24. In order to obtain an even illumination of 10 ft.-candles on a horizontal plane, the intensity distribution must be $I = 10h^2 \sec^3 \theta$, where h is the height of the source above the plane. Draw the distribution curve if a circular area of 10 ft. diameter, with its centre directly beneath the source, is to be uniformly illuminated by a lamp 5 ft. above it.

25. A point-source has a candle-power distribution in the lower hemisphere given by the equation $I = 50(\cos \theta + \sin \theta)$. Draw the polar curve.

26. A curve is symmetrical about the initial line XOX' and, for values of θ between 0° and 180°, $r = k\theta$, where k is a constant. Draw the curve.

Show that if a cam with this curve as profile rotates about O with constant angular velocity, a follower which is free to move in a vertical line through O will move up and down with constant speed.

27. Draw the polar curve $r = 1 - \cos\theta$. [This is called a *cardioid*. It is the path traced out by a point on the circumference of a circle which rolls on the outside of another circle of equal radius.]

28. Show that if values of θ are chosen which are in arithmetical progression, the corresponding radii of the curve $r = ae^{k\theta}$ (where a and k are constants) are in geometrical progression. Hence draw the curve. [It is called an *equiangular spiral* or *logarithmic spiral*.]

Draw the following polar curves :

29. $r = \sin 2\theta$.

30. $r^2 = \cos 2\theta$.   [*Lemniscate.*]

31. $r = 1 + 2\cos\theta$.

CHAPTER IV

TRIGONOMETRY

Formulæ for $\sin (A \pm B)$, $\cos (A \pm B)$, $\sin 2A$, $\cos 2A$, **etc.**

The following formulæ have been proved in Part II (pages 284–5) :

$$\sin (A+B) = \sin A \cos B + \cos A \sin B \quad . \quad . \quad (1)$$
$$\sin (A-B) = \sin A \cos B - \cos A \sin B \quad . \quad . \quad (2)$$
$$\cos (A+B) = \cos A \cos B - \sin A \sin B \quad . \quad . \quad (3)$$
$$\cos (A-B) = \cos A \cos B + \sin A \sin B \quad . \quad . \quad (4)$$

They are true for all values of the angles A and B.

From formulæ (1) and (3) we obtain the following :

$$\sin 2A = \sin (A+A)$$
$$= \sin A \cos A + \cos A \sin A$$

i.e. $\qquad \sin 2A = 2 \sin A \cos A \quad . \quad . \quad . \quad . \quad . \quad (5)$

Also $\qquad \cos 2A = \cos (A+A)$
$$= \cos A \cos A - \sin A \sin A$$

i.e. $\qquad \cos 2A = \cos^2 A - \sin^2 A \quad . \quad . \quad . \quad . \quad (6)$

By writing $\sin^2 A = 1 - \cos^2 A$ or $\cos^2 A = 1 - \sin^2 A$ in this formula we obtain two other forms for $\cos 2A$, viz. :

$$\cos 2A = 2 \cos^2 A - 1 . \quad . \quad . \quad . \quad . \quad (7)$$

and $\qquad \cos 2A = 1 - 2 \sin^2 A \quad . \quad . \quad . \quad . \quad . \quad (8)$

From (7), $\qquad 2 \cos^2 A = 1 + \cos 2A$

$\qquad\qquad \therefore \cos^2 A = \tfrac{1}{2}(1 + \cos 2A) \quad . \quad . \quad . \quad . \quad (9)$

and from (8), $\qquad 2 \sin^2 A = 1 - \cos 2A$

$\qquad\qquad \therefore \sin^2 A = \tfrac{1}{2}(1 - \cos 2A) \quad . \quad . \quad . \quad . \quad (10)$

Formulæ (9) and (10) are especially useful in integration.

Example.—Find the value of sin 15° without using tables of sines or cosines :

$$\sin 15° = \sin (45° - 30°)$$
$$= \sin 45° \cos 30° - \cos 45° \sin 30°$$
$$= \frac{1}{\sqrt{2}} \cdot \frac{\sqrt{3}}{2} - \frac{1}{\sqrt{2}} \cdot \frac{1}{2}$$
$$= \frac{\sqrt{3} - 1}{2\sqrt{2}} = \frac{(\sqrt{3} - 1)\sqrt{2}}{4} = \frac{\sqrt{6} - \sqrt{2}}{4}$$
$$\simeq \frac{2 \cdot 449 - 1 \cdot 414}{4} = \frac{1 \cdot 035}{4} \simeq 0 \cdot 259.$$

Example.—Express cos 3x in terms of cos x.

$$\cos 3x = \cos (2x + x)$$
$$= \cos 2x \cos x - \sin 2x \sin x$$
$$= (2 \cos^2 x - 1) \cos x - (2 \sin x \cos x) \sin x$$
$$= 2 \cos^3 x - \cos x - 2 \sin^2 x \cos x$$
$$= 2 \cos^3 x - \cos x - 2 (1 - \cos^2 x) \cos x$$
$$= 2 \cos^3 x - \cos x \ - 2 \cos x + 2 \cos^3 x$$
$$= 4 \cos^3 x - 3 \cos x.$$

Example.—Prove that sin (α + 60°) + sin (α − 60°) = sin α.

$$\sin (\alpha + 60°) + \sin (\alpha - 60°)$$
$$= (\sin \alpha \cos 60° + \cos \alpha \sin 60°) + (\sin \alpha \cos 60° - \cos \alpha \sin 60°)$$
$$= 2 \sin \alpha \cos 60°$$
$$= 2 \sin \alpha \cdot \tfrac{1}{2}$$
$$= \sin \alpha.$$

Example.—Prove that $\sin^4 \theta = \tfrac{1}{8}(3 - 4 \cos 2\theta + \cos 4\theta)$.

$$\sin^4 \theta = (\sin^2 \theta)^2$$
$$= \{\tfrac{1}{2}(1 - \cos 2\theta)\}^2$$
$$= \tfrac{1}{4}(1 - 2 \cos 2\theta + \cos^2 2\theta)$$
$$= \tfrac{1}{4}\{1 - 2 \cos 2\theta + \tfrac{1}{2}(1 + \cos 4\theta)\}$$
$$= \tfrac{1}{4}\{\tfrac{3}{2} - 2 \cos 2\theta + \tfrac{1}{2} \cos 4\theta\}$$
$$= \tfrac{1}{8}(3 - 4 \cos 2\theta + \cos 4\theta).$$

Example.—In a certain type of bevel gearing the velocity ratio k is given by $k = -\dfrac{\cos \alpha}{\cos 2\alpha}$, where α is the angle between the shafts of the pinion and gear. Find the value of α when $k = 6$. [In this type of gearing α is essentially less than 90°.]

We have to solve the equation

$$6 = -\frac{\cos \alpha}{\cos 2\alpha}.$$

$$6 \cos 2\alpha = -\cos \alpha$$

$$6 (2 \cos^2 \alpha - 1) = -\cos \alpha$$

$$12 \cos^2 \alpha + \cos \alpha - 6 = 0.$$

This is a quadratic equation for $\cos \alpha$, giving

$$\cos \alpha = \frac{-1 \pm \sqrt{1 + 288}}{24}$$

$$= \frac{-1 \pm \sqrt{289}}{24} = \frac{-1 \pm 17}{24}$$

$$= \tfrac{16}{24} \text{ or } -\tfrac{18}{24}$$

$$= \tfrac{2}{3} \text{ or } -\tfrac{3}{4}.$$

Since $\alpha < 90°$, $\cos \alpha$ must be positive.

$$\therefore \cos \alpha = \tfrac{2}{3} \fallingdotseq 0\cdot6667$$

$$\therefore \alpha = 48° \ 11'.$$

Example.—The equation $\dfrac{\cos (30° + \phi)}{\cos (30° - \phi)} = n$ occurs in the two-wattmeter method of measuring power in three-phase circuits, being the ratio of the readings of the two wattmeters. Prove that $\tan \phi = \sqrt{3}\left(\dfrac{1 - n}{1 + n}\right)$, and find the angle ϕ (assumed to be acute) when $n = 0\cdot3$.

The equation for ϕ is

$$\cos (30° + \phi) = n \cos (30° - \phi)$$

$$\cos 30° \cos \phi - \sin 30° \sin \phi = n(\cos 30° \cos \phi + \sin 30° \sin \phi)$$

$$\frac{\sqrt{3}}{2} \cos \phi - \frac{1}{2} \sin \phi = n\left(\frac{\sqrt{3}}{2}\cos \phi + \frac{1}{2} \sin \phi\right)$$

Collecting the terms in $\sin \phi$ on one side of the equation and those in $\cos \phi$ on the other,

$$\frac{1}{2}(1 + n) \sin \phi = \frac{\sqrt{3}}{2}(1 - n) \cos \phi$$

$$\sin \phi = \sqrt{3}\left(\frac{1 - n}{1 + n}\right) \cos \phi$$

Dividing through by $\cos \phi$, we obtain

$$\tan \phi = \sqrt{3}\left(\frac{1 - n}{1 + n}\right).$$

When $n = 0.3$,

$$\tan \phi = \sqrt{3}\left(\frac{1 - 0.3}{1 + 0.3}\right) = \sqrt{3} \times \frac{0.7}{1.3}$$

$$= \frac{7\sqrt{3}}{13} \mathrel{\widehat{=}} \frac{7 \times 1.7321}{13} = \frac{12.1247}{13}$$

$$\mathrel{\widehat{=}} 0.9327$$

$$\therefore \phi \mathrel{\widehat{=}} 43° \, 0'.$$

Exercise IX.

[For additional examples, see Part II, Exercise XXXVI.]

[NOTE. When angles are expressed without units, the units are always understood to be radians.]

1. Expand (i) $\sin (\alpha + 60°)$, (ii) $\sin (150° - \theta)$, (iii) $\cos \left(x + \frac{\pi}{4}\right)$.

2. Express as a single trigonometric ratio :

   (i) $\sin 35° \cos 25° + \cos 35° \sin 25°$,

   (ii) $\cos 2y \cos y + \sin 2y \sin y$,

   (iii) $\cos (A + B) \cos (A - B) - \sin (A + B) \sin (A - B)$.

3. Find sin 75° and cos 75° without using tables of sines or cosines.

4. If $v = 220 \sin (100\pi t + 0.3)$ express v in the form

$$a \sin 100\pi t + b \cos 100\pi t,$$

finding the values of a and b. Calculate the value of v when $t = 0.018$ from both forms and verify that the two values are equal, to the degree of accuracy obtainable from the tables.

5. If $\sin A = 0.8$, $\sin B = 0.25$, and A, B are both acute angles, find the values of $\sin (A - B)$ and $\cos (A - B)$ without using trigonometric tables.

6. If $\tan \theta = \frac{4}{3}$, $\tan \phi = \frac{5}{12}$, and θ, ϕ are acute angles, find the values of $\sin (\theta + \phi)$, $\sin 2\theta$ and $\cos 2\phi$ without using tables.

7. ABC is a triangle and $\cos A = \frac{4}{5}$, $\cos B = \frac{5}{13}$; find $\cos C$ without using tables.

8. Prove that $(\sin x + \cos x)^2 = 1 + \sin 2x$.

9. Prove that

$$(\sin A + \sin B)^2 + (\cos A + \cos B)^2 = 2\{1 + \cos (A - B)\}$$

$$= 4 \cos^2 \left(\frac{A - B}{2}\right).$$

10. Prove that

$$\cos (A + B) \cos (A - B) = \cos^2 A - \sin^2 B = \cos^2 B - \sin^2 A.$$

11. What are the maximum and minimum values, as θ varies, of (i) $\sin \theta \cos \theta$, (ii) $\frac{2}{3} \sin 3\theta$, (iii) $\sin^2 \theta - \cos^2 \theta$?

12. Simplify $\sin \alpha + \sin \beta \cos (\alpha + \beta)$.

13. If $\sin (\alpha + \beta) : \sin (\alpha - \beta) = (p + q) : (p - q)$, prove that $\tan \alpha : \tan \beta = p : q$.

14. The efficiency η of a screw gearing is given by

$$\eta = \frac{1 - \mu \sec \theta \tan \alpha}{1 + \mu \sec \theta \tan \alpha}.$$

If $\mu = \sin \theta$ show that $\eta = \dfrac{\cos (\theta + \alpha)}{\cos (\theta - \alpha)}$.

15. Solve the equation $\cos (45° + x) + \cos (45° - x) = 0.7$, giving the values of x between 0° and 360°.

16. Find the value of θ between 0 and π which satisfies the equation $\sin \left(\theta - \dfrac{\pi}{4}\right) = 2 \cos \theta$.

17. The thrust T along the crank in a reciprocating engine is given by $T = p \dfrac{\cos(\theta + \phi)}{\cos \phi}$ where $\sin \phi = \dfrac{r}{l} \sin \theta$. Prove that

$$T = p\left\{ \cos \theta - \frac{r \sin^2 \theta}{\sqrt{l^2 - r^2 \sin^2 \theta}} \right\},$$

and that the values of θ for which T is zero are given by

$$\tan \theta = \pm \frac{l}{r}$$

[Hint. Solve the equation $T = 0$ for $\cos \theta$, and thence deduce the above values of $\tan \theta$.]

18. The equation $F_2 + F_3 \sin \alpha = \mu F_3 \cos \alpha$ occurs in the design of a cone clutch, α being the cone angle and μ the coefficient of friction. If $\mu = \tan \lambda$, prove that $\alpha = \lambda - \sin^{-1}\left(\dfrac{F_2}{F_3} \cos \lambda \right)$.

Prove the following identities :

19. $\cos^4 A - \sin^4 A = \cos 2A$.

20. $\cos^4 A + \sin^4 A = 1 - \frac{1}{2} \sin^2 2A = \frac{1}{4}(3 + \cos 4A)$.

21. $(\sin x + \cos x)(\sin y + \cos y) = \sin(x + y) + \cos(x - y)$.

22. $\cot \theta - \tan \theta = 2 \cot 2\theta$.

23. $\dfrac{\sin 3x}{\sin x} - \dfrac{\cos 3x}{\cos x} = 2$.

24. $\dfrac{1 + \sin \theta - \cos \theta}{1 + \sin \theta + \cos \theta} = \tan \dfrac{\theta}{2}$.

25. $\sin^2\left(\dfrac{\pi}{4} - \dfrac{\theta}{2} \right) = \frac{1}{2}(1 - \sin \theta)$.

26. $\dfrac{(1 + \cos 2\theta)(1 + \cos 4\theta)}{\sin 2\theta \sin 4\theta} = \cot \theta \cot 2\theta$.

27. Solve the equation $\sin(2x + 1 \cdot 36) = 4 \sin(2x - 0 \cdot 64)$, giving the values of x between 0 and 2π.

28. Find the values of θ between 0 and 2π which satisfy the equation $\cos 2\theta = 2 \cos \theta + 1$.

29. Solve the equation $\sin 2\theta = 2 \sin \theta$.

30. Prove that $\cos^4 \theta = \frac{1}{8}(3 + 4 \cos 2\theta + \cos 4\theta)$.

31. Solve the cubic equation $4x^3 - 3x + 1 = 0$ by putting $x = \cos \theta$ and using the fact that $\cos 3\theta = 4 \cos^3 \theta - 3 \cos \theta$.

32. Solve the cubic equation $12x^3 - x - 0 \cdot 065 = 0$ by putting $x = \frac{1}{3} \cos \theta$.

Formulæ for tan $(A \pm B)$ and tan $2A$

$$\mathbf{tan}\,(A+B) = \frac{\sin(A+B)}{\cos(A+B)}$$

$$= \frac{\sin A \cos B + \cos A \sin B}{\cos A \cos B - \sin A \sin B}$$

This fraction is unaltered if we divide both **numerator and denominator** by $\cos A \cos B$. Thus

$$\tan(A+B) = \frac{\dfrac{\sin A}{\cos A} + \dfrac{\sin B}{\cos B}}{1 - \dfrac{\sin A}{\cos A} \cdot \dfrac{\sin B}{\cos B}}$$

i.e. $$\mathbf{tan}\,(A+B) = \frac{\tan A + \tan B}{1 - \tan A \tan B} \quad \cdots \quad (11)$$

This formula is true for all values of the angles A and B. We can therefore write $-B$ in place of B; hence

$$\tan(A-B) = \frac{\tan A + \tan(-B)}{1 - \tan A \tan(-B)}$$

i.e. $$\mathbf{tan}\,(A-B) = \frac{\tan A - \tan B}{1 + \tan A \tan B} \quad \cdots \quad (12)$$

From (11) we can derive a formula for $\tan 2A$ in terms of $\tan A$, viz.

$$\tan 2A = \tan(A+A) = \frac{\tan A + \tan A}{1 - \tan A \cdot \tan A}$$

i.e. $$\mathbf{tan}\,2A = \frac{2 \tan A}{1 - \tan^2 A} \quad \cdots \cdots \cdots \quad (13)$$

Example.—Prove that

$$\tan\left(\frac{\pi}{4} + \theta\right) = \frac{1 + \tan\theta}{1 - \tan\theta} \quad \text{and} \quad \tan\left(\frac{\pi}{4} - \theta\right) = \frac{1 - \tan\theta}{1 + \tan\theta}.$$

$$\tan\left(\frac{\pi}{4} + \theta\right) = \frac{\tan\dfrac{\pi}{4} + \tan\theta}{1 - \tan\dfrac{\pi}{4}\tan\theta} = \frac{1 + \tan\theta}{1 - \tan\theta}$$

$$\tan\left(\frac{\pi}{4}-\theta\right) = \frac{\tan\frac{\pi}{4}-\tan\theta}{1+\tan\frac{\pi}{4}\tan\theta} = \frac{1-\tan\theta}{1+\tan\theta}$$

Example.—If α, β are both acute angles and $\tan\alpha = \frac{1}{2}$, $\tan\beta = \frac{1}{3}$, show, without using tables, that $\alpha+\beta = 45°$. Also verify this by finding α and β from tables.

$$\tan(\alpha+\beta) = \frac{\tan\alpha+\tan\beta}{1-\tan\alpha\tan\beta}$$

$$= \frac{\frac{1}{2}+\frac{1}{3}}{1-\frac{1}{6}} = \frac{\frac{5}{6}}{\frac{5}{6}} = 1$$

$\therefore \alpha+\beta = 45° \pm n \,.\, 180°$, where n is any integer.

Since α and β are both acute angles, $\alpha+\beta$ lies between $0°$ and $180°$.

Hence $\alpha+\beta = 45°$.

Using tables of tangents, we find that

$\alpha = 26° \, 34'$, $\beta = 18° \, 26'$, whence $\alpha+\beta = 45° \, 0'$.

Example.—If $\tan 2x = 4$, and x is an acute angle, find $\tan x$ without using tables of tangents.

$$\tan 2x = \frac{2\tan x}{1-\tan^2 x}.$$

$$\therefore \frac{2\tan x}{1-\tan^2 x} = 4$$

$$\therefore \tan x = 2(1-\tan^2 x)$$

$$\therefore 2\tan^2 x + \tan x - 2 = 0.$$

This is a quadratic for $\tan x$; solving,

$$\tan x = \frac{-1 \pm \sqrt{17}}{4}.$$

Since x is an acute angle, $\tan x$ is positive.

$$\therefore \tan x = \frac{-1+\sqrt{17}}{4} \simeq \frac{-1+4 \cdot 123}{4} = \frac{3 \cdot 123}{4} \simeq 0 \cdot 781.$$

Angle between two straight lines whose equations are given

The graph of $y = mx + c$ is a straight line whose gradient is m. If the scales for x and y are the same and the line makes an angle α with the positive direction of the x-axis, the gradient of the line is $\tan \alpha$; thus $m = \tan \alpha$.

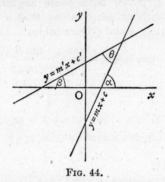

Fig. 44.

If a second line, whose equation is $y = m'x + c'$, makes an angle β with the x-axis, $m' = \tan \beta$.

If θ is the angle between the two straight lines, $\theta = \alpha - \beta$.

$$\therefore \tan \theta = \tan(\alpha - \beta) = \frac{\tan \alpha - \tan \beta}{1 + \tan \alpha \tan \beta} = \frac{m - m'}{1 + mm'}.$$

As a special case, if the lines are at right angles, $\theta = 90°$ and $\tan \theta$ is infinitely large. Hence $1 + mm' = 0$, that is, $mm' = -1$.

Expressions for sin θ, cos θ and tan θ in terms of $\tan \dfrac{\theta}{2}$

$$\sin \theta = \sin \left(2 \times \frac{\theta}{2} \right) = 2 \sin \frac{\theta}{2} \cos \frac{\theta}{2}$$

$$= \frac{2 \sin \dfrac{\theta}{2} \cos \dfrac{\theta}{2}}{\cos^2 \dfrac{\theta}{2} + \sin^2 \dfrac{\theta}{2}} \qquad \left(\text{since } \cos^2 \frac{\theta}{2} + \sin^2 \frac{\theta}{2} = 1 \right)$$

$$= \frac{\dfrac{2\sin\theta/2}{\cos\theta/2}}{1+\dfrac{\sin^2\theta/2}{\cos^2\theta/2}} \qquad \left(\begin{array}{l}\text{on dividing numerator and}\\ \text{denominator by } \cos^2\dfrac{\theta}{2}\end{array}\right)$$

$$= \frac{2\tan\dfrac{\theta}{2}}{1+\tan^2\dfrac{\theta}{2}}.$$

$$\cos\theta = \cos\left(2\times\frac{\theta}{2}\right) = \cos^2\frac{\theta}{2}-\sin^2\frac{\theta}{2}$$

$$= \frac{\cos^2\dfrac{\theta}{2}-\sin^2\dfrac{\theta}{2}}{\cos^2\dfrac{\theta}{2}+\sin^2\dfrac{\theta}{2}}$$

$$= \frac{1-\dfrac{\sin^2\theta/2}{\cos^2\theta/2}}{1+\dfrac{\sin^2\theta/2}{\cos^2\theta/2}} \qquad \left(\begin{array}{l}\text{on dividing numerator and}\\ \text{demoninator by } \cos^2\dfrac{\theta}{2}\end{array}\right)$$

$$= \frac{1-\tan^2\dfrac{\theta}{2}}{1+\tan^2\dfrac{\theta}{2}}.$$

$$\tan\theta = \tan\left(2\times\frac{\theta}{2}\right)$$

$$= \frac{2\tan\dfrac{\theta}{2}}{1-\tan^2\dfrac{\theta}{2}}.$$

These formulæ are important because they express all the trigonometric ratios of any angle θ in terms of a single trigonometric ratio (of $\theta/2$) without any square roots occurring.

They are extremely useful for many purposes (for example, in integration and in solving trigonometric equations) and are usually remembered in the following form :

Denote $\tan \dfrac{\theta}{2}$ by t ; then

$$\sin \theta = \frac{2t}{1+t^2}, \quad \cos \theta = \frac{1-t^2}{1+t^2}, \quad \tan \theta = \frac{2t}{1-t^2}. \quad . \quad (14)$$

[As a check,

$$\frac{\sin \theta}{\cos \theta} = \frac{2t}{1+t^2} \div \frac{1-t^2}{1+t^2} = \frac{2t}{1+t^2} \times \frac{1+t^2}{1-t^2} = \frac{2t}{1-t^2} = \tan \theta.]$$

Example.—Find the values of θ between 0° and 360° which satisfy the equation $3 \sin \theta + 4 \cos \theta = 2$.

Put $\tan \dfrac{\theta}{2} = t$; then, substituting the expressions for $\sin \theta$ and $\cos \theta$ in terms of t, the equation becomes

$$3\left(\frac{2t}{1+t^2}\right) + 4\left(\frac{1-t^2}{1+t^2}\right) = 2.$$

Multiplying both sides of the equation by $1+t^2$,

$$6t + 4 - 4t^2 = 2 + 2t^2$$
$$6t^2 - 6t - 2 = 0$$
$$3t^2 - 3t - 1 = 0$$
$$t = \frac{3 \pm \sqrt{9+12}}{6} = \frac{3 \pm \sqrt{21}}{6} \eqsim \frac{2 \pm 4 \cdot 583}{6}$$
$$= \frac{7 \cdot 583}{6} \quad \text{or} \quad -\frac{1 \cdot 583}{6}$$

i.e. $\tan \dfrac{\theta}{2} \eqsim 1 \cdot 264 \quad \text{or} \quad -0 \cdot 264$

$$\therefore \frac{\theta}{2} = 51° \ 39' \pm n \ . \ 180° \quad \text{or} - 14° \ 47' \pm n \ . \ 180°,$$

where n is any integer.

$$\therefore \theta = 103° \ 18' \pm n \ . \ 360° \quad \text{or} - 29° \ 34' \pm n \ . \ 360°.$$

The values of θ between $0°$ and $360°$ are

$$\theta = 103° \ 18' \quad \text{or} \quad 330° \ 26'.$$

[Another method of solving equations of this type has been given in Part II, page 295.]

Exercise X.

1. Verify the formulæ for $\tan(A \pm B)$ when $A = 38°$, $B = 20°$.

2. Verify the formulæ for $\tan(A \pm B)$ when $A = 45°$, $B = 135°$.

3. Verify the formula for $\tan 2A$ when $A = 60°$.

4. Find $\tan 15°$ without tables.

5. Find $\tan 22\frac{1}{2}°$ without tables.

6. Prove that $\tan 3\theta = \dfrac{3 \tan \theta - \tan^3 \theta}{1 - 3 \tan^2 \theta}$.

7. If θ is the acute angle $\tan^{-1} 0.8$, find $\tan 2\theta$ and $\tan \theta/2$ without tables.

8. Prove that—

$$\text{(i)} \quad \tan\left(\frac{\pi}{4} + x\right) - \tan\left(\frac{\pi}{4} - x\right) = 2 \tan 2x,$$

$$\text{(ii)} \quad \tan\left(\frac{\pi}{4} + x\right) + \tan\left(\frac{\pi}{4} - x\right) = 2 \sec 2x.$$

9. If α, β are acute angles and $\tan \alpha = \frac{1}{7}$, $\tan \beta = \frac{3}{4}$, prove without using tables that $\alpha + \beta = \frac{1}{4}\pi$.

10. If $\tan(x + y) = 2$ and $\tan y = \frac{1}{3}$, find $\tan x$ without tables.

11. AN is a vertical pole of height a, N being on the ground, and Q is a point on the pole at height b above N. If O is a point on the ground distant c from N and PQ subtends an angle θ at O, prove that $\tan \theta = \dfrac{(a-b)c}{ab + c^2}$.

12. Prove that $\cot(A + B) = \dfrac{\cot A \cot B - 1}{\cot A + \cot B}$, and find a similar expression for $\cot(A - B)$.

13. The formula $x = h\{\cot(\alpha - \phi) - \cot \alpha\}$ occurs in the design of a Davis's steering gear. Prove that

$$\cot \phi = \operatorname{cosec}^2 \alpha \left\{ \frac{h}{x} + \tfrac{1}{2} \sin 2\alpha \right\}.$$

14. Prove the following identities :

   (i) $\cot \theta - \tan \theta = 2 \cot 2\theta$,

   (ii) $\tan (45° + \theta) \tan (45° - \theta) = 1$,

   (iii) $\sec \theta + \tan \theta = \tan \left(\dfrac{\pi}{4} + \dfrac{\theta}{2} \right)$.

15. Find, by calculation, the angle between the lines $y = 4x + 3$ and $y = x - 1$. Verify by drawing the lines on squared paper and measuring the angle.

16. Show, without drawing, that the lines $y = 2x - 3$ and $y = -\frac{1}{2}x + 1$ are at right angles, and verify by drawing on squared paper.

17. Find the equation of the straight line which is perpendicular to the line $y = 3x + 7$ and passes through the point $(6, 2)$.

18. If $\tan \dfrac{\alpha}{2} = \frac{3}{4}$ calculate $\sin \alpha$, $\cos \alpha$ and $\tan \alpha$ without tables.

19. If $\sin 2\theta = \frac{3}{5}$ and $0° < \theta < 45°$, find $\tan \theta$ without tables.

20. Prove that $\sqrt{\dfrac{1 - \sin x}{1 + \sin x}} = \dfrac{1 - \tan \dfrac{x}{2}}{1 + \tan \dfrac{x}{2}}$.

21. If $\cos \theta = \dfrac{\cos \phi - e}{1 - e \cos \phi}$, prove that $\tan \dfrac{\theta}{2} = \pm \sqrt{\dfrac{1 + e}{1 - e}} \tan \dfrac{\phi}{2}$.

22. Fig. 45 shows a railway track of mean radius R turning out from a straight main line. If the width of the track is G and the angle of crossing is θ, show that $\cos \theta = \dfrac{R - \frac{1}{2}G}{R + \frac{1}{2}G}$ and hence that $\cot \dfrac{\theta}{2} = \sqrt{\dfrac{2R}{G}}$.

23. If in Question **22** both tracks are curved (with similar flexure) and their mean radii are R and r (see Fig. 46), show, by applying the cosine rule to $\triangle OCA$, that

$$\cos \theta = \frac{2Rr - G(r - R) + \frac{1}{2}G^2}{2Rr + G(r - R) - \frac{1}{2}G^2}$$

and hence that

$$\cot \frac{\theta}{2} = \sqrt{\frac{2Rr}{G(r - R - \frac{1}{2}G)}}$$

$$\simeq \sqrt{\frac{2R}{G\left(1 - \dfrac{R}{r}\right)}}$$

24. Find the angles between $-180°$ and $180°$ which satisfy the equation $\sin x - 2 \cos x = 1$.

25. Solve the equation $9 \sin \theta - 16 \cos \theta = -12$, giving the angles between $0°$ and $360°$.

26. Show that, if h is small, $\tan (x + h) \fallingdotseq \tan x + h \sec^2 x$, the angles being in radians.

Calculate the value of $\tan 45° \; 18'$ from this approximation and compare with the value given in the tables.

[Hint: $\tan (x + h) = \dfrac{\tan x + \tan h}{1 - \tan h \tan x}.$

If h is small, $\tan (h \text{ radians})$ is approximately equal to h, and hence

$$\tan (x + h) \fallingdotseq \frac{\tan x + h}{1 - h \tan x} = (\tan x + h)(1 - h \tan x)^{-1}.$$

Expand $(1 - h \tan x)^{-1}$ by the binomial theorem.]

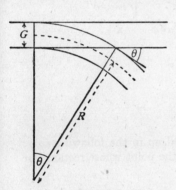

Fig. 45.

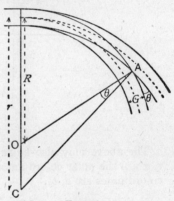

Fig. 46.

To convert $a \sin \theta + b \cos \theta$ into the form $r \sin (\theta + \alpha)$

We have shown in Part II (pages 292–5) how to convert any expression of the type $a \sin \theta + b \cos \theta$, where a and b are constants, into the form $r \sin (\theta + \alpha)$. We shall recapitulate briefly in this paragraph.

$$\begin{aligned} r \sin (\theta + \alpha) &= r(\sin \theta \cos \alpha + \cos \theta \sin \alpha) \\ &= r \cos \alpha \, . \, \sin \theta + r \sin \alpha \, . \, \cos \theta. \end{aligned}$$

This is identical with $a \sin \theta + b \cos \theta$ if

$$r \cos a = a \quad \text{and} \quad r \sin \alpha = b.$$

Since $r \cos \alpha$, $r \sin \alpha$ are the resolved parts along two perpendicular directions of the vector r_a, the required constants r and α are the magnitude and direction-angle of the vector whose resolved parts are a and b. The angle α may be in any of the four quadrants, according as a and b are positive or negative (see Part II, page 275); the particular quadrant is determined by drawing a rough sketch.

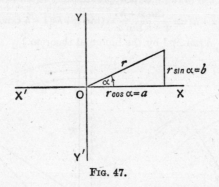

FIG. 47.

The above may also be summed up in the following rule : r, α are the polar co-ordinates of the point whose rectangular co-ordinates are a, b.

Example.—Convert (i) $3 \sin \theta + 4 \cos \theta$, (ii) $7 \cdot 2 \cos \theta - 1 \cdot 6 \sin \theta$ into the form $r \sin (\theta + \alpha)$.

(i) In this example $a = 3$, $b = 4$.

The point (3, 4) is marked in Fig. 48, from which it is seen that

$$r = \sqrt{3^2 + 4^2} = \sqrt{9 + 16} = \sqrt{25} = 5$$
$$\alpha = \tan^{-1} \tfrac{4}{3} = \tan^{-1} 1 \cdot 3333 = 53° \; 8'$$
$$\therefore 3 \sin \theta + 4 \cos \theta \equiv 5 \sin (\theta + 53° \; 8').$$

(ii) Writing the expression as $-1·6 \sin \theta + 7·2 \cos \theta$, we have in this case $a = -1·6$, $b = 7·2$.

The point $(-1·6, 7·2)$ is shown in Fig. 49.

$$r = \sqrt{1·6^2 + 7·2^2} = \sqrt{2·56 + 51·84} = \sqrt{54·4} \risingdotseq 7·376.$$

The angle α is in the second quadrant.

The acute angle shown $= \tan^{-1} \dfrac{7·2}{1·6} = \tan^{-1} 4·5 = 77° \, 28'.$

$$\therefore \alpha = 180° - 77° \, 28' = 102° \, 32'.$$

$$\therefore 7·2 \cos \theta - 1·6 \sin \theta \equiv 7·376 \sin (\theta + 102° \, 32').$$

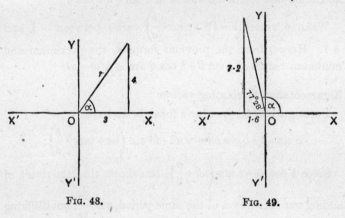

FIG. 48.   FIG. 49.

In the general case, $a \sin \theta + b \cos \theta = r \sin (\theta + \alpha)$ where $r \cos \alpha = a$, $r \sin \alpha = b$.

Squaring and adding, $r^2 = a^2 + b^2$.

$$\therefore r = \sqrt{a^2 + b^2} \, ;$$

also dividing, $\tan \alpha = \dfrac{b}{a}$

$$\therefore \alpha = \tan^{-1} \dfrac{b}{a}.$$

The particular value of $\tan^{-1}\dfrac{b}{a}$ to be taken has to be decided by the signs of a and b which determine the quadrant in which α lies.

Thus we have the general formula

$$a \sin \theta + b \cos \theta \equiv \sqrt{a^2 + b^2} \sin \left(\theta + \tan^{-1}\frac{b}{a}\right),$$

where the value of $\tan^{-1}\dfrac{b}{a}$ is determined by the signs of a and b.

Maximum and minimum values of $a \sin \theta + b \cos \theta$

When θ varies, $\sin \left(\theta + \tan^{-1}\dfrac{b}{a}\right)$ varies between -1 and $+1$. Hence, from the previous formula, the maximum and minimum values of $a \sin \theta + b \cos \theta$ are $\pm \sqrt{a^2 + b^2}$.

Representation by rotating vectors

Putting $\theta = \omega t$ in the above formula we have

$$a \sin \omega t + b \cos \omega t = \sqrt{a^2 + b^2} \sin \left(\omega t + \tan^{-1}\frac{b}{a}\right).$$

Since $b \cos \omega t = b \sin \left(\omega t + \dfrac{\pi}{2}\right)$, this shows that the result of adding two sine-waves of the same period, viz. $\dfrac{2\pi}{\omega}$, but differing in phase by $\dfrac{\pi}{2}$, is a single sine-wave of the same period.

This can be seen also by using the idea of rotating vectors (Part II, pages 238, 242). If OP_1 is a vector, or crank, of length a rotating about O with angular velocity ω, starting from the position OA (Fig. 50) when $t = 0$, its projection OQ_1 on the line OY perpendicular to OA is of length $a \sin \omega t$. If OP_2 is a second crank of length b, which leads the former by an angle $\dfrac{\pi}{2}$, then

$$OQ_2 = b \sin \left(\omega t + \frac{\pi}{2} \right) = b \cos \omega t.$$

Thus $a \sin \omega t + b \cos \omega t$ is the sum of the projections on OY of the vectors OP_1, OP_2 and is therefore equal to the projection ON on OY of the resultant OR of those vectors (Part II, page 277). Since the angle P_1OP_2 is constant, viz. $\frac{\pi}{2}$, it is evident that OR rotates at the same speed ω as OP_1 and OP_2; in fact, OP_1RP_2 rotates like a rigid framework about

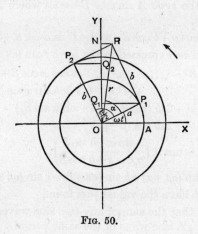

Fig. 50.

O. Thus N executes a simple harmonic oscillation about O of period $\frac{2\pi}{\omega}$ and of amplitude equal to the length of OR.

From the figure, $OR = \sqrt{a^2 + b^2}$ and $P_1\widehat{O}R = \tan^{-1}\frac{b}{a}$. Thus OR leads OP_1 by an angle $\tan^{-1}\frac{b}{a}$, and the motion of N is given by $y = \sqrt{a^2 + b^2} \sin \left(\omega t + \tan^{-1}\frac{b}{a} \right)$.

Addition of any two sine-waves of the same period

Any two sine-waves of the same period are represented by equations $y = a \sin (\omega t + \alpha)$ and $y = b \sin (\omega t + \beta)$. Their common period is $\dfrac{2\pi}{\omega}$, their amplitudes are a and b, their phase-difference is $\beta - \alpha$.

$a \sin (\omega t + \alpha) + b \sin (\omega t + \beta)$
$= a (\sin \omega t \cos \alpha + \cos \omega t \sin \alpha) + b (\sin \omega t \cos \beta + \cos \omega t \sin \beta)$
$= (a \cos \alpha + b \cos \beta) \sin \omega t + (a \sin \alpha + b \sin \beta) \cos \omega t.$

This is of the type $A \sin \omega t + B \cos \omega t$ where A and B are constants, viz.

$$A \equiv a \cos \alpha + b \cos \beta \quad \text{and} \quad B \equiv a \sin \alpha + b \sin \beta,$$

and hence can be expressed in the form $r \sin (\omega t + \phi)$, where

$$r = \sqrt{A^2 + B^2} = \sqrt{\{(a^2 \cos^2 \alpha + 2ab \cos \alpha \cos \beta + b^2 \cos^2 \beta)}$$
$$+ (a^2 \sin^2 \alpha + 2ab \sin \alpha \sin \beta + b^2 \sin^2 \beta)\}$$
$$= \sqrt{\{a^2 + b^2 + 2ab (\cos \alpha \cos \beta + \sin \alpha \sin \beta)\}}$$
$$= \sqrt{\{a^2 + b^2 + 2ab \cos (\beta - \alpha)\}} ;$$
$$\phi = \tan^{-1} \frac{B}{A} = \tan^{-1} \left(\frac{a \sin \alpha + b \sin \beta}{a \cos \alpha + b \cos \beta} \right).$$

Hence $\quad a \sin (\omega t + \alpha) + b \sin (\omega t + \beta) = r \sin (\omega t + \phi)$,

where r and ϕ have the values just found.

This shows that the sum of any two sine-waves of the same period is a single sine-wave of the same period.

We can illustrate this result by means of rotating vectors. The two cranks OP_1, OP_2 now have a constant phase-difference $\beta - \alpha$, as shown in Fig. 51. If OR is the resultant of the vectors OP_1, OP_2, the figure $OP_1 R P_2$ rotates about O like a rigid framework, and thus OR rotates with the same angular velocity ω as each of the cranks and leads OP_1 by a constant angle $\phi - \alpha$.

The expression $a \sin (\omega t + \alpha) + b \sin (\omega t + \beta)$, being the sum of the projections of OP_1 and OP_2 on OY, is equal to the projection of OR on OY, which is $r \sin \widehat{XOR}$, i.e. $r \sin (\omega t + \phi)$.

From the formula for the magnitude of the resultant of two vectors (Part II, page 310)

$$r = \sqrt{a^2 + b^2 + 2ab \cos (\beta - \alpha)}.$$

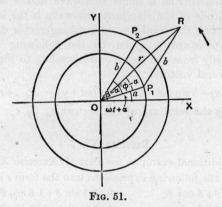

FIG. 51.

The value of $\tan \phi$ is most easily found from Fig. 52, in which OH is the line making an angle α with OP_1.

$$\tan \phi = \frac{FR}{OF} = \frac{FG + GR}{OE + EF} = \frac{EP_1 + GR}{OE + P_1G} = \frac{a \sin \alpha + b \sin \beta}{a \cos \alpha + b \cos \beta}.$$

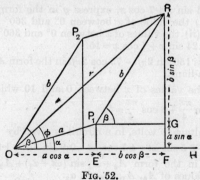

FIG. 52.

Addition of any number of sine-waves of the same period

If we have more than two sine-waves of the same period it is clear, by adding two at a time, that the result of adding them all together is a single sine-wave of the same period. The amplitude of the resultant sine-wave is the length of the resultant of all the cranks in the rotating-vector diagram, and its phase-constant is given by the following rule, which follows easily from the figure corresponding to Fig. 52 for the case of several vectors :

$$a \sin (\omega t + \alpha) + b \sin (\omega t + \beta) + c \sin (\omega t + \gamma) + \ldots = r \sin (\omega t + \phi),$$

where r_ϕ is the resultant of the vectors a_α, b_β, c_γ, $\ldots$

Exercise XI.

[For additional examples see Part II, Exercise XXXVII.]

Convert the following expressions into the form $r \sin (\theta + \alpha)$:

1. $2 \sin \theta + 5 \cos \theta$.   **2.** $3 \cdot 1 \sin \theta + 1 \cdot 8 \cos \theta$.

3. $4 \sin \theta - 3 \cos \theta$.   **4.** $75 \sin \theta - 110 \cos \theta$.

5. $- \sin \theta + 2 \cos \theta$.   **6.** $8 \cos \theta - 15 \sin \theta$.

7. Determine A and α such that $10 \sin \theta - 6 \cos \theta = A \sin (\theta - \alpha)$. Sketch in one diagram the graphs of $10 \sin \theta$, $6 \cos \theta$ and $A \sin (\theta - \alpha)$ for values of θ from $0°$ to $360°$.

8. The third harmonic of a voltage wave is given as $0 \cdot 11 \cos 3\theta - 0 \cdot 13 \sin 3\theta$. Express this in the form $r \sin (3\theta + \alpha)$.

9. If $y = 24 \sin x + 7 \cos x$, express y in the form $a \sin (x + \theta)$. Hence find (i) the value of x between $0°$ and $360°$ for which y is a maximum, (ii) the values of x between $0°$ and $360°$ which satisfy the equation $24 \sin x + 7 \cos x = 15$.

10. Express $150 \sin 2\pi ft - 75 \cos 2\pi ft$ in the form $A \sin (2\pi ft - \alpha)$, giving α in radians.

11. Find the values of x between 0 and 10 which satisfy the equation $6 \sin \dfrac{\pi x}{4} + 8 \cos \dfrac{\pi x}{4} = 5$.

12. The voltage, v volts, in a circuit is given by

$$v = 120 + 8 \cdot 5 \sin \omega t + 4 \cdot 7 \cos \omega t - 0 \cdot 9 \sin 3\omega t + 1 \cdot 3 \cos 3\omega t.$$

Express v in the form $A_0 + A_1 \sin (\omega t + \alpha_1) + A_2 \sin (3\omega t + \alpha_2)$ finding the values of A_0, A_1. A_2, α_1, α_2.

13. The e.m.f., v volts, required to maintain a current $I_m \sin \omega t$ ampères in a circuit containing a resistance R ohms, an inductance L henrys and a condenser of capacity C farads in series, is given by

$$v = I_m \left\{ R \sin \omega t + \left(\omega L - \frac{1}{\omega C} \right) \cos \omega t \right\}.$$

Express this in the form $v = ZI_m \sin (\omega t + \phi)$, and calculate Z and ϕ when $R = 0.5$, $L = 0.005$, $C = 200 \times 10^{-6}$, $\omega = 100\pi$.

14. Express $8 \sin (\theta + 30°) + 10 \sin (\theta - 60°)$ in the form $r \sin (\theta + \alpha)$.

15. Express $4.5 \sin \theta + 6.2 \sin (\theta - 30°)$ in the form $A \sin (\theta - \alpha)$; state the maximum and minimum values of the expression, and find the values of θ between $-180°$ and $180°$ for which those maxima and minima occur.

16. For what values of θ between $0°$ and $360°$ is the expression $5 \sin \theta - 7 \cos \theta$ positive ?

17. The formula $E_s{}^2 = (E_R \cos \phi + RI)^2 + (E_R \sin \phi + XI)^2$ occurs in connection with a high-pressure transmission line, E_s being the voltage at the sending end and E_R that at the receiving end. Express $E_s{}^2$ in the form $a + b \sin (\phi + \alpha)$, giving the values of a, b and α, and find the maximum and minimum values of E_s as ϕ varies.

18. A current when analysed as far as the fifth harmonic is found to be given by the formula

$$i = 14.8 \sin \omega t + 5.7 \sin 3\omega t - 0.26 \sin 5\omega t$$
$$- 6.1 \cos \omega t + 4.4 \cos 3\omega t + 1.95 \cos 5\omega t.$$

Express i as the sum of three sine-waves.

19. Draw a diagram showing the rotating vectors which represent the following e.m.f.'s :

$$e_1 = 200 \sin 100\pi t, \qquad e_2 = 120 \cos 100\pi t,$$
$$e_3 = 150 \sin (100\pi t - \tfrac{1}{3}\pi), \qquad e_4 = 50 \sin (100\pi t - \tfrac{1}{4}\pi).$$

If $e = e_1 - e_2 - e_3 + e_4$, show the vector representing e, and find the sine-wave expression for e.

Transformation of products into sums or differences

From the formulæ

$$\sin (A + B) = \sin A \cos B + \cos A \sin B,$$
$$\sin (A - B) = \sin A \cos B - \cos A \sin B,$$

we obtain, on adding,

$$\sin (A + B) + \sin (A - B) = 2 \sin A \cos B,$$

and, on subtracting,

$$\sin (A + B) - \sin (A - B) = 2 \cos A \sin B.$$

Also from the formulæ

$$\cos (A + B) = \cos A \cos B - \sin A \sin B,$$
$$\cos (A - B) = \cos A \cos B + \sin A \sin B,$$

we obtain, on adding and subtracting,

$$\cos (A + B) + \cos (A - B) = 2 \cos A \cos B,$$
$$\cos (A - B) - \cos (A + B) = 2 \sin A \sin B.$$

The importance of these four formulæ is more apparent when they are written in the following forms :

$$2 \sin A \cos B = \sin (A + B) + \sin (A - B) \quad . \quad (15)$$
$$2 \cos A \sin B = \sin (A + B) - \sin (A - B) \quad . \quad (16)$$
$$2 \cos A \cos B = \cos (A + B) + \cos (A - B) \quad . \quad (17)$$
$$2 \sin A \sin B = \cos (A - B) - \cos (A + B) \quad . \quad (18)$$

These enable us to express products of sines and cosines as the sum or difference of two sines or cosines. They may be memorized thus :

$$2\ sin \times cos = sin\ (sum) + sin\ (difference),$$
$$2\ cos \times sin = sin\ (sum) - sin\ (difference),$$
$$2\ cos \times cos = cos\ (sum) + cos\ (difference),$$
$$2\ sin \times sin = cos\ (difference) - cos\ (sum),$$

where " difference " denotes " first angle – second angle."

Examples.—

(1) $2 \sin 50° \cos 20° = \sin (50° + 20°) + \sin (50° - 20°)$
$$= \sin 70° + \sin 30°.$$

(2) $2 \sin 10° \cos 45° = \sin (10° + 45°) + \sin (10° - 45°)$
$$= \sin 55° + \sin (-35°)$$
$$= \sin 55° - \sin 35° ;$$

or $2 \sin 10° \cos 45°$ $= 2 \cos 45° \sin 10°$
$= \sin (45° + 10°) - \sin (45° - 10°)$
$= \sin 55° - \sin 35°.$

(3) $\cos 75° \cos 15°$ $= \frac{1}{2}(2 \cos 75° \cos 15°)$
$= \frac{1}{2}\{\cos (75° + 15°) + \cos (75° - 15°)\}$
$= \frac{1}{2}\{\cos 90° + \cos 60°\}$
$= \frac{1}{2}\{0 + \frac{1}{2}\}$
$= \frac{1}{4}.$

(4) $2 \sin 112° \sin 38°$ $= \cos (112° - 38°) - \cos (112° + 38°)$
$= \cos 74° - \cos 150°.$

(5) $\sin 20° \sin 50°$ $= \frac{1}{2}(2 \sin 20° \sin 50°)$
$= \frac{1}{2}\{\cos (20° - 50°) - \cos (20° + 50°)\}$
$= \frac{1}{2}\{\cos (-30°) - \cos 70°\}$
$= \frac{1}{2}\{\cos 30° - \cos 70°\} ;$

or $\sin 20° \sin 50°$ $= \sin 50° \sin 20°$
$= \frac{1}{2}\{\cos (50° - 20°) - \cos (50° + 20°)\}$
$= \frac{1}{2}\{\cos 30° - \cos 70°\}.$

NOTE. In Examples (2) and (5) above we have given alternative methods, the object of the second method in each case being to avoid negative differences by writing the larger angle first. The student will probably find it advisable to do this, at any rate until he is thoroughly accustomed to dealing with negative angles.

Example.—In an alternating-current circuit the power, p watts, at any instant is equal to the product ei, where e volts is the e.m.f. and i amp. is the current. If $e = E_m \sin \omega t$ and $i = I_m \sin (\omega t - \phi)$, what are the maximum and minimum values of p as the time t varies ?

$$p = ei = E_m I_m \sin \omega t \cdot \sin (\omega t - \phi)$$

Using formula (18) with ωt for A and $\omega t - \phi$ for B,

$$2 \sin \omega t \sin (\omega t - \phi) = \cos \phi - \cos (2\omega t - \phi)$$
$$\therefore \; p = \frac{1}{2} E_m I_m \{\cos \phi - \cos (2\omega t - \phi)\}.$$

As t varies, $\cos(2\omega t - \phi)$ varies between -1 and $+1$, and hence $\cos\phi - \cos(2\omega t - \phi)$ varies between $\cos\phi - 1$ and $\cos\phi + 1$, since $\cos\phi$ is constant.

Thus $p_{\max.} = \frac{1}{2}E_m I_m(\cos\phi + 1)$ and $p_{\min.} = \frac{1}{2}E_m I_m(\cos\phi - 1)$.

Since $\cos\phi = 2\cos^2\dfrac{\phi}{2} - 1 = 1 - 2\sin^2\dfrac{\phi}{2}$, we can express these in another form, viz. :

$$p_{\max.} = E_m I_m \cos^2\frac{\phi}{2}, \qquad p_{\min.} = -E_m I_m \sin^2\frac{\varphi}{2}.$$

GRAPHS OF $e = 6\sin 100\pi t$, $\ i = 2\sin(100\pi t - \frac{1}{5}\pi)$
and $p = 12\sin 100\pi t . \sin(100\pi t - \frac{1}{5}\pi)$

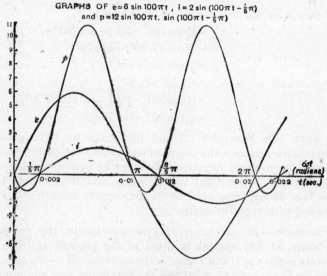

FIG. 53.

In the above example, since $\cos\phi$ is constant and $\cos(2\omega t - \phi)$ is a periodic function of t of period $\dfrac{2\pi}{2\omega}$, i.e. $\dfrac{\pi}{\omega}$, we see that p is itself a periodic function of t—in fact, a sine-wave—of period

$\dfrac{\pi}{\omega}$. The period of p is therefore half that of i and e, and its frequency is twice that of i and e.

Fig. 53 shows the graphs of e, i and p for the case in which $E_m = 6$, $I_m = 2$, $\omega = 100\pi$ (i.e. frequency 50), $\phi = \frac{1}{5}\pi(=36°)$. The scale for t is marked below the axis, the scale for ωt above the axis. The maximum and minimum values of p are 10·854 and −1·146 respectively.

Exercise XII.

Express the following products as sums or differences of sines or cosines, and verify from tables in Questions 1–9 :

1. $2 \sin 32° \cos 18°$.

2. $2 \sin 100° \cos 20°$.

3. $2 \cos 43° \sin 15°$.

4. $2 \cos 31° \cos 51°$.

5. $\sin 25° \cos 65°$.

6. $\cos 130° \cos 46°$.

7. $2 \sin 84° \sin 6°$.

8. $\sin 26° \sin 50°$.

9. $\cos 16° \sin 72°$.

10. $\sin 5x \cos x$.

11. $\cos 2\alpha \cos 3\alpha$.

12. $\sin 2\pi ft \sin (2\pi ft + \alpha)$.

13. Deduce formula (16) on page 100 from formula (15) by writing $2 \cos A \sin B$ as $2 \sin B \cos A$.

14. Deduce formula (17) on page 100 from formula (15) by writing $2 \cos A \cos B$ as $2 \sin (90° − A) \cos B$.

15. Show that $\cos \left(\dfrac{\pi}{4} + \theta \right) \cos \left(\dfrac{\pi}{4} - \theta \right) = \frac{1}{2} \cos 2\theta$.

16. Express $2 \sin 45° \sin 15°$ as the difference of two cosines, and deduce the value of $\sin 15°$.

17. Prove that $4 \cos x \cos 2x \cos 3x = 1 + \cos 2x + \cos 4x + \cos 6x$.
[Hint.   Write the left-hand side as $2 \cos x \times 2 \cos 2x \cos 3x$.]

18. Prove that $\sin 3\theta = 4 \sin \theta \sin \left(\theta + \dfrac{\pi}{3} \right) \sin \left(\theta + \dfrac{2\pi}{3} \right)$.

19. Find the maximum and minimum values of the expression $\sin (\theta + 20°) \cos (\theta - 10°)$ as θ varies between 0° and 180°, and state the values of θ for which the maximum and minimum values occur.

20. The efficiency η of a screw is equal to $\dfrac{\tan \alpha}{\tan (\alpha + \phi)}$, where α is the angle of pitch and ϕ the angle of friction. Prove that

$$\eta = \frac{\sin (2\alpha + \phi) - \sin \phi}{\sin (2\alpha + \phi) + \sin \phi}$$

and hence that

$$\eta = 1 - \frac{2 \sin \phi}{\sin (2\alpha + \phi) + \sin \phi}.$$

Deduce that for varying values of α the efficiency is a maximum when $2\alpha = \dfrac{\pi}{2} - \phi$, and hence show that the maximum efficiency is $\tan^2 \left(\dfrac{\pi}{4} - \dfrac{\phi}{2} \right)$.

21. Show that the expression in Question **19** is a periodic function of θ, state its period and draw a sketch of its graph.

22. Convert $\cos x \sin 2x$ into a sum of sines and hence draw the graph of the function.

Transformation of sums and differences into products

In formulæ (15)–(18) on page 100 let us write

$$A + B = P \quad \text{and} \quad A - B = Q,$$

so that

$$A = \frac{P + Q}{2} \quad \text{and} \quad B = \frac{P - Q}{2}.$$

Then, on interchanging the two sides of the formulæ, we obtain the following four formulæ :

$$\sin P + \sin Q = 2 \sin \frac{P + Q}{2} \cos \frac{P - Q}{2} \quad . \quad . \quad (19)$$

$$\sin P - \sin Q = 2 \cos \frac{P + Q}{2} \sin \frac{P - Q}{2} \quad . \quad . \quad (20)$$

$$\cos P + \cos Q = 2 \cos \frac{P + Q}{2} \cos \frac{P - Q}{2} \quad . \quad . \quad (21)$$

$$\cos Q - \cos P = 2 \sin \frac{P + Q}{2} \sin \frac{P - Q}{2} \quad . \quad . \quad (22)$$

These are true for all values of the angles P and Q.   If we interchange P and Q in the last formula it takes the form :

$$\cos P - \cos Q = 2 \sin \frac{P+Q}{2} \sin \frac{Q-P}{2} \quad . \quad . \quad (22)$$

These enable us to express the sum or difference of two sines or cosines as a product of sines and cosines.

They may be memorized thus :

sin + sin = 2 sin (half sum) cos (half difference),

sin − sin = 2 cos (half sum) sin (half difference),

cos + cos = 2 cos (half sum) cos (half difference),

cos − cos = 2 sin (half sum) sin (half difference reversed),

where " difference " means " first angle − second angle."

Examples.—

(1) $\sin 32° + \sin 24° = 2 \sin \dfrac{32° + 24°}{2} \cos \dfrac{32° - 24°}{2}$

$= 2 \sin 28° \cos 4°.$

(2) $\sin 4x + \sin 2x = 2 \sin \dfrac{4x + 2x}{2} \cos \dfrac{4x - 2x}{2}$

$= 2 \sin 3x \cos x.$

(3) $\sin 75° - \sin 15° = 2 \cos \dfrac{75° + 15°}{2} \sin \dfrac{75° - 15°}{2}$

$= 2 \cos 45° \sin 30°$

$= 2 \cdot \dfrac{1}{\sqrt{2}} \cdot \dfrac{1}{2}.$

$= \dfrac{1}{\sqrt{2}}.$

(4) $\cos 3A + \cos 2A = 2 \cos \dfrac{3A + 2A}{2} \cos \dfrac{3A - 2A}{2}$

$= 2 \cos \dfrac{5A}{2} \cos \dfrac{A}{2}.$

(5) $\cos 80° - \cos 40° = 2 \sin \dfrac{80° + 40°}{2} \sin \dfrac{40° - 80°}{2}$

$$= 2 \sin 60° \sin (-20°)$$

$$= 2 \cdot \frac{\sqrt{3}}{2} \cdot (-\sin 20°)$$

$$= -\sqrt{3} \sin 20°.$$

(6) $\cos (x - h) - \cos (x + h)$

$$= 2 \sin \left\{ \frac{(x - h) + (x + h)}{2} \right\} \sin \left\{ \frac{(x + h) - (x - h)}{2} \right\}$$

$$= 2 \sin x \sin h.$$

Example.—Prove that $\sin \alpha + \sin \left(\alpha + \dfrac{2\pi}{3} \right) + \sin \left(\alpha + \dfrac{4\pi}{3} \right) \equiv 0.$

Rearranging the terms on the left-hand side,

$$\sin \alpha + \sin \left(\alpha + \frac{2\pi}{3} \right) + \sin \left(\alpha + \frac{4\pi}{3} \right)$$

$$= \sin \left(\alpha + \frac{2\pi}{3} \right) + \left\{ \sin \left(\alpha + \frac{4\pi}{3} \right) + \sin \alpha \right\}$$

$$= \sin \left(\alpha + \frac{2\pi}{3} \right) + 2 \sin \left(\alpha + \frac{2\pi}{3} \right) \cos \frac{2\pi}{3}$$

$$= \sin \left(\alpha + \frac{2\pi}{3} \right) \left\{ 1 + 2 \cos \frac{2\pi}{3} \right\}$$

$$= \sin \left(\alpha + \frac{2\pi}{3} \right) \left\{ 1 + 2 \left(-\frac{1}{2} \right) \right\}$$

$$= 0.$$

Example.—Solve the equation

$$\cos \theta + \cos (\theta + 50°) = 1 \cdot 3,$$

giving the values of θ between 0° and 360°.

Expressing the left-hand side as a product, the equation becomes

$$2 \cos (\theta + 25°) \cos 25° = 1 \cdot 3$$

$$\therefore \cos (\theta + 25°) = \frac{1 \cdot 3}{2 \cos 25°}$$

$$= \frac{0 \cdot 65}{\cos 25°} = \frac{0 \cdot 65}{0 \cdot 9063}$$

$$= 0 \cdot 7172$$

$\therefore \theta + 25° = \pm 44° \ 10' \pm n \ . \ 360°$, where n is any integer.

$\therefore \theta = 19° \ 10' \pm n \ . \ 360°$ or $-69° \ 10' \pm n \ . \ 360°$.

Selecting the values of θ between 0° and 360° we have

$$\theta = 19° \ 10' \quad \text{or} \quad 290° \ 50'.$$

Addition of sine-waves of slightly different frequencies. Beats

Fig. 54 shows the result of adding the two sine-waves $y = \sin 100\pi t$ and $y = \sin 120\pi t$. These have the same amplitude 1, but their frequencies are 50 and 60 respectively. The resultant curve is not a sine-wave, though it is periodic, its period being $\frac{1}{10}$ sec.

If we take two sine-waves, each of amplitude a, of frequencies f and f', their equations are

$$y = a \sin 2\pi f t \quad \text{and} \quad y = a \sin 2\pi f' t.$$

Adding these gives the curve

$$y = a \ (\sin 2\pi f t + \sin 2\pi f' t)$$

$$= 2a \sin \pi(f + f')t \ . \ \cos \pi(f - f')t.$$

This is not a pure sine-wave, but if we write it as

$$y = 2a \cos \pi(f - f')t \ . \ \sin \pi(f + f')t$$

we can regard it as a sine-wave of frequency $\frac{1}{2}(f + f')$ with a variable amplitude $2a \cos \pi(f - f')t$. If the frequencies f and f' are high but nearly equal, so that $f - f'$ is small, the result is a high-frequency wave of slowly varying amplitude or intensity, that is, a wave which " beats." The *wave-frequency*

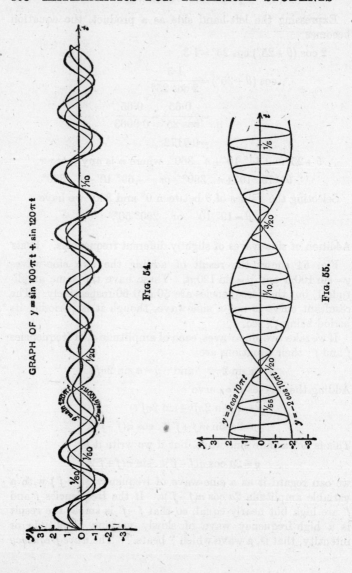

GRAPH OF $y = \sin 100\pi t + \sin 120\pi t$

Fig. 54.

Fig. 55.

is the average of the two component frequencies; the time between two maximum amplitudes is $\frac{1}{f-f'}$, so that the *beat-frequency* is the difference of the component frequencies.

The phenomenon of beats is well illustrated in the case of sound waves. If two notes of only slightly different frequencies, say 512 and 516, are sounded together, a listener does not perceive two distinct notes but a single note of varying intensity.

The variation of amplitude of the curve

$$y = \sin 100\pi t + \sin 120\pi t$$

is shown more clearly in Fig. 55.

$$y = \sin 100\pi t + \sin 120\pi t$$
$$= 2 \cos 10\pi t \cdot \sin 110\pi t.$$

Since $\sin 110\pi t$ always lies between ± 1, the curve lies between the two cosine curves $y = \pm 2 \cos 10\pi t$; it touches them at the points where $\sin 110\pi t = \pm 1$, i.e. when $t = \frac{1}{220}, \frac{3}{220}, \frac{5}{220}$, etc.

Beats are also produced when the amplitudes of the component waves are not equal, as is shown in Fig. 56, which represents the graph of

$$y = 5 \sin 280\pi t + 4 \sin 240\pi t.$$

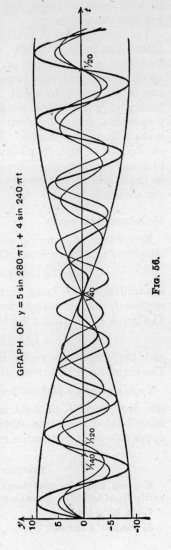

GRAPH OF $y = 5 \sin 280\pi t + 4 \sin 240\pi t$

Fig. 56.

In such cases, however, not only is the amplitude variable but also the frequency.

The principle of "beating" is made use of in super-heterodyne radio receivers. Wireless waves are of very high frequency, a wave-length of 300 metres, for example, corresponding to a frequency of about 1,000,000 cycles per sec. and one of 30 metres to about 10,000,000 cycles per sec. The tuning of a resonance circuit is however sharper for low frequencies, and so for short-wave reception it is desirable to make a frequency change. This is done by setting up local oscillations of high frequency within the receiver, by means of a valve oscillator or other means, and superimposing them on the oncoming wireless waves, when beats of lower frequency are obtained.

Modulated sine-waves

Sine-waves of varying amplitude are used both in line telephony and in wireless. Currents of the type

$$i = I_0(1 + k \sin 2\pi f_2 t) \sin 2\pi f_1 t$$

are transmitted, f_1 being high, f_2 low, and k, the *modulation-coefficient*, being essentially less than 1 and usually less than $\frac{1}{2}$. The graph of i against t lies between the curves

$$i = \pm I_0(1 + k \sin 2\pi f_2 t),$$

and the amplitude varies between $I_0(1 - k)$ and $I_0(1 + k)$. The current can be written in the form

$$i = I_0 \sin 2\pi f_1 t + \tfrac{1}{2} I_0 k \cos 2\pi (f_1 - f_2) t - \tfrac{1}{2} I_0 k \cos 2\pi (f_1 + f_2) t ;$$

the first term, $I_0 \sin 2\pi f_1 t$ represents the *carrier wave* (the unmodulated wave), the other two terms show the lower and upper side-band frequencies respectively.

Exercise XIII.

Express the following sums or differences as products, and verify from tables in Questions 1–6 :

1. $\sin 85° + \sin 21°$.　　　　2. $\sin 40° - \sin 10°$.

3. $\cos 100° + \cos 44°$.　　　　4. $\cos 34° - \cos 76°$.

5. $\cos 52° - \cos 18°$.   **6.** $\sin 25° + \sin 62°$.

7. $\sin \alpha + \sin 7\alpha$.   **8.** $\cos \frac{5}{2}\beta + \cos \frac{3}{2}\beta$.

9. $\cos (45° - A) - \cos (45° + A)$.   **10.** $\sin (pt + \alpha) + \sin (pt - \alpha)$.

11. Prove that $\sin x + \cos x = \sqrt{2} \sin \left(x + \dfrac{\pi}{4}\right)$. [Hint. Write $\cos x$ as $\sin \left(x + \dfrac{\pi}{2}\right)$.]

12. Prove that $\dfrac{\sin A + \sin B}{\cos A + \cos B} = \tan \dfrac{A + B}{2}$.

13. Prove that

    (i) $\sin (x + h) - \sin x = 2 \sin \dfrac{h}{2} \cos \left(x + \dfrac{h}{2}\right)$,

    (ii) $\cos (x + h) - \cos x = -2 \sin \dfrac{h}{2} \sin \left(x + \dfrac{h}{2}\right)$.

14. Show that the area of the rectangle $DEBF$ in Fig. 57 can be expressed in each of the forms $2a^2 (\sin \alpha - \sin 2\alpha)$ and $-4a^2 \sin \frac{1}{2}\alpha \cos \frac{3}{2}\alpha$.

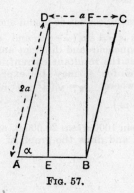

FIG. 57.

15. Prove, without using tables, that
$$\cos 24° + \cos 96° + \cos 144° = 0.$$

16. Solve the equation $\sin 2x + \sin 4x = \sin 3x$.

17. Find the angles between 0° and 180° which satisfy the equation $\cos \theta + \cos 3\theta = \sin \theta + \sin 3\theta$.

Prove the following identities :

18. $\cos \alpha + \cos \left(\alpha + \dfrac{2\pi}{3} \right) + \cos \left(\alpha + \dfrac{4\pi}{3} \right) = 0.$

19. $\sin^2 \theta + \sin^2 \left(\theta + \dfrac{\pi}{3} \right) + \sin^2 \left(\theta + \dfrac{2\pi}{3} \right) = \dfrac{3}{2}.$

[Hint. Write $\sin^2 \theta$ as $\frac{1}{2}(1 - \cos 2\theta)$, with similar expressions for the other terms, and use Question 18.]

20. $\dfrac{\sin 2x + \sin 3x}{\cos 2x - \cos 3x} = \cot \dfrac{x}{2}.$

21. $\dfrac{\sin A + \sin 3A + \sin 5A}{\cos A + \cos 3A + \cos 5A} = \tan 3A.$

22. The total flux density B in a three-phase circuit is given by

$$B = B_m \left\{ \cos \dfrac{2\pi x}{\lambda} \cos \omega t + \cos \left(\dfrac{2\pi x}{\lambda} + \dfrac{2\pi}{3} \right) \cos \left(\omega t + \dfrac{2\pi}{3} \right) \right.$$

$$\left. + \cos \left(\dfrac{2\pi x}{\lambda} + \dfrac{4\pi}{3} \right) \cos \left(\omega t + \dfrac{4\pi}{3} \right) \right\}.$$

Prove that $B = \frac{3}{2} B_m \cos \left(\dfrac{2\pi x}{\lambda} - \omega t \right).$

[Hint. Express each product as a sum and use Question 18.]

23. Two currents $i = A \sin (\omega + p)t$ and $i = B \sin (\omega - p)t$, of slightly different frequencies and different amplitudes, are superimposed. Show that the resultant current, obtained by adding the two expressions for i, may be expressed in the form $i = i_0 \sin (\omega t + \phi)$, where $i_0 = \sqrt{(A^2 + B^2 + 2AB \cos 2pt)}$ and $\phi = \tan^{-1} \left(\dfrac{A - B}{A + B} \tan pt \right).$

24. If $i = (1 + 0 \cdot 4 \sin 1000\pi t) \sin 20,000\pi t$, express i as the sum of three sine-waves, and draw the graph of i against t between $t = 0$ and $t = \frac{1}{500}$.

CHAPTER V

DIFFERENTIATION OF x^n

Velocity of a body moving at a variable rate

Fig. 58 shows the graph of the distance s moved by a body in time t.

P and Q are two points on the graph; PM, QN are the ordinates at P and Q and PK is perpendicular to QN. Hence MP is the distance the body moves in the time OM and NQ is the distance the body moves in the time ON. Therefore the distance the body moves in the time MN

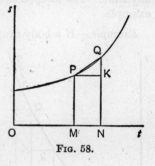

FIG. 58.

$$= NQ - MP = NQ - NK = KQ.$$

Hence the body moves the same distance in the time MN, which equals PK, as if it had moved at a constant velocity $\dfrac{KQ}{PK}$; this ratio is the gradient of the chord PQ.

If N is taken nearer and nearer to M the chord PQ approaches the tangent at P and hence the velocity $\dfrac{KQ}{PK}$ approaches a value equal to the gradient of the tangent at P. This value is called "the velocity at the instant when the time is OM."

The idea of velocity at an instant is one with which we are all familiar in everyday life. When a motorist says his speed is 35 m.p.h. he means that at that *instant* the hand of his speedometer is over the line marked 35 on the dial; he does not mean that he will travel 35 miles in the next hour, or even that he will travel at 35 m.p.h. for the next two seconds, though, unless he puts on the brake very suddenly, his average speed for the next two seconds will not be far from 35 m.p.h.

If the distance s moved by the body in time t has been determined experimentally, the velocity at any instant is found by plotting the graph of s against t, drawing the tangent at the correct point and measuring its gradient. Since a tangent can only be drawn approximately the value of the velocity so obtained is only approximate.

If, however, we know the mathematical relation between s and t, we can find an exact expression for the velocity at any time. The method of doing this is shown in the following example.

Example.—If a body drops under gravity, the distance s ft. which it falls in t sec. is given by $s = 16t^2$. Show that the velocity after t sec. is $32t$ ft./sec.

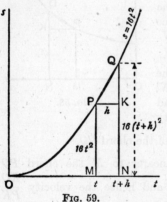

Fig. 59.

Fig. 59 shows the graph of $s = 16t^2$. P and Q are points on the graph having abscissæ t and $t + h$.

Since $s = 16t^2$ the distances MP and NQ which the body moves in t sec. and $t + h$ sec. respectively are given by

$$MP = 16t^2, \quad NQ = 16(t+h)^2.$$

Hence the distance moved in h sec. from t sec. to $t + h$ sec. is given by

$$KQ = NQ - MP = 16(t+h)^2 - 16t^2$$
$$= 16(t^2 + 2th + h^2) - 16t^2$$
$$= 16t^2 + 32th + 16h^2 - 16t^2$$
$$= 32th + 16h^2.$$

If this distance were covered at a constant velocity this velocity would be

$$\frac{KQ}{PK} = \frac{32th + 16h^2}{h} = 32t + 16h \text{ ft./sec.}$$

If we now consider h as becoming smaller and smaller, this velocity becomes nearer and nearer to $32t$ ft./sec. For instance, when h is less than $\frac{1}{2000}$, this velocity is within 0·001 ft./sec. of $32t$ ft./sec. Geometrically the meaning of this is that the gradient of the chord PQ approaches the value $32t$. Therefore at the instant t sec. after the body is dropped its velocity is $32t$ ft./sec.

The value $32t$ to which the fraction $\dfrac{32th + h^2}{h}$ approaches as h approaches zero is called the limiting value of the fraction as h approaches 0, and we write this

$$\lim_{h \to 0} \frac{32th + h^2}{h} = 32t,$$

where $h \to 0$ stands for " h approaches 0," and the left-hand side of the equation is read " the limiting value (or limit), as h approaches 0, of $\dfrac{32th + h^2}{h}$."

Differentiation

The velocity $\dfrac{KQ}{PK}$ is really the ratio of two differences. KQ is the difference of the distances NQ and MP, and PK is the difference of the times ON and OM. We call their ratio a difference ratio. The time difference, called h above, is usually denoted by δt—a symbol meaning " an increase of t." Notice that this symbol does not mean $\delta \times t$. In the same way the distance KQ travelled in this time is denoted by δs, which means " an increase of s." Using this notation

$$MP = s = 16t^2, \quad NQ = s + \delta s = 16(t + \delta t)^2$$

$$\therefore \quad \delta s = 16(t + \delta t)^2 - 16t^2$$

$$= 16\{t^2 + 2t \cdot \delta t + (\delta t)^2\} - 16t^2$$

$$= 16t^2 + 32t \cdot \delta t + 16(\delta t)^2 - 16t^2$$

$$= 32t \cdot \delta t + 16(\delta t)^2.$$

$$\therefore \quad \frac{\delta s}{\delta t} = 32t + 16\delta t.$$

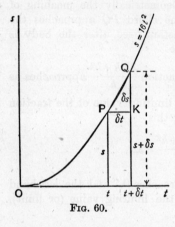

FIG. 60.

The limiting value of this ratio as δt approaches 0 is the velocity of the body at the instant t, or the rate of increase of s with respect to t. It is denoted by $\dfrac{ds}{dt}$, a notation due to Leibniz, or by $\dot{s}$, a notation due to Newton.

$$\therefore \quad \frac{ds}{dt} \ (\text{or } \dot{s}) = \lim_{\delta t \to 0} \frac{\delta s}{\delta t}$$

$$= \lim_{\delta t \to 0} (32t + 16\delta t)$$

$$= 32t.$$

$\dfrac{ds}{dt}$ is also called *the differential coefficient of s with respect to t* or *the derivative of s with respect to t*. The graph of $\dfrac{ds}{dt}$ is called the derived curve of the graph of s against t. The process of finding a differential coefficient is called differentiation.

Differential coefficient with respect to any other variable

Suppose y is a function of x. Then, as in the case of t and s, δx and δy denote the increases of x and y respectively, and y increases to $y + \delta y$ when x increases to $x + \delta x$.

As before, the difference ratio $\dfrac{\delta y}{\delta x} = \dfrac{KQ}{PK} =$ the gradient of the chord PQ (Fig. 61), and as δx approaches 0 this difference ratio approaches a limiting value equal to the gradient of the tangent at P.

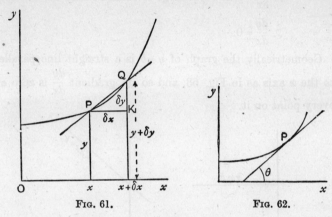

FIG. 61.   FIG. 62.

Just as the limiting value of $\dfrac{\delta s}{\delta t}$ as δt approaches 0 is written $\dfrac{ds}{dt}$, the limiting value of $\dfrac{\delta y}{\delta x}$ as δx approaches 0 is written $\dfrac{dy}{dx}$ and is called the differential coefficient of y with respect to x; in symbols

$$\frac{dy}{dx} = \lim_{\delta x \to 0} \frac{\delta y}{\delta x}$$

[The dot notation, i.e. $\dot{s}$ for $\dfrac{ds}{dt}$, is usually reserved for differentiation with respect to time.]

If the scales on the axes of x and y are equal

$$\frac{dy}{dx} = \text{gradient of tangent at } P = \tan \theta$$

where θ is the angle which the tangent makes with Ox (Fig. 62).

Differential coefficients of particular functions

(i) $y = b$, *where b is a fixed number*

When x increases by δx, there is no change in y, i.e. $\delta y = 0$.

$$\therefore \frac{\delta y}{\delta x} = 0 \text{ however large or small } \delta x \text{ may be.}$$

$$\therefore \frac{dy}{dx} = 0.$$

Geometrically the graph of $y = b$ is a straight line parallel to the x axis as in Fig. 63, and so its gradient $\frac{dy}{dx}$ is zero at every point on it.

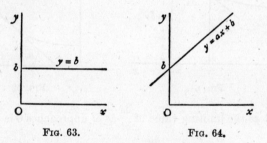

FIG. 63.   FIG. 64.

1i) $y = ax + b$, *where a and b are fixed numbers*

Since y becomes $y + \delta y$ when x becomes $x + \delta x$,

$$y + \delta y = a(x + \delta x) + b = ax + a\delta x + b.$$

Hence since $y = ax + b$, $\delta y = a\delta x$

$$\therefore \frac{\delta y}{\delta x} = a.$$

Since this is true for every value of δx, the limiting value as δx approaches 0 must also be a.

$$\therefore \frac{dy}{dx} = a.$$

In this case the graph of y is a sloping straight line of gradient a as in Fig. 64. Consequently the gradient of the join of any pair of points on the line is a.

(iii) $y = ax^2$

In the same way as with $s = 16t^2$ on page 116 we find that

$$\frac{dy}{dx} = 2ax.$$

This is left as an exercise for the student.

In calculating a limiting value it is often more convenient to use a single letter such as h for the increment of x instead of δx. We use h instead of δx in finding the differential coefficient of ax^3 below.

(iv) $y = ax^3$

Writing h for δx

$$y + \delta y = a(x + \delta x)^3 = a(x + h)^3$$
$$\therefore \; \delta y = a(x + h)^3 - ax^3$$
$$= a(x^3 + 3x^2 h + 3xh^2 + h^3) - ax^3$$
$$= ax^3 + 3ax^2 h + 3axh^2 + ah^3 - ax^3$$
$$= 3ax^2 h + 3axh^2 + ah^3$$
$$\therefore \; \frac{\delta y}{\delta x} = \frac{3ax^2 h + 3axh^2 + ah^3}{h}$$
$$= 3ax^2 + 3axh + ah^2.$$

If we now make δx, which is h, approach 0, the terms $3axh$ and ah^2 approach 0, and hence $\dfrac{\delta y}{\delta x}$ approaches the limiting value $3ax^2$.

$$\therefore \; \frac{dy}{dx} = 3ax^2.$$

Using the notation for a limiting value

$$\frac{dy}{dx} = \lim_{\delta x \to 0} \frac{\delta y}{\delta x} = \lim_{h \to 0} \frac{3ax^2h + 3axh^2 + ah^3}{h}$$

$$= \lim_{h \to 0} (3ax^2 + 3axh + ah^2)$$

$$= 3ax^2.$$

(v) $y = \dfrac{1}{x^2}$

$$y + \delta y = \frac{1}{(x + \delta x)^2} = \frac{1}{(x + h)^2}$$

$$\therefore \delta y = \frac{1}{(x + h)^2} - \frac{1}{x^2}$$

$$= \frac{x^2 - (x + h)^2}{(x + h)^2 x^2}$$

$$= \frac{x^2 - x^2 - 2xh - h^2}{(x + h)^2 x^2}$$

$$= -\frac{2xh + h^2}{(x + h)^2 x^2}$$

$$\therefore \frac{\delta y}{\delta x} = -\frac{2xh + h^2}{h(x + h)^2 x^2} = -\frac{2x + h}{(x + h)^2 x^2}$$

$$\therefore \frac{dy}{dx} = \lim_{h \to 0} \frac{2x + h}{(x + h)^2 x^2} = -\frac{2x}{x^2 \cdot x^2} = -\frac{2}{x^3}.$$

In the last line $2x + h$ approaches $2x$ and $(x + h)^2$ approaches x^2 as h approaches 0.

All the above examples are special cases of the general rule.

$$\text{If } y = ax^n, \quad \frac{dy}{dx} = anx^{n-1},$$

which is true for all values of the constants n and a.

A proof of the rule for differentiating ax^n for the case when n is a positive whole number is given on page 124 and a proof for the case when n is any positive or negative whole number or fraction is given on page 272.

For instance, when $n = 3$

$$y = ax^3 \quad \therefore \frac{dy}{ax} = a \cdot 3x^{3-1} = 3ax^2.$$

Also, when $y = \dfrac{1}{x^2}$,

$$y = x^{-2} \quad \therefore \frac{dy}{dx} = -2x^{-2-1} = -2x^{-3} = -\frac{2}{x^3},$$

which agrees with the result obtained above.

There is no need to write y for the function we are differentiating. We can write instead the function itself. For instance, we write the derivative of x^3 either as $\dfrac{d(x^3)}{dx}$ or as $\dfrac{d}{dx}(x^3)$.

Examples.—Find the derivatives of (*a*) $\frac{1}{6}m^{1\cdot8}$, (*b*) $\dfrac{4}{x^7}$, (*c*) $\dfrac{10}{\sqrt{y}}$ with respect to the variable in each expression.

(*a*) $\dfrac{d(\frac{1}{6}m^{1\cdot8})}{dm} = \frac{1}{6} \cdot 1\cdot8m^{1\cdot8-1} = 0\cdot3m^{0\cdot8}.$

(*b*) $\dfrac{d}{dx}\left(\dfrac{4}{x^7}\right) = \dfrac{d}{dx}(4x^{-7}) = 4 \times (-7)x^{-7-1} = -28x^{-8} = -\dfrac{28}{x^8}.$

(*c*) $\dfrac{d}{dy}\left(\dfrac{10}{\sqrt{y}}\right) = \dfrac{d}{dy}(10y^{-\frac{1}{2}}) = 10(-\tfrac{1}{2})y^{-\frac{1}{2}-1} = -5y^{-\frac{3}{2}} = -\dfrac{5}{y^{\frac{3}{2}}}.$

Exercise XIV.

1. The following table gives the distance s ft. of a point in a piece of mechanism to the right of a fixed point O after t sec. Draw a graph of s against t and from it find the value of the velocity $\dfrac{ds}{dt}$ at $t=0, 1, 2, \ldots 12$. Draw a graph of $\dfrac{ds}{dt}$ against t. What is the greatest speed of the point (a) to the right, (b) to the left ?

t ..	0	1	2	3	4	5	6	7	8	9	10	11	12
s ..	0	2·4	5·7	9·5	13·6	17·6	20·8	22·1	19·8	14·0	7·8	3·5	1·0

2. Draw a graph of $y=\dfrac{1}{x}$ from $x=\frac{1}{2}$ to $x=3$. By drawing the tangents at $x=1$ and 2, find the values of $\dfrac{dy}{dx}$ at $x=1$ and $x=2$ respectively.

3. The following table gives the potential difference, V volts, across the plates of a condenser which is being charged through a resistance. The current, i amp., which is entering a plate of the condenser after t sec., is given by $i=C\dfrac{dV}{dt}$, where C farads is the capacity of the condenser. Draw a graph of V against t and hence find the values of i when $t=0\cdot08$ and $0\cdot3$, given that $C=50\times10^{-6}$.

V ..	0	200	400	600	800	1000	1200	1400	1600	1800
$100t$ ..	0	2·11	4·46	7·13	10·21	13·86	18·32	24·07	32·15	46·06

4. The following table gives the volume v cu. ft. of a quantity of steam when its pressure is p lb. wt./ft.^{2}. Draw a graph of p against v and from it find the values of $\dfrac{dp}{dv}$ when v is 1·5 and 2·5.

p ..	52,000	40,000	21,500	14,600	8200	5200	3000	1600	1350
v ..	0·4	0·5	0·75	1·0	1·5	2·0	3	4	5

5. A body moves so that the distance s ft. described in t sec. is given by $s=10t-2t^2$. Draw the space-time graph from $t=0$ to 5, taking values of the time at intervals of $\frac{1}{2}$ sec. Find the velocity of the body at each $\frac{1}{2}$ sec. and draw a velocity-time graph for the motion.

6. If the distance s ft. moved by a body in t sec. is given by $s=5t^2$, find the distance δs ft. moved in the time δt sec. from

t to $t+\delta t$, and deduce the value of the velocity $\dfrac{ds}{dt}$ ft./sec. at the instant t sec.

For each of the following values of y find the value of δy when x increases by δx (or h), and hence find $\dfrac{dy}{dx}$ as the limiting value of $\dfrac{\delta y}{\delta x}$ as δx approaches 0. In each case verify that your answer agrees with that obtained by using the rule for differentiating x^n.

7. $\frac{1}{4}x^2$. 8. $\dfrac{3}{x}$. 9. $2x^4$. 10. $\frac{1}{100}x^3$.

By using the rule for differentiating x^n find the differential coefficients with respect to x of :

11. $9x^7$. 12. $\frac{1}{20}x^{10}$. 13. $0{\cdot}1x^{2{\cdot}7}$. 14. $\sqrt{x^5}$.

15. $10x^{-3{\cdot}5}$. 16. $\dfrac{15}{x^{14}}$. 17. $-\dfrac{3}{2x^2}$. 18. $\dfrac{1}{ax^n}$.

Find the values of :

19. $\dfrac{d}{dh}(h^{\frac{3}{2}})$. 20. $\dfrac{d}{dv}(100v^{-1{\cdot}2})$. 21. $\dfrac{d}{dm}(84m^{\frac{1}{6}})$.

22. $\dfrac{d}{d\lambda}\left(\dfrac{1}{3\lambda}\right)$. 23. $\dfrac{d}{dz}\left(\dfrac{4}{\sqrt{z}}\right)$. 24. $\dfrac{d}{dp}\left\{\left(\dfrac{p}{20}\right)^{\frac{n+1}{n}}\right\}$.

Find the derivatives of each of the following expressions with respect to the variable :

25. $20x^{\frac{2}{5}}$. 26. $\sqrt{5m}$. 27. $\dfrac{1}{6k^2}$.

28. $36v^{\frac{7}{6}}$. 29. $\dfrac{0{\cdot}04}{x^{10}}$. 30. $(2z^{\frac{1}{4}})^5$.

31. Find the gradients of the tangents to the graph of $y=\frac{1}{2}x^4$ at the points where $x=\frac{1}{2}$, $x=-1$ and $x=2$ respectively.

In Questions 32 to 36 the scales on the axes are the same :

32. Find the co-ordinates of the point on the graph of $y=x^2$ at which the tangent makes $60°$ with the x axis.

33. Find the angles which the tangents at the points given by $x=1$, $x=-2$ on the curve $y=\frac{1}{2}x^3-2x$ make with the x axis.

34. At what points on the graph of $y=1+4x-2x^2$ does the tangent make (a) $45°$, (b) $135°$ with Ox ?

35. Find where the graphs of $y=x+2$ and $y=x^2$ cut, and find the acute angle between the graphs at each point of intersection.

36. The distance s in. moved by a body in t sec. is given by $s = 3t^2$. What is its velocity after t sec. ? What is the increase of the velocity from the end of the third second to the end of the fifth second ?

37. A spherical balloon is blown up so that its volume increases at a constant rate of 2 cu. in. per sec. Show that after t sec. its radius is r in. is given by $r = \sqrt[3]{\dfrac{3t}{2\pi}}$. Hence find the rate at which the radius is increasing (a) after t sec., (b) after 4 sec.

38. The volume v cu. ft. of a gas expanding adiabatically is related to the pressure p lb. wt./in.^{2} by the formula $pv^{1\cdot4} = 512$. Find the value of $\dfrac{dp}{dv}$ when $v = 12\cdot7$.

39. The curves $pv^n = A$ and $pv = B$ where A and B are constants are plotted with p axis vertical and v axis horizontal. Prove that the ratio of the gradients of their tangents at the point where they intersect is $n : 1$. [These curves are those showing the pressure and volume of a gas during adiabatic and isothermal expansions respectively ; n is always greater than 1 and so the adiabatic curve is steeper than the isothermal at their point of intersection.]

Proof of the rule for differentiating ax^n when n is a positive integer

If $y = ax^n$,

$$y + \delta y = a(x + \delta x)^n = a(x + h)^n, \quad \text{where } h = \delta x.$$

Substitute x and h for a and b in the formulæ for $(a+b)^n$ given in an example on page 46 we find that, when n is a positive integer, $(x+h)^n = x^n + nx^{n-1}h + \text{terms containing } h^2$ and higher powers of h.

$$\therefore \ \delta y = a(x + h)^n - ax^n$$

$$= ax^n + anx^{n-1}h + a(\text{terms containing } h^2 \text{ and higher power of } h) - ax^n$$

$$= anx^{n-1}h + a(\text{terms containing } h^2 \text{ and higher powers of } h)$$

$\therefore$ dividing by h, i.e. δx,

$$\frac{\delta y}{\delta x} = anx^{n-1} + a(\text{terms containing } h \text{ and higher powers of } h).$$

Now, when δx approaches 0, every term containing h as a factor approaches 0, and hence in the limit all the terms in the bracket become zero.

$$\therefore \frac{dy}{dx} = anx^{n-1}.$$

Functional notation

Instead of writing a new letter such as y or z for a function of x we sometimes write $f(x)$, $F(x)$ or $\phi(x)$. The differential coefficient of $f(x)$ with respect to x is denoted by $f'(x)$. When x is given a special value, say 3, the values taken by $f(x)$ and $f'(x)$ are written $f(3)$, $f'(3)$; thus $f'(3)$ means the value obtained by putting $x = 3$ after differentiating $f(x)$.

Example.—If $f(x) = x^3 - 5x^2 + 7x$, find the values of $f(\frac{1}{2})$, $f(-2)$, $f'(-2)$.

$$f(\tfrac{1}{2}) = \frac{1}{2^3} - \frac{5}{2^2} + \frac{7}{2} = \tfrac{1}{8} - \tfrac{5}{4} + \tfrac{7}{2} = 2\tfrac{3}{8}.$$

$$f(-2) = (-2)^3 - 5(-2)^2 + 7(-2) = -8 - 20 - 14 = -42.$$

Differentiating $f(x)$

$$f'(x) = 3x^2 - 10x + 7.$$

$$\therefore f'(-2) = 3(-2)^2 - 10(-2) + 7 = 12 + 20 + 7 = 39.$$

$f'(x)$ as a limiting value.

If $y = f(x)$, $y + \delta y = f(x + \delta x)$.

$$\therefore \delta y = f(x + \delta x) - f(x).$$

$$\therefore \frac{\delta y}{\delta x} = \frac{f(x + \delta x) - f(x)}{\delta x}.$$

$$\therefore f'(x) = \frac{dy}{dx} = \lim_{\delta x \to 0} \frac{\delta y}{\delta x} = \lim_{\delta x \to 0} \frac{f(x + \delta x) - f(x)}{\delta x},$$

or
$$f'(x) = \lim_{h \to 0} \frac{f(x + h) - f(x)}{h}.$$

Alternative method of finding $f'(x)$

Let P, Q, R be points on the graph of $f(x)$ having abscissæ x, $x+h$ and $x-h$. So far we have found $f'(x)$ as the limit of

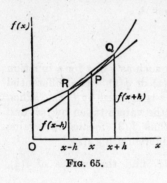

FIG. 65.

the gradient of the chord PQ as Q approaches P, i.e. as h approaches 0, but it is clear that the gradient of the chord RQ will also approach the gradient of the tangent at P as h approaches 0. The gradient of RQ is

$$\frac{f(x+h)-f(x-h)}{2h}.$$

$$\therefore f'(x) = \lim_{h\to 0}\frac{f(x+h)-f(x-h)}{2h}.$$

Differentiation of cu where c is a constant

Let $y=cu$, where c is constant and u is a function of x. Let u and y increase by δu and δy when x increases by δx. Then

$$y+\delta y=c(u+\delta u)=cu+c\delta u$$

$$\therefore \delta y=c\delta u$$

$$\therefore \frac{\delta y}{\delta x}=c\frac{\delta u}{\delta x}$$

Hence, when δx approaches 0,

$$\frac{dy}{dx}=c\frac{du}{dx}$$

Thus, as we have already seen on page 120,

$$\frac{d(ax^n)}{dx}=a\frac{d(x^n)}{dx}=anx^{n-1}.$$

Differentiation of a sum or difference

Suppose two taps are filling a bath and at the same time the water is running out through a drain-pipe; then the increase of the amount of water in the bath in any interval of time equals the sum of the amounts that have flowed in from the two taps minus the amount that has flowed out. In the same way, if $y = 7x^3 + 3x^2 - 5x$, when x increases by δx, increase in $y =$ increase in $7x^3$ + increase in $3x^2$ − increase in $5x$ or in symbols

$$\delta y = \delta(7x^3) + \delta(3x^2) - \delta(5x)$$

$$\therefore \frac{\delta y}{\delta x} = \frac{\delta(7x^3)}{\delta x} + \frac{\delta(3x^2)}{\delta x} - \frac{\delta(5x)}{\delta x}$$

$$\therefore \frac{dy}{dx} = \lim_{\delta x \to 0} \frac{\delta(7x^3)}{\delta x} + \lim_{\delta x \to 0} \frac{\delta(3x^2)}{\delta x} - \lim_{\delta x \to 0} \frac{\delta(5x)}{\delta x}$$

$$= \frac{d(7x^3)}{dx} + \frac{d(3x^2)}{dx} - \frac{d(5x)}{dx}$$

$$= 21x^2 + 6x - 5.$$

In general, if $y = u + v + w$, where u, v, w are functions of x,

$$\frac{dy}{dx} = \frac{du}{dx} + \frac{dv}{dx} + \frac{dw}{dx}.$$

Example.—If $f(x) = 4\sqrt{x} - 0.4x^{1.2} + \dfrac{1}{6x^3}$, find $f'(x)$:

$$f(x) = 4x^{\frac{1}{2}} - 0.4x^{1.2} + \tfrac{1}{6}x^{-3}.$$

$$\therefore f'(x) = \frac{d(4x^{\frac{1}{2}})}{dx} - \frac{d(0.4x^{1.2})}{dx} + \frac{d(\frac{1}{6}x^{-3})}{dx}$$

$$= 4 \times \tfrac{1}{2}x^{-\frac{1}{2}} - 0.4 \times 1.2x^{0.2} + \tfrac{1}{6}(-3)x^{-4}$$

$$= \frac{2}{\sqrt{x}} - 0.48x^{0.2} - \frac{1}{2x^4}.$$

Small Increments

In Fig. 61, if δx is small enough, $\dfrac{KQ}{PK}$ is a good approxima-

tion to the gradient of the tangent at P, which is $\dfrac{dy}{dx}$. Hence, when δx is small enough

$$\frac{\delta y}{\delta x} = \frac{KQ}{PK} \backsimeq \frac{dy}{dx}$$

$$\therefore \ \delta y \backsimeq \frac{dy}{dx} \cdot \delta x.$$

Example.—A cube has edges of length x in. If the length of an edge is increased by δx in., find the approximate increase in the volume of the cube. Calculate this increase when $x = 8$ and $\delta x = 0\cdot01$; also find what δx must be for the increase in the volume of the cube to be $0\cdot6$ cu. in. when $x = 10$.

Let the volume of the cube be V cu. in. ; then $V = x^3$ and hence

$$\delta V \backsimeq \frac{dV}{dx}\delta x = 3x^2\delta x.$$

When $x = 8$ and $\delta x = 0\cdot01$, $\delta V \backsimeq 3 \times 64 \times 0\cdot01 = 1\cdot92$ and therefore the increase in the volume of the cube is $1\cdot92$ cu. in. nearly.

When $\delta V = 0\cdot6$ and $x = 10$, $0\cdot6 \backsimeq 3 \times 10^2\delta x$, whence $\delta x \backsimeq 0\cdot002$.

Exercise XV.

1. Write out the complete expansion of $(x + h)^7$ in powers of x and h (see page 46). Use this to find the differential coefficient of $4x^7$ from first principles.

2. If $f(x) = 2x^2 + 3x + 1$, find the values of $f(2), f(1), f'(2), f'(-1)$.

3. If $f(t) = t + \dfrac{1}{t}$, find the values of $f(3), f(\frac{1}{3}), f'(3), f'(\frac{1}{3})$. Also show that $f\left(\dfrac{1}{t}\right) = f(t)$.

4. Find the values of $f(1), f(1\cdot6), f'(1), f'(1\cdot6)$ when $f(u) = \sqrt{10u}$.

5. If $f(x) = \dfrac{1}{x}$ prove that $f(x+h) - f(x-h) = -\dfrac{2h}{x^2 - h^2}$, and verify that the limiting value of $\dfrac{f(x+h) - f(x-h)}{2h}$ as h approaches 0 is $-\dfrac{1}{x^2}$.

6. If $f(x) = x^3$ find $f'(x)$ from the limiting value of

$$\frac{f(x+h) - f(x-h)}{2h}.$$

7. The values of a function $J(x)$ near $x = 2$ are given by

x	1·9	2·0	2·1
$J(x)$	0·28132	0·22389	0·16661

Find the value of $J'(2)$ approximately.

8. From a table of logs to base 10, find the approximate values of $\dfrac{d(\log_{10} x)}{dx}$ when $x = 1, 2, 3, 4$ and 5. Make a table of the values of $x\dfrac{d}{dx}(\log_{10} x)$. What do you notice about the numbers in this table and what conclusion do you draw ?

9. From a table of cubes, $7 \cdot 9^3 = 493 \cdot 04$, $8 \cdot 1^3 = 531 \cdot 44$. Use these to find the approximate value of $\dfrac{d(x^3)}{dx}$ when $x = 8$, and compare your answer with the value of $3x^2$ when $x = 8$.

By using the rule for differentiating x^n find the derivatives of :

10. $2x^{10} - 9x^5 + 7$. **11.** $4x^{6\cdot3} - 1 \cdot 4x^{2\cdot5}$. **12.** $0 \cdot 1x^{1\cdot8} + 0 \cdot 3x^{0\cdot9}$.

13. $\dfrac{1}{5x} - \dfrac{3}{2x^2}$. **14.** $8x^4 - 7x^3 + 2x^2 - 3$. **15.** $\sqrt{x} + \dfrac{1}{\sqrt{x}}$.

Find the values of :

16. $\dfrac{d}{dp}(p^2 + 4p)$. **17.** $\dfrac{d}{dr}(r^2 - 2r + 3)$. **18.** $\dfrac{d}{dz}\left(z + \dfrac{1}{z}\right)$.

19. $\dfrac{d}{dk}\left(\dfrac{1}{2\sqrt{k}} - \dfrac{1}{2k^2}\right)$. **20.** $\dfrac{d}{d\mu}\left(\mu^2 - \dfrac{2}{\mu}\right)$. **21.** $\dfrac{d}{dx}\left(x^{0\cdot8} + \dfrac{1}{x^{0\cdot2}}\right)$.

22. If $f(x) = \dfrac{2x^2 + 5}{x^3}$, express $f(x)$ as the sum of two fractions and hence find $f'(x)$.

5

Find the following differential coefficients, assuming that all the quantities are constants except the one with respect to which you are differentiating.

23. $\dfrac{d}{di}(Ei - Ri^2)$.

24. $\dfrac{d}{dr}\left(ar^2 + \dfrac{b}{r^2}\right)$.

25. $\dfrac{d}{dx}\left(Rgx - \dfrac{Cx^3}{6l}\right)$.

26. $\dfrac{d}{dR_2}\left(R_2 + \dfrac{x^2}{R_2}\right)$.

27. $\dfrac{d}{dH}\left(\frac{4}{15}B\sqrt{2g}H^{\frac{3}{2}}\right)$.

28. $\dfrac{d}{dv}\left\{\dfrac{C}{1-n}(v^{1-n} - v_1^{1-n})\right\}$.

29. $\dfrac{d}{dI}\left(\dfrac{aI^2 + b}{I}\right)$.

30. $\dfrac{d}{dp_2}\left[\left(\dfrac{p_2}{p_1}\right)^{\frac{n-1}{n}} + \left(\dfrac{p_3}{p_2}\right)^{\frac{n-1}{n}}\right]$.

31. $\dfrac{d}{du}\left(\dfrac{f-u}{u^2}\right)$.

32. A body moves so that the distance s ft. described in t sec. is given by $s = 10t - 8t^2$. What is its velocity after t sec. ?

33. The resistance R lb. wt. (per ton wt. of the train) to the motion of a train is given in terms of the velocity V m.p.h. by $R = 5 \cdot 25 + 0 \cdot 0513V + 0 \cdot 00162V^2$. At what rate is R increasing with respect to V when (a) $V = 20$, (b) $V = 80$?

34. The length l of a gold bar is given in terms of the temperature t by $l = 1 + 0 \cdot 0000136t + 0 \cdot 0000000112t^2$. Find the rate at which l increases with respect to the temperature when (a) $t = 100$, (b) $t = 500$.

35. The luminosity, I candles, of a lamp is given in terms of the voltage V by $I = 9 \times 10^{-7}V^{3 \cdot 9}$. Find the rate at which I is increasing with respect to V, and calculate its value when $V = 100$.

36. A man 6 ft. tall walks from a lamp directly towards a wall 20 ft. away at a speed of 4 ft./sec. If the lamp is 10 ft. above the ground, show that t sec. (where $t > 2$) after he leaves the post

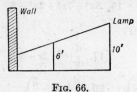

FIG. 66.

the top of his shadow on the wall is at a height $10 - \dfrac{20}{t}$ ft. At what speed is this height increasing when $t = 4$? Show also that this height increases at a decreasing rate.

37. What is the approximate increase of the area of a circle of radius r when r increases by a small quantity δr ?

38. Find the approximate increase in y when x increases by δx if y is (a) x^4, (b) $\dfrac{1}{x}$. Explain the meaning of the negative sign in the answer to (b).

39. What is the length of a side of a square of area A sq. in. ? What is the approximate increase in the length of a side if A increases by δA ? Calculate this increase when A is 36 and δA is 0·01.

40. Find the approximate increase in the volume of a sphere when its radius increases from 3 to 3·01 in.

41. In Question 35 what is the approximate increment in I when V increases by δV ? Calculate this increment when V is 100 and δV is 0·5.

42. Find the approximate decrease in $\dfrac{1}{x^3}$ when x increases by δx, and hence calculate the approximate value of $\dfrac{1}{3^3} - \dfrac{1}{3\cdot1^3}.$

CHAPTER VI

MAXIMUM AND MINIMUM VALUES
RATES OF INCREASE

The sign of $\dfrac{dy}{dx}$

If $\dfrac{dy}{dx}$ is positive at $x = a$, y is increasing as x increases

through a, whereas, if $\dfrac{dy}{dx}$ is negative at $x = a$, y is decreasing

as x increases through a. On the graph of y this means that

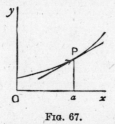
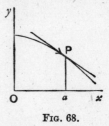

FIG. 67.   FIG. 68.

the tangent at the point P, given by $x = a$, slopes upwards or

downwards to the right according as $\dfrac{dy}{dx}$ is positive (Fig. 67) or

negative (Fig. 68).

Example.—If $y = 2x^3 - 6x^2 + 3$, find whether y is increasing or decreasing as x increases through (a) -1, (b) 1, (c) 2, (d) 2·5.

$$\frac{dy}{dx} = 6x^2 - 12x.$$

$\therefore$ at $x = -1$, $\dfrac{dy}{dx} = 6 + 12 = 18$. $\therefore$ y is increasing ;

at $x = 1$, $\dfrac{dy}{dx} = 6 - 12 = -6$. $\therefore$ y is decreasing ;

at $x = 2$, $\dfrac{dy}{dx} = 24 - 24 = 0$. $\therefore$ y is neither increasing nor decreasing ;

at $x = 2\cdot5$, $\dfrac{dy}{dx} = 37\cdot5 - 30 = 7\cdot5$. $\therefore$ y is increasing.

Fig. 69 shows the graph of y.

GRAPH OF $y = 2x^3 - 6x^2 + 3$

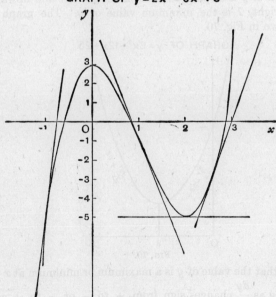

Fig. 69.

When we say either that y is increasing or that y is decreasing we shall always imply that this happens as x increases. When y is increasing the point on the graph of y is moving upwards and when y is decreasing it is moving downwards.

Example.—If $y = 2x^2 - 12x + 25$, show that y is decreasing when x is less than 3, and increasing when x is greater than 3. Sketch a graph of y from $x = -1$ to 5.

$$\frac{dy}{dx} = 4x - 12 = 4(x - 3).$$

$\therefore \dfrac{dy}{dx} = 0$ at $x = 3$, and when x is less than 3 the value of $\dfrac{dy}{dx}$ is negative and hence y is decreasing. Also when x is greater than 3, $\dfrac{dy}{dx}$ is positive and y is increasing. At $x = 3$, $y = 7$ and since the graph of y is sloping downwards on the left and upwards on the right, 7 is the minimum value of y. The graph of y is shown in Fig. 70.

GRAPH OF $y = 2x^2 - 12x + 25$

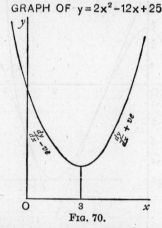

Fig. 70.

Note that the value of y is a maximum or minimum at $x = a$ according as $\dfrac{dy}{dx}$ changes sign from $+$ to $-$ or $-$ to $+$ as x increases through a.

Second and higher differential coefficients

The differential coefficient of $\dfrac{dy}{dx}$ with respect to x is written

$\dfrac{d^2y}{dx^2}$, which is pronounced *dee two y by dee x squared*.

Thus
$$\frac{d^2y}{dx^2} = \frac{d\left(\dfrac{dy}{dx}\right)}{dx}.$$

In the same way

$$\frac{d^3y}{dx^3} = \frac{d\left(\dfrac{d^2y}{dx^2}\right)}{dx}.$$

If $y = f(x)$, $\dfrac{d^2y}{dx^2}$, $\dfrac{d^3y}{dx^3}$, etc., are written $f''(x)$, $f'''(x)$, etc.

Example.—If $y = 4\sqrt{x} - \dfrac{2}{x}$, find $\dfrac{d^2y}{dx^2}$.

$$y = 4x^{\frac{1}{2}} - 2x^{-1}$$

$$\therefore \frac{dy}{dx} = 4 \times \tfrac{1}{2}x^{-\frac{1}{2}} - 2(-1)x^{-2} = 2x^{-\frac{1}{2}} + 2x^{-2}$$

$$\therefore \frac{d^2y}{dx^2} = 2(-\tfrac{1}{2})x^{-\frac{3}{2}} + 2(-2)x^{-3}$$

$$= x^{-\frac{3}{2}} - 4x^{-3}$$

$$= -\frac{1}{x^{\frac{3}{2}}} - \frac{4}{x^3}.$$

The meaning of $\dfrac{d^2y}{dx^2}$ on the graph of y.

Because $\dfrac{d^2y}{dx^2}$ is the rate of increase of $\dfrac{dy}{dx}$ it tells us the same

things about $\dfrac{dy}{dx}$ as $\dfrac{dy}{dx}$ tells us about y.   Just as y is increasing when $\dfrac{dy}{dx}$ is positive, so $\dfrac{dy}{dx}$ is increasing when $\dfrac{d^2y}{dx^2}$ is positive. This means that when $\dfrac{d^2y}{dx^2}$ is positive the gradient of the tangent is increasing with x, i.e. as a point moves along the graph to the right the tangent is turning anti-clockwise, as at A in Fig. 71. Similarly when $\dfrac{d^2y}{dx^2}$ is negative, $\dfrac{dy}{dx}$ is

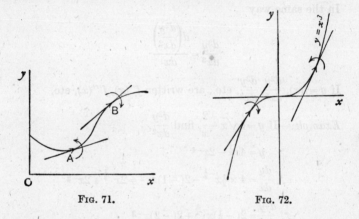

FIG. 71.   FIG. 72.

decreasing; in this case the tangent is turning clockwise, as at B in Fig. 71.

For instance, if $y = x^3$ (Fig. 72),

$$\frac{dy}{dx} = 3x^2 \quad \text{and} \quad \frac{d^2y}{dx^2} = 6x.$$

Hence, $\dfrac{d^2y}{dx^2}$ is negative at every point on the graph of y to the left of the y-axis, and therefore the tangent is turning clockwise. In the same way at any point on the graph to the right of the y-axis, the tangent is turning anti-clockwise.

Velocity and acceleration

Suppose a point moves a distance x from O along a straight line in time t. Then its velocity v is the rate of increase of x, i.e. $\dfrac{dx}{dt}$ or $\dot{x}$. This gives the velocity in the direction of increase of x, i.e. to the right. When $\dfrac{dx}{dt}$ is negative, x is decreasing as t increases and the point is moving to the left.

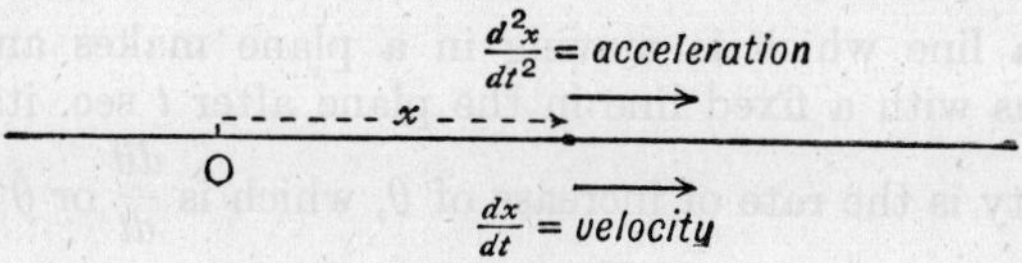

$$\frac{d^2x}{dt^2} = acceleration$$

$$\frac{dx}{dt} = velocity$$

Fig. 73.

The acceleration of the point in the direction of increase of x is the rate of increase of its velocity, i.e. $\dfrac{dv}{dt}$ or $\dot{v}$. Since

$$v = \frac{dx}{dt}, \quad \frac{dv}{dt} = \frac{d^2x}{dt^2}, \text{ sometimes written } \ddot{x}.$$

Example.—If a ball starts to roll with a velocity of 6 ft./sec. up an inclined plane of inclination 1/100, its distance x ft. up the plane after t sec. is given approximately by $x = 6t - 0.12t^2$. Find its velocity and acceleration after t sec. and describe the motion.

Differentiating x with respect to t,

$$\frac{dx}{dt} = 6 - 0.24t, \quad \frac{d^2x}{dt^2} = -0.24.$$

Since $\dfrac{d^2x}{dt^2}$ is constant and is negative the ball has a constant acceleration down the plane, i.e. at the beginning it has a retardation 0.24 ft./sec². The velocity of the ball decreases at this rate until the ball comes to rest, when $\dfrac{dx}{dt} = 0$; this occurs

5*

when $t = \dfrac{6}{0\cdot24} = 25$.   After this the ball still has an acceleration $0\cdot24$ ft./sec.[2] down the plane, and so the ball rolls back with a velocity which increases at this rate.   Note that, after $t = 25$, $\dfrac{dx}{dt}$ is negative, which indicates that the ball is rolling down the plane.

Angular velocity and acceleration

If a line which is moving in a plane makes an angle θ radians with a fixed line in the plane after t sec. its angular velocity is the rate of increase of θ, which is $\dfrac{d\theta}{dt}$ or $\dot{\theta}$ rad./sec., and it is often denoted by ω.   Its angular acceleration is the rate of increase of its angular velocity, i.e. $\dfrac{d\omega}{dt}$ rad./sec.[2], which equals $\dfrac{d^2\theta}{dt^2}$ or $\ddot{\theta}$ rad./sec.[2].

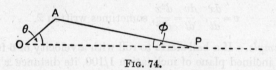

FIG. 74.

Angular velocity can also be expressed in degrees per sec. or revolutions per sec.   Thus, if a propeller shaft is rotating at n rev./sec. every line in a normal cross-section of the shaft has an angular velocity of n rev./sec. or $2n\pi$ rad./sec.

Fig. 74 shows the crank OA and the connecting rod AP of an engine.   The piston head P moves in a straight line through O.   If the crank and connecting rod make angles θ and ϕ respectively with this line at a time t, the angular velocities of the crank and connecting rod are $\dot{\theta}$ and $\dot{\phi}$, and their angular accelerations are $\ddot{\theta}$ and $\ddot{\phi}$.   In most cases $\dot{\theta}$ is nearly constant, i.e. $\ddot{\theta} = 0$, but $\dot{\phi}$ and $\ddot{\phi}$ vary considerably. The following example shows how $\dot{\phi}$ varies.

Example.—In a certain motor-car engine the crank is $1\frac{1}{2}$ in. long and the connecting rod is 6 in. long. The crank rotates at a uniform rate of 2800 rev./min. Calculate the approximate angular velocity of the connecting rod when the crank makes (i) 15°, (ii) 75° with the line of stroke.

From Fig. 74 by the sine rule

$$\frac{\sin \phi}{1\frac{1}{2}} = \frac{\sin \theta}{6}$$

$$\therefore \sin \phi = \tfrac{1}{4} \sin \theta.$$

To find the rate at which ϕ is increasing when θ is 15° we calculate the increase in ϕ as θ increases from 14° to 16°.

θ				14°	16°
$\sin \theta$	..	..	..	0·2419	0·2756
$\sin \phi$	..	..	..	0·0605	0·0689
ϕ	..	..	..	3° 28′	3° 57′

Thus ϕ increases from 3° 28′ to 3° 57′, i.e. 29′, while θ increases by 120′. Hence the ratio of the angular velocity, $\dot{\phi}$, of the connecting rod to that of the crank is nearly $\frac{29}{120}$.

Therefore, when $\theta = 15°$, $\dot{\phi} \fallingdotseq \frac{29}{120} \times 2800 \fallingdotseq 680$ rev./min.

In the same way, as θ increases from 74° to 76° we find that ϕ increases by approximately 8′,

thus, when θ is 75°, $\dot{\phi} \fallingdotseq \frac{8}{120} \times 2800 \fallingdotseq 190$ rev./min.

This example is solved by another method on page 271

Relation between linear and angular velocity in circular motion

Suppose that the radius OP of the circle in Fig. 75 is rotating about O. Let OA be any fixed radius and let the arc AP have a length s when the angle AOP is θ^c.

Then, if r is the radius of the circle, $s = r\theta$.

Differentiating this equation and remembering that r is constant

$$\frac{ds}{dt} = r\frac{d\theta}{dt} = r\omega.$$

Thus, when OP is rotating at any instant with an angular velocity ω, the velocity of P at this instant is $r\omega$.

Maximum and minimum values

If $\dfrac{dy}{dx}=0$ and $\dfrac{d^2y}{dx^2}$ is negative at $x=a$, the tangent is horizontal at the point A given by $x=a$ (Fig. 76) and it is turning clockwise.

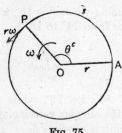

FIG. 75.

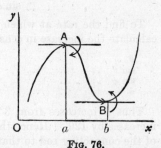

FIG. 76.

Thus y has a maximum value at $x=a$. In the same way, if $\dfrac{dy}{dx}=0$ and $\dfrac{d^2y}{dx^2}$ is positive at $x=b$, the tangent is horizontal at the point B given by $x=b$ and it is turning anti-clockwise. Thus y has a minimum value at $x=b$. Hence we have the rule :

At any value of x which makes

$$\dfrac{dy}{dx}=0 \quad \text{and} \quad \dfrac{d^2y}{dx^2} \begin{cases} \text{negative, } y \text{ is a maximum;} \\ \text{positive, } y \text{ is a minimum.} \end{cases}$$

In applications it is often possible to distinguish between a maximum and a minimum from practical considerations. It is then unnecessary to find $\dfrac{d^2y}{dx^2}$.

Example.—Find the maximum and minimum values of y when $y = 2x^3 + 3x^2 - 12x + 4$.

Differentiating $$\frac{dy}{dx} = 6x^2 + 6x - 12$$

$$\frac{d^2y}{dx^2} = 12x + 6.$$

$$\therefore \frac{dy}{dx} = 0 \quad \text{when} \quad 6x^2 + 6x - 12 = 0.$$

$$\text{whence } x^2 + x - 2 = 0.$$

$$x = -2 \text{ or } 1.$$

At $x = -2$, $\frac{d^2y}{dx^2} = -24 + 6 = -18$, which is negative. Therefore y has a maximum value at $x = -2$, and substituting this value of x in y we find

$$y_{\text{max.}} = 2(-2)^3 + 3(-2)^2 - 12(-2) + 4$$
$$= -16 + 12 + 24 + 4 = 24.$$

At $x = 1$, $\frac{d^2y}{dx^2} = 12 + 6$, which is positive. Therefore y has a minimum value at $x = 1$ and hence

$$y_{\text{min.}} = 2 + 3 - 12 + 4 = -3.$$

GRAPH OF $y = 2x^3 + 3x^2 - 12x + 4$

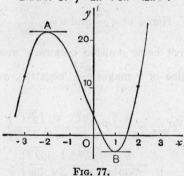

Fig. 77.

The values of $y_{\text{max.}}$ and $y_{\text{min.}}$ give the ordinates at the important points A and B on the graph of y in Fig. 77.   Since these are the only turning points on the graph, they enable us to draw a rough sketch of the graph without finding any other points, though the sketch is much improved by finding one point to the left at A and one to the right of B which give a rough idea how steep the graph is in these parts. In Fig. 77 the points given by $x = -3$, and $x = 2$ are plotted in addition to A and B.

Example.—The horse-power P transmitted by a belt is given by $P = \dfrac{k}{550}\left(Tv - \dfrac{wv^3}{g}\right)$, where k is a number depending on the friction and the angle of lap, T lb. wt. is the tension of the belt on the driving side, v ft./sec. is its velocity and w lb. wt./ft. its weight per unit length. Find the speed at which P is greatest and also the greatest value of P.

$$\frac{dP}{dv} = \frac{k}{550}\left(T - \frac{3wv^2}{g}\right),$$

$$\therefore \frac{d^2P}{dv^2} = \frac{k}{550}\left(-\frac{6wv}{g}\right) = -\frac{6kwv}{550g}.$$

$$\therefore \frac{dP}{dv} = 0 \quad \text{when} \quad T - \frac{3wv^2}{g} = 0.$$

$$\text{Hence } v^2 = \frac{gT}{3w} \text{ and } v = \sqrt{\frac{gT}{3w}},$$

the negative root being omitted because v must be positive here. This value of v makes $\dfrac{d^2P}{dv^2}$ negative, and hence P a maximum.

$$\therefore P_{\max.} = \frac{k}{550}\left\{T\sqrt{\frac{gT}{3w}} - \frac{w}{g}\sqrt{\frac{g^3T^3}{27w^3}}\right\}$$

$$= \frac{k}{550}\left\{\sqrt{\frac{gT^3}{3w}} - \frac{1}{3}\sqrt{\frac{gT^3}{3w}}\right\}$$

$$= \frac{2k}{1650}\sqrt{\frac{gT^3}{3w}}.$$

It is not always necessary to differentiate in order to find a maximum or minimum value. It is often possible to write an expression so that the variable terms in it make up a square and then to use the fact that a square is always positive or zero. Two examples are given below.

Example.—The impedance Z of a circuit containing a resistance R, an inductance L and a capacity C is given by

$$Z = \sqrt{R^2 + \left(\omega L - \frac{1}{\omega C}\right)^2},$$

where $\dfrac{\omega}{2\pi}$ is the frequency of the oscillations. Find the minimum value of Z as ω varies and the value of ω which makes Z a minimum.

Here the terms involving ω already form the square $\left(\omega L - \dfrac{1}{\omega C}\right)^2$. The minimum value of this square is zero. Therefore the least value of Z is R and it occurs when

$$\omega L = \frac{1}{\omega C}, \text{ i.e. } \omega = \frac{1}{\sqrt{LC}}.$$

Example.—Show that the sum of two positive numbers whose product is a constant C is a minimum when the numbers are equal.

Let one number be x; then the other is $\dfrac{C}{x}$, and their sum S is given by

$$S = x + \frac{C}{x}$$

$$= \left(\sqrt{x} - \frac{\sqrt{C}}{\sqrt{x}}\right)^2 + 2\sqrt{C},$$

because $\left(\sqrt{x} - \dfrac{\sqrt{C}}{\sqrt{x}}\right)^2 = x - 2\sqrt{C} + \dfrac{C}{x}.$

Hence, by the same argument as in the previous example, the sum has a minimum value $2\sqrt{C}$ when

$$\sqrt{x} = \frac{\sqrt{C}}{\sqrt{x}}, \quad \text{i.e.} \quad x = \frac{C}{x}.$$

Hence the two numbers, which are x and $\dfrac{C}{x}$, are equal.

The student should also work out this example by differentiation.

If the two numbers are the lengths of the sides of a rectangle their product is the area of the rectangle and their sum is half the perimeter of the rectangle. Hence the rectangle of given area and minimum perimeter is a square. The result proved above is useful in many practical problems as, for instance, in the following example.

Example.—The time of oscillation of a rigid body about an axis at a distance h from the centre of gravity is given by $T = 2\pi \sqrt{\dfrac{h^2 + k^2}{gh}}$, where k is constant. Find the value of h for which T is a minimum and the minimum value of T.

$$T = \frac{2\pi}{\sqrt{g}} \sqrt{h + \frac{k^2}{h}}.$$

Hence T is a minimum when $h + \dfrac{k^2}{h}$ is a minimum. The product of h and $\dfrac{k^2}{h}$ is k^2, which is constant,

$$\therefore h + \frac{k^2}{h} \text{ is a minimum when}$$

$$h = \frac{k^2}{h}, \quad \text{i.e.} \quad h = k.$$

$$\therefore T_{\min.} = \frac{2\pi}{\sqrt{g}} \sqrt{k + k} = 2\pi \sqrt{\frac{2k}{g}}.$$

The graph of T when $k^2 = 1200$ is shown on page 33, Part II.

In two examples above we have found the minimum value of an expression of the form $\sqrt{v}$ (as for instance in the last example where $v = h + \dfrac{k^2}{h}$) by finding the minimum value of v. It should be noted that

(a) if $y = +\sqrt{v}$, y is a maximum or a minimum when v is a maximum or a minimum;

(b) if $y = \dfrac{1}{v}$, y is a maximum when v is a minimum and vice versa.

Exercise XVI.

1. If $y = x^2 - x + 1$ find the values of $\dfrac{dy}{dx}$ at $x = -1, 0, 1$, and state whether y is increasing or decreasing as x increases through each value.

2. If $y = \dfrac{2}{x} - \dfrac{3}{x^2}$ find whether y is increasing or decreasing at $x = 1$ and $x = 5$.

3. If $y = x + \dfrac{1}{x}$ show that y is increasing from $x = -\infty$ to $x = -1$, decreasing from $x = -1$ to $x = 0$ and from $x = 0$ to $x = 1$ and increasing from $x = 1$ to ∞. Draw a rough sketch of the graph of y in the neighbourhoods of the points given by $x = -1$ and $x = 1$.

4. If $y = \sqrt{x} - x$, show that $\dfrac{dy}{dx}$ is positive if $x < \tfrac{1}{4}$ and negative if $x > \tfrac{1}{4}$. What conclusion do you draw from this?

Find $\dfrac{d^2y}{dx^2}$ when y is:

5. $\dfrac{2}{x}$.   6. $4x^2$.   7. $2x^4 - 5x^3$.   8. $\dfrac{1}{\sqrt{x}}$.   9. $x^{0.4} + \dfrac{1}{x^{0.4}}$.

10. Show by a figure the direction in which the tangent to $y = x^3 - 3x$ is turning as x increases at the points where (a) $x = -1$, (b) $x = 1$, (c) $x = 2$.

11. If the distance moved by a body in t sec. is $(8t - 0.1t^3)$ ft., find (a) its velocity, (b) its acceleration after 4 sec.

12. If the angle θ radians turned through by a body in t sec. is given by $\theta = 4t + \frac{1}{16}t^2$, find its angular velocity after t sec. and show that the angular acceleration of the body is constant.

13. A flywheel of radius 4 ft. is slowing down. What is the velocity of a point on its rim at the instant when its angular velocity is (a) 200 rev./min., (b) 40 rev./min. ?

14. A flywheel weighs W and its weight may be considered as concentrated in a thin rim of radius r. Show that its kinetic energy when it is rotating at angular velocity ω is $\frac{1}{2}\dfrac{W}{g}r^2\omega^2$. Evaluate the kinetic energy when $W = 50$ lb., $r = 0\cdot8$ ft., $\omega = 4$ rad./sec., and $g = 32$ ft./sec.^{2} and state the units in which it is measured.

Find the maximum and minimum values of y, if any, and sketch a rough graph of y when y is :

15. $1 + 3x - x^2$.

16. $2x^2 - 4x + 5$.

17. $x^3 - 3x^2 + 4$.

18. $p^3 - 6p^2$.

19. $2x^3 - 3x^2 - 12x + 4$.

20. $r^3 - 12r$.

21. $x + 1 + \dfrac{1}{x}$.

22. $\dfrac{1}{u} - \dfrac{1}{u^2}$.

23. $4\sqrt{N} - N$ $(N > 0)$.

24. $\sqrt{x} - 2x^2$ $(x > 0)$.

25. $x^{1\cdot5} - x^{2\cdot5}$.

26. $v^{1\cdot2} - 2\cdot4v$.

27. The bending moment M of a beam at a distance x from one end is given by $M = \frac{1}{2}w(lx - x^2)$. Find its maximum value.

28. To drive an electrical machine between C and D an electromotive force, E volts, is applied between A and B. The power,

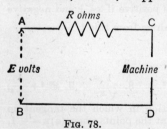

W watts, available to drive the machine is given by $W = Ei - Ri^2$ where i amp. is the current. Find the value of i for which W is a maximum, and show that the maximum value of W is $\dfrac{E^2}{4R}$.

Fig. 78.

29. If a beam AB of length l is supported at its ends at the same level and a load is hung from it at $\frac{6}{7}l$ from A, the deflection y at a distance $x(<\frac{6}{7}l)$ from A is proportional to $48l^2x - 49x^3$. For what value of x is the deflection a maximum ?

30. A tank has a volume 4 cu. ft., a square base and an open top. Show that if a side of the base is x ft., the total area of the material used in making the tank is $x^2 + \dfrac{16}{x}$ sq. ft. Find the value of x for which this is a minimum, and its minimum value.

31. The sum of two numbers is 20. Show that the sum of their product and their difference is a maximum when the numbers are 11 and 9.

32. When the current through a certain transformer is i amp. its efficiency is $\dfrac{200i}{200i + 350 + 0 \cdot 64i^2}$. If the efficiency is $\dfrac{1}{y}$, show that $y = 1 + \dfrac{1 \cdot 75}{i} + 0 \cdot 0032i$. Find the value of i which makes y a minimum and hence the efficiency a maximum. Calculate the maximum efficiency.

33. A closed cylindrical can is to hold 1 pint. Show that if its radius is r ft. its height is $\dfrac{0 \cdot 02}{\pi r^2}$ ft., and hence show that the total area of the metal of which it is made is $2\pi r^2 + \dfrac{0 \cdot 04}{r}$ sq. ft. Find the value of r for which this is a minimum. Hence, find to the nearest $\frac{1}{10}$ in. (a) the radius, (b) the height of the can of minimum surface area which will hold 1 pint. Find also the area of the metal used in making it, to the nearest sq. in. [1 gallon $= 0 \cdot 16$ cu. ft.]

34. Show by a graph that if $f(x)$ is continuous from $x = a$ to $x = b$ and has one minimum and no maximum value between $x = a$ and $x = b$, the greatest value of $f(x)$ in the interval from $x = a$ to b, including $x = a$ and $x = b$, is either $f(b)$ or $f(a)$.

Find the greatest and least values of $x^2 - 4x + 10$ between $x = 1$ and $x = 4$.

35. If gas flows through a nozzle from a chamber where the pressure is p_1 to a chamber where the pressure is p_2, the weight of gas that flows per second is greatest when $x^{\frac{2}{n}} - x^{\frac{n+1}{n}}$ is a maximum, where $x = p_2/p_1$ and n is greater than 1. Show that the weight is a maximum when $x = \left(\dfrac{2}{n+1}\right)^{\frac{n}{n-1}}$. and calculate this value of x when $n = 1 \cdot 3$.

36. If the sum of two numbers is constant, prove that their product is a maximum when they are equal.

Find the area of the largest rectangle which can be enclosed by 200 yd. of fencing. Is this area larger or smaller than the area enclosed when the fence is a circle ?

37. The velocity U of waves of length λ in a canal is given by $U^2 = \dfrac{g\lambda}{2\pi} + \dfrac{2\pi T}{\rho\lambda}$ where T is the surface tension of the water and ρ is its density. Show that U is least when $\lambda = 2\pi\sqrt{\dfrac{T}{g\rho}}$. Find the least value of U.

38. In a two-stage air compressor in which air at a pressure p_1 is taken into the low-pressure cylinder, compressed to a pressure p_2, then cooled to its original temperature at constant pressure p_2 and finally compressed in the high-pressure cylinder to a pressure p_3, the work done per cycle is proportional to

$$\left(\frac{p_2}{p_1}\right)^{\frac{n-1}{n}} + \left(\frac{p_3}{p_2}\right)^{\frac{n-1}{n}} - 2.$$

Taking p_1 and p_3 as constant, show that the work is a minimum when $p_2 = \sqrt{p_1 p_3}$. [This may be proved either by differentiation or by noting that the product of the two numbers $\left(\dfrac{p_2}{p_1}\right)^{\frac{n-1}{n}}$ and $\left(\dfrac{p_3}{p_2}\right)^{\frac{n-1}{n}}$ is constant for all values of p_2.]

39. At noon a ship A is 30 sea miles north of a ship B. A then sails due west at 10 knots, and B due north at 20 knots. Show that after t hours they are $\sqrt{500t^2 - 1200t + 900}$ sea miles apart. Find when they are nearest, and their nearest distance. [Square the distance before differentiating.]

40. Fig. 79 shows the cross-section of a channel for the flow of water. If the cross-section has an area of 60 sq. ft., show that

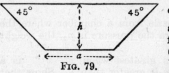

Fig. 79.

$a = \dfrac{60}{h} - h$ and deduce that the area of the wetted surface per foot length of the channel is $\dfrac{60}{h} - h + 2\sqrt{2}h$ when the channel is full. The resistance to the flow of water along the channel is least when the area of the wetted surface is least. Find the value of h when the resistance is a minimum, and calculate the corresponding value of a.

41. In Exercise XV, Question 36, show that, if $t > 2$, the total ength of the man's shadow on the ground and on the wall is $30 - 4t - \dfrac{20}{t}$ ft. At what instant is this greatest, and what is its greatest value ?

42. If in Fig. 78, Question 28, the resistance of the machine is r ohms, $W = \dfrac{E^2 r}{(R+r)^2}$. Show that $\dfrac{1}{W} = \dfrac{1}{E^2}\left(\dfrac{R^2}{r} + r + 2\,R\right)$. Hence, assuming that E and R are constant, show that W is greatest when $r = R$. [This is really the same problem as that in Question 28, only here r is taken as the variable quantity instead of i. The relation between r and i is $i = \dfrac{E}{R+r}$].

Rates of change

Suppose we wish to find the rate at which the area of a circle is increasing when its radius r in. is increasing at u in./sec. Let the area be A sq. in. and the radius be r in. after t sec., and let r and A increase by δr and δA when t increases by δt. Fig. 80 shows the increase of A when r increases by δr. By multiplication of fractions

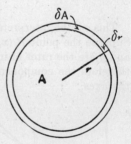

Fig. 80.

$$\frac{\delta A}{\delta t} = \frac{\delta A}{\delta r} \times \frac{\delta r}{\delta t}.$$

But this equation is true however small δt, δr and δA may be, and so we may make δt, δr, δA approach 0 and then each difference ratio approaches the corresponding differential coefficient.

$$\therefore \frac{dA}{dt} = \frac{dA}{dr} \times \frac{dr}{dt}.$$

But we know that $A = \pi r^2$

$$\therefore \frac{dA}{dr} = 2\pi r.$$

As we are given that $\dfrac{dr}{dt} = u$

$$\therefore \frac{dA}{dt} = 2\pi r u.$$

For instance, if $u = 0.3$ and $r = 2$, the circle is increasing its area at a rate $1.2\pi \fallingdotseq 3.77$ in.^{2}/sec.

If x and y are functions of t we may prove, as in the case of A and r above, that

$$\frac{dy}{dt} = \frac{dy}{dx} \times \frac{dx}{dt}.$$

We may write this also as

$$\frac{dy}{dx} = \frac{\dfrac{dy}{dt}}{\dfrac{dx}{dt}} \quad \text{or} \quad \frac{\dot{y}}{\dot{x}}.$$

This can be interpreted in the motion of a point in a plane. Suppose the point $P\,(x, y)$ is moving along a curve. Then $\dot{x}$ and $\dot{y}$ are the rates of increase of its two co-ordinates and are therefore the components of its velocity in the directions of the axes.

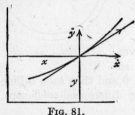

FIG. 81.

FIG. 82.

Now the tangent at P must be in the direction of the velocity of P, and hence its gradient is $\dfrac{\dot{y}}{\dot{x}}$ or in symbols

$$\frac{dy}{dx} = \frac{\dot{y}}{\dot{x}} \text{ as above.}$$

Example.—A cone with a vertical angle of 60° is held with its axis vertical and with its vertex downwards. If water is poured into it at a uniform rate of 12 cu. in. per sec., find the rate at which the surface is rising when the water is 6 in. deep. Also find the rate at which the water is rising when its depth is h in.

If after t sec. the depth of the water is h in., the radius of the surface of the water is $h \tan 30°$,

i.e. $\dfrac{h}{\sqrt{3}}$ in.

Hence the volume V cu. in. of the water in the cone is given by

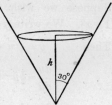

FIG. 83.

$$V = \tfrac{1}{3}\pi h \cdot \left(\dfrac{h}{\sqrt{3}}\right)^2 = \tfrac{1}{9}\pi h^3.$$

Now we know $\dfrac{dV}{dt} = 12$ and we want to find $\dfrac{dh}{dt}$, so we differentiate with respect to t.

$$\frac{dV}{dt} = \frac{dV}{dh} \times \frac{dh}{dt} = \tfrac{1}{3}\pi h^2 \cdot \frac{dh}{dt}.$$

Putting $\qquad h = 6$ and $\dfrac{dV}{dt} = 12$

$$12 = 12\pi \frac{dh}{dt}$$

$$\therefore \frac{dh}{dt} = \frac{1}{\pi} \simeq 0.318 \frac{\text{in.}}{\text{sec.}}$$

This is, of course, the rate at which the water is rising at this instant. The rate depends on the depth h. When the depth is h in.

$$\frac{dh}{dt} = \frac{3}{\pi h^2} \frac{dV}{dt} = \frac{36}{\pi h^2} \frac{\text{in.}}{\text{sec.}}$$

Differentiation by means of a substitution

If we write x instead of t and u instead of x the formula

$$\frac{dy}{dt} = \frac{dy}{dx} \times \frac{dx}{dt}$$

becomes

$$\frac{dy}{dx} = \frac{dy}{du} \times \frac{du}{dx}.$$

Suppose we wish to find the differential coefficient of $\sqrt{1+x^2}$. We write $y = \sqrt{1+x^2}$ and $1 + x^2 = u$.

Then $\qquad y = \sqrt{u} = u^{\frac{1}{2}}, \qquad u = 1 + x^2.$

$$\therefore \frac{dy}{du} = \tfrac{1}{2} u^{-\frac{1}{2}} = \frac{1}{2\sqrt{u}}, \quad \frac{du}{dx} = 2x.$$

$$\therefore \frac{dy}{dx} = \frac{dy}{du} \times \frac{du}{dx} = \frac{1}{2\sqrt{u}} \times 2x = \frac{x}{\sqrt{u}} = \frac{x}{\sqrt{1+x^2}}.$$

$$\therefore \frac{d}{dx}\sqrt{1+x^2} = \frac{x}{\sqrt{1+x^2}}.$$

The student should verify the rule $\dfrac{dy}{dx} = \dfrac{dy}{du} \times \dfrac{du}{dx}$ by applying it in a case where he knows the answer, as in the following example :

If $\qquad\qquad y = x^{10}$ and we write $u = x^2$

$$y = u^5 \text{ and } u = x^2$$

$$\therefore \frac{dy}{du} = 5u^4, \quad \frac{du}{dx} = 2x.$$

$$\therefore \frac{dy}{dx} = 5u^4 \times 2x = 10 \cdot x^8 \cdot x = 10x^9,$$

which we know is the differential coefficient of x^{10}.

The following case occurs so frequently that it is of special importance.

If $y = (ax + b)^n$ and we put $u = ax + b$,

$$y = u^n$$

$$\therefore \frac{dy}{du} = nu^{n-1}, \ \frac{du}{dx} = a.$$

$$\therefore \frac{dy}{dx} = nu^{n-1} \cdot a = an(ax + b)^{n-1}.$$

$$\therefore \frac{d}{dx}(ax + b)^n = an(ax + b)^{n-1}$$

To show that
$$\frac{dy}{dx} = \frac{1}{\dfrac{dx}{dy}}.$$

Whatever values δx and δy may have

$$\frac{\delta y}{\delta x} = \frac{1}{\dfrac{\delta x}{\delta y}}.$$

Now if we make δx and δy approach 0, $\dfrac{\delta y}{\delta x}$ and $\dfrac{\delta x}{\delta y}$ approach

the limiting values $\dfrac{dy}{dx}$ and $\dfrac{dx}{dy}$ respectively and hence

$$\frac{dy}{dx} = \frac{1}{\dfrac{dx}{dy}}.$$

Example.—Find $\dfrac{dy}{dx}$ if $y^2 = x$, and interpret the answers.

Since
$$x = y^2, \qquad \frac{dx}{dy} = 2y.$$

$$\therefore \frac{dy}{dx} = \frac{1}{\dfrac{dx}{dy}} = \frac{1}{2y} = \pm \frac{1}{2\sqrt{x}}.$$

Now if $y^2 = x$, y can be $\sqrt{x}$ or $-\sqrt{x}$. When it has the first value, $\dfrac{dy}{dx} = \dfrac{1}{2\sqrt{x}}$ which can easily be verified by differentiating $\sqrt{x}$. In the same way when $y = -\sqrt{x}$, $\dfrac{dy}{dx} = -\dfrac{1}{2\sqrt{x}}$.

Exercise XVII.

1. A point moves in a plane so that its co-ordinates x and y with respect to two perpendicular axes Ox and Oy are given in terms of the time t by $x = 3t^2$, $y = t^3$. Find its component velocities parallel to the axes, and deduce that when $t = 2$ the direction of motion of the body is equally inclined to the axes. Show also that after time t the body is moving at an angle with Ox whose tangent is $\frac{1}{2}t$.

2. Find $\dfrac{d(x^2)}{dt}$. At what rate is the area of a square increasing when its sides are 6 in. long and they are increasing at 2 in. per sec. ?

3. Using the formula $V = \frac{4}{3}\pi r^3$ for the volume of a sphere of radius r, find $\dfrac{dV}{dt}$ in terms of r and $\dfrac{dr}{dt}$. How fast is the volume increasing when the radius of the sphere is 2 ft. and it is increasing at 3 in. per sec. ?

4. During the expansion of a gas its pressure p lb. wt./in.^{2} and its volume v ft.^{3} are related by the formula $pv = 100$. If the volume is increasing at $0 \cdot 2$ ft.^{3} per sec. when the volume is 4 cu. ft., find the rate in lb. wt./in.^{2} per sec. at which the pressure is decreasing.

Find the value of $\dfrac{dy}{dt}$ in terms of x and $\dfrac{dx}{dt}$ when :

5. $y = x^4$.   **6.** $y = \dfrac{4}{x}$.   **7.** $y = \sqrt{x}$.

8. If the area of a circle is increasing at a constant rate of 2 sq. in. per sec., at what rate is the radius increasing when the radius of the circle is r in. ? Calculate this rate when $r = 4$.

9. A reservoir with a square base of side 100 ft. and a square top of side 120 ft. is 10 feet deep and it has plane sloping sides. Find the area of the surface of the water when it is x ft. deep. At what rate is the area of the surface increasing when the water is 4 ft. deep, if it is rising at $\frac{1}{20}$ in. per sec. ?

10. If the volume of a sphere is V, show that the area of its surface is $(36\pi)^{\frac{1}{3}} V^{\frac{2}{3}}$. If the volume of a spherical balloon is increasing at a uniform rate of 4 cu. in. per sec., at what rate is the area of the surface increasing when the volume is 1000 cu. in. ?

11. If a brass cube is being heated so that the length of an edge increases at a rate of 0·2% of the length per hour. At what rate is the volume increasing (a) of a cube of side 5 in., (b) of a cube of side x in. ?

12. A trough, which is 10 ft. long and 1 ft. deep, is 2 ft. wide at the bottom and 3 ft. wide at the top. It has plane sloping sides and vertical ends. If the volume of water in the trough is increasing at a constant rate of 2 cu. ft. per min., find the rate at which the depth of the water is increasing when the depth is h ft.

13. The figure shows a cylinder in which a gas is being compressed by the pressure of a piston. The diameter of the cylinder is 4 in. and the pressure, p lb. wt./in.^{2}, and the volume, v in.^{3}, of the gas are related by the equation $pv = 120$. Find the rate at which the pressure of the gas is increasing when the clearance of the piston is x in. and the piston is moving inwards at $\frac{1}{2}$ in. per sec. Calculate this rate when $x = 8$.

FIG. 84.

Differentiate with respect to x:

14. $(4 + 5x)^6$. **15.** $\sqrt{1 + 2x}$. **16.** $(1 - 3x^2)^4$.

17. $\dfrac{1}{(1 + x^3)^2}$. **18.** $(a - x)^n$. **19.** $\sqrt{ax + b}$.

Find the values of :

20. $\dfrac{d\sqrt{1 + v^2}}{dv}$. **21.** $\dfrac{d(3 - 4l)^6}{dl}$. **22.** $\dfrac{d}{dt}\left\{\dfrac{1}{(1 + t)^2}\right\}$.

23. $\dfrac{d}{dr}\left(\dfrac{1}{1 + 4r^2}\right)$. **24.** $\dfrac{d(2z + 3)^{20}}{dz}$. **25.** $\dfrac{d(am + b)^t}{dm}$.

26. $\dfrac{d(x^2 + 2x)^3}{dx}$. **27.** $\dfrac{d}{dn}\left(\dfrac{1}{1 + n - n^2}\right)$. **28.** $\dfrac{d}{du}\left(\dfrac{1}{\sqrt{1 - u^2}}\right)$.

29. A disc of radius 2 ft. is 4 ft. in front of a wall and parallel to it. A lamp is held at a point on the axis of the disc at a distance x ft. from the disc. Show that the radius r ft. of its shadow is given by $r = 2 + \dfrac{8}{x}$. At what rate is the radius of the shadow decreasing when the lamp is 7 ft. from the wall and is being moved away from it at $\frac{1}{2}$ ft. per sec. ? At what rate is the area of the shadow decreasing at the same instant ?

30. The velocity V ft./sec. of a sound wave in air at a temperature of $t°$ C. is given by $V = 1092\sqrt{1 + \dfrac{t}{273}}$. Find the rate at which the velocity increases with respect to the temperature.

31. If the point (x, y) is on a circle of radius a with centre at the origin, $x^2 + y^2 = a^2$. Hence, if (x, y) is a point above the x axis, $y = +\sqrt{a^2 - x^2}$. Find $\dfrac{dy}{dx}$ from this equation.

32. Find $\dfrac{dy}{dx}$ from $\dfrac{dx}{dy}$ if $y^3 = 2x$.

33. When a body is thrown vertically upwards with a velocity 20 ft./sec. its velocity v ft./sec., when it is at a height x ft., is given by $v = \sqrt{400 - 64x}$. Find $\dfrac{dv}{dt}$ in terms of x and $\dfrac{dx}{dt}$, and hence (remembering that $\dfrac{dx}{dt} = v$) show that $\dfrac{dv}{dt} = -32$.

34. When a point N moves in a straight line with simple harmonic motion of period $2\pi/n$, its velocity v, when it is at a distance x from the centre of the motion is given by $v = n\sqrt{a^2 - x^2}$, where a is the amplitude. Prove that the acceleration of N, i.e. $\dfrac{dv}{dt}$, is equal to $-n^2x$.

CHAPTER VII

INTEGRATION OF x^n

We will now see how to find a function which has a given differential coefficient, that is, to answer such a question as " If $\dfrac{dz}{dx} = x^2$, what is z ? " We will first answer the easier question " If $\dfrac{dz}{dx} = 3x^2$, what is z ? " On page 119 we saw that $\dfrac{d(x^3)}{dx} = 3x^2$, and hence one answer to the question is $z = x^3$. This is not the only answer, however, because $\dfrac{d(x^3 + 2)}{dx} = 3x^2$ and $\dfrac{d(x^3 - 1)}{dx} = 3x^2$; in fact $\dfrac{d(x^3 + c)}{dx} = 3x^2$ where c is any constant number. Therefore the complete answer to the question is $z = x^3 + c$, where c is a constant to which we can give any value whatever ; for this reason c is called an arbitrary constant.

Now we will return to the original question : " If $\dfrac{dz}{dx} = x^2$, what is z ? "

Since
$$\frac{d(x^3)}{dx} = 3x^2,$$

$$\frac{d(\tfrac{1}{3}x^3)}{dx} = \tfrac{1}{3} \cdot 3x^2 = x^2.$$

$$\therefore \frac{d(\tfrac{1}{3}x^3 + c)}{dx} = x^2.$$

Hence
$$z = \tfrac{1}{3}x^3 + c.$$

The graphical meaning of this answer is that, whatever value is given to c, the graph of the equation $z = \frac{1}{3}x^3 + c$ has the gradient x^2 at the point whose abscissa is x. Fig. 85 shows the graphs of $z = \frac{1}{3}x^3$, $z = \frac{1}{3}x^3 + 4$ and $z = \frac{1}{3}x^3 - 7$. It is clear that the second graph is obtained by raising the first graph 4 units, and the third graph by lowering the first graph

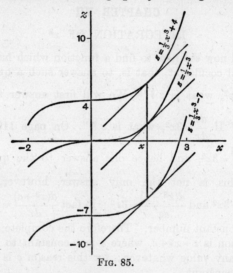

FIG. 85.

7 units. Thus the tangents to these graphs at the points whose abscissa is x are parallel and have the gradient x^2.

The following table gives the values of z when $\dfrac{dz}{dx}$ has the values in the left-hand column :

$\dfrac{dz}{dx}$	z
1	$x + c$
x	$\frac{1}{2}x^2 + c$
x^2	$\frac{1}{3}x^3 + c$
x^3	$\frac{1}{4}x^4 + c$
x^4	$\frac{1}{5}x^5 + c$
x^5	$\frac{1}{6}x^6 + c.$

The student can easily verify any one of these by differentiating the value of z; e.g. when $z = \frac{1}{6}x^6 + c$, $\dfrac{dz}{dx} = \frac{1}{6} \cdot 6x^5 = x^5$. This table suggests that if

$$\frac{dz}{dx} = x^n, \quad z = \frac{x^{n+1}}{n+1} + c,$$

which again is easily verified by differentiating z;

$$\frac{dz}{dx} = \frac{(n+1)x^{n+1-1}}{n+1} = x^n.$$

It is shown in the same way that if

$$\frac{dz}{dx} = ax^n, \quad z = \frac{ax^{n+1}}{n+1} + c.$$

When $n = -1$, $\dfrac{x^{n+1}}{n+1}$ does not give a function of x and so this formula does not tell us of what function x^{-1} is the differential coefficient. It is shown in Chapter X that if

$$\frac{dz}{dx} = x^{-1}, \ z = \log_e x + c.$$

Example.—Find z when $\dfrac{dz}{dx}$ is (a) $x^{2 \cdot 7}$, (b) $4\sqrt{x}$, (c) $\dfrac{10}{x^3}$, (d) $\dfrac{1}{2x^{1 \cdot 4}}$.

(a) Putting $n = 2 \cdot 7$ in the rule above

$$z = \frac{x^{2 \cdot 7 + 1}}{2 \cdot 7 + 1} + c = \frac{x^{3 \cdot 7}}{3 \cdot 7} + c.$$

(b) $\dfrac{dz}{dx} = 4\sqrt{x} = 4x^{\frac{1}{2}}$.

Therefore, putting $a = 4$, $n = \frac{1}{2}$, in the rule

$$z = \frac{4x^{\frac{1}{2}+1}}{\frac{1}{2}+1} + c = \frac{4x^{\frac{3}{2}}}{\frac{3}{2}} + c = \frac{8}{3}x^{\frac{3}{2}} + c.$$

(c) $\dfrac{dz}{dx} = \dfrac{10}{x^3} = 10x^{-3}$

$$\therefore z = \frac{10x^{-3+1}}{-3+1} + c = \frac{10x^{-2}}{-2} + c = -\frac{5}{x^2} + c.$$

(d) $\dfrac{dz}{dx} = \dfrac{1}{2x^{1\cdot4}} = \dfrac{x^{-1\cdot4}}{2}$

$$\therefore z = \frac{x^{-1\cdot4+1}}{2(-1\cdot4+1)} + c = \frac{x^{-0\cdot4}}{-0\cdot8} + c = -1\cdot25x^{-0\cdot4} + c.$$

Example.—Find z when $\dfrac{dz}{dx} = 3x^3 - 5x^2 + 4$.

Since $\quad 3x^3 = \dfrac{d(\frac{3}{4}x^4)}{dx}, \quad 5x^2 = \dfrac{d(\frac{5}{3}x^3)}{dx} \quad$ and $\quad 4 = \dfrac{d(4x)}{dx}$,

$$\frac{dz}{dx} = \frac{d(\frac{3}{4}x^4)}{dx} - \frac{d(\frac{5}{3}x^3)}{dx} + \frac{d(4x)}{dx}$$

$$= \frac{d(\frac{3}{4}x^4 - \frac{5}{3}x^3 + 4x + c)}{dx}$$

$$\therefore z = \tfrac{3}{4}x^4 - \tfrac{5}{3}x^3 + 4x + c.$$

This example shows that when $\dfrac{dz}{dx}$ is the sum of two or more terms the value of z is found by applying the rule to each term and adding the results. It is not necessary to add more than one constant because, if in the above example we added say 7 to the first term $\frac{3}{4}x^4$, 5 to $\frac{5}{3}x^3$ and 4 to $4x$, this would be the same as giving c the value $7 - 5 + 4 = 6$.

Example.—Find z if $\dfrac{dz}{dx} = \dfrac{1}{4\sqrt{x}} + \dfrac{2}{x^3}$

$$\frac{dz}{dx} = \frac{x^{-\frac{1}{2}}}{4} + 2x^{-3}$$

$$\therefore z = \frac{x^{-\frac{1}{2}+1}}{4(-\frac{1}{2}+1)} + \frac{2x^{-3+1}}{-3+1} + c$$

$$= \frac{x^{\frac{1}{2}}}{2} - x^{-2} + c$$

$$= \tfrac{1}{2}\sqrt{x} - \frac{1}{x^2} + c.$$

Example.—A body moves with an acceleration which is $(0 \cdot 3 + 0 \cdot 04t)$ ft./sec.^{2} after t sec. Find its velocity after t sec. if it has a velocity of 5 ft./sec. at $t = 0$. Hence calculate its velocity after 20 sec.

If its velocity after t sec. is v ft./sec. its acceleration is $\dfrac{dv}{dt}$ ft./sec.^{2}

$$\therefore \frac{dv}{dt} = 0 \cdot 3 + 0 \cdot 04t$$

$$\therefore v = 0 \cdot 3t + 0 \cdot 04 \times \tfrac{1}{2}t^2 + c$$

$$= 0 \cdot 3t + 0 \cdot 02t^2 + c$$

But $v = 5$ when $t = 0$.

$$\therefore 5 = 0 + 0 + c, \quad \text{whence } c = 5.$$

$$\therefore v = 0 \cdot 3t + 0 \cdot 02t^2 + 5.$$

When $t = 20$

$$v = 6 + 8 + 5 = 19.$$

Notice that the constant c ft./sec. is the velocity at $t = 0$. If another body started with a velocity of 8 ft./sec. and moved with the same acceleration, then c would be 8 for this body, and it would therefore move 3 ft./sec. faster than the former body at each instant.

Exercise XVIII.

1. What is the value of $\dfrac{d(x^5)}{dx}$? If $\dfrac{dz}{dx} = x^4$, find z.

2. If $\dfrac{ds}{dt} = 16t^2$, what is the value of s ?

6

3. Write down the value of $\dfrac{d}{dx}\left(\dfrac{1}{x^2}\right)$. If $\dfrac{dz}{dx}=\dfrac{1}{x^3}$, find z.

Find the value of z when $\dfrac{dz}{dx}$ is :

4. $4x$.

5. $3\sqrt{x}$.

6. $\dfrac{1}{5x^2}$.

7. x^2+2x-3.

8. $\dfrac{4}{x^9}$.

9. $x^3+\dfrac{1}{x^3}$.

10. $x^{2\cdot6}$.

11. $x^{-2\cdot6}$.

12. $\sqrt{10x^5}$.

13. $1\cdot6x^3-2\cdot4x^2-0\cdot6x+3\cdot5$.

14. $(x+1)^3$.

15. If the acceleration of a body is $0\cdot6t^2$ ft./sec.^{2} after t sec. and its velocity is 4 ft./sec. when $t=2$, find its velocity in terms of t. What are the velocities when $t=0$ and $t=5$ respectively ?

16. The bending moment M lb. ft. of a beam is given by $\dfrac{dM}{dx}=1-2x$ and $M=28$ at $x=2$. Find M in terms of x and verify that $M=0$ at $x=6$.

17. If $\dfrac{dM}{dx}=-W(l-x)$, where W and l are constants, and $M=0$ at $x=l$, find M in terms of W, l and x. What is the value of M at $x=0$?

18. If $\dfrac{dz}{dx}=3x^2+5x$ and $z=2$ at $x=1$, find z.

19. The angular velocity of a wheel rotating in a vertical plane is given by $\omega=(10+4t)$ rad./sec. after t seconds. Find a general expression for the angle turned through by a spoke in terms of t. If a spoke makes an angle $\frac{1}{4}\pi$ with the upward vertical at $t=0$ and turns away from the upward vertical, what angle does it make with the upward vertical t sec. later ?

Definition of an integral

We write $\displaystyle\int y\,dx$, which is read "the integral of $y\,dx$" or briefly "integral $y\,dx$," for a function whose differential coefficient with respect to x is y. The reason for this notation is given on page 173.

Thus $z = \int y \, dx$ is another way of writing $\dfrac{dz}{dx} = y$; so the statement $\dfrac{d}{dx}\left(\dfrac{ax^{n+1}}{n+1} + c\right) = ax^n$ may be written in the alternative form

$$\int ax^n \, dx = \frac{ax^{n+1}}{n+1} + c.$$

Using this notation, the answers to the example on page 159 are written :

(a) $z = \quad x^{2 \cdot 7} dx = \dfrac{x^{3 \cdot 7}}{3 \cdot 7} + c.$

(b) $z = \displaystyle\int 4\sqrt{x} \, dx = \int 4x^{\frac{1}{2}} dx = \dfrac{4x^{\frac{3}{2}}}{\frac{3}{2}} + c = \tfrac{8}{3} x^{\frac{3}{2}} + c.$

(c) $z = \displaystyle\int \dfrac{10}{x^3} \, dx = \int 10x^{-3} dx = \dfrac{10x^{-2}}{-2} + c = -\dfrac{5}{x^2} + c.$

(d) $z = \displaystyle\int \dfrac{1}{2x^{1 \cdot 4}} \, dx = \int \tfrac{1}{2} x^{-1 \cdot 4} dx = \dfrac{x^{-0 \cdot 4}}{-0 \cdot 8} + c = -1 \cdot 25 x^{-0 \cdot 4} + c.$

Some further examples are given below.

Example.—Find   (a) $\displaystyle\int (6x^8 - 4x^{11}) dx$;   (b) $\displaystyle\int \left(\dfrac{1}{2\sqrt{t}} - \dfrac{3}{t^{\frac{3}{2}}}\right) dt$;

(c) $\displaystyle\int p \, dv$, if $pv^{1 \cdot 2} = 360$.

(a) $\displaystyle\int (6x^8 - 4x^{11}) dx$ $= \dfrac{6x^{8+1}}{8+1} - \dfrac{4x^{11+1}}{11+1} + c$

$$= \frac{6x^9}{9} - \frac{4x^{12}}{12} + c$$

$$= \tfrac{2}{3} x^9 - \tfrac{1}{3} x^{12} + c.$$

(b) $\int \left(\dfrac{1}{2\sqrt{t}} - \dfrac{3}{t^{\frac{3}{2}}} \right) dt$ $= \int (\frac{1}{2}t^{-\frac{1}{2}} - 3t^{-\frac{3}{2}})dt$

$$= \frac{t^{-\frac{1}{2}+1}}{2(-\frac{1}{2}+1)} - \frac{3t^{-\frac{3}{2}+1}}{-\frac{3}{2}+1} + c$$

$$= t^{\frac{1}{2}} + 6t^{\frac{1}{2}-} + c$$

$$= \sqrt{t} + \frac{6}{\sqrt{t}} + c.$$

(c) Since $pv^{1\cdot 2} = 360$, $p = \dfrac{360}{v^{1\cdot 2}} = 360v^{-1\cdot 2}$.

$$\therefore \int pdv = \int 360v^{-1\cdot 2}dv$$

$$= \frac{360v^{-1\cdot 2+1}}{-1\cdot 2+1} + c$$

$$= -\frac{360v^{-0\cdot 2}}{0\cdot 2} + c$$

$$= -1800v^{-0\cdot 2} + c.$$

Definite integral

The notation $\left[x^2 \right]_1^2$ is used to indicate the increase of x^2 from $x = 1$ to $x = 2$, i.e.

$$\left[x^2 \right]_1^2 = 2^2 - 1^2 = 4 - 1 = 3.$$

Similarly $\left[\dfrac{1}{x^3} \right]_a^b = \dfrac{1}{b^3} - \dfrac{1}{a^3}$;

$$\left[\tfrac{1}{2}\sqrt{t} \right]_4^{16} = \tfrac{1}{2}\sqrt{16} - \tfrac{1}{2}\sqrt{4} = \tfrac{1}{2} \cdot 4 - \tfrac{1}{2} \cdot 2 = 1.$$

If y is a function of x, then $\int y\,dx$ is itself a function of x, and its increase as x increases from a to b is $\left[\int y\,dx\right]_a^b$. For simplicity we usually omit the brackets in this case and attach the letters a and b directly to the $\int$ sign; thus we write it as $\int_a^b y\,dx$.

The value thus obtained is called " the definite integral of $y\,dx$ from $x=a$ to $x=b$." a is called the lower limit and b the upper limit.

Example.—Find the value of (a) $\int_1^2 2x\,dx$, (b) $\int_4^{16} \dfrac{1}{4\sqrt{t}}\,dt$, (c) $\int_4^7 9x^{2\cdot6}\,dx$.

(a) $\int_1^2 2x\,dx$

$\qquad = \left[\int 2x\,dx\right]_1^2$

$\qquad = \left[x^2 + c\right]_1^2$

$\qquad = 2^2 + c - (1^2 + c)$

$\qquad = 2^2 - 1^2$

$\qquad = 3.$

(b) $\int_4^{16} \dfrac{1}{4\sqrt{t}}\,dt$

$\qquad = \left[\int \tfrac{1}{4}t^{-\frac{1}{2}}\,dt\right]_4^{16}$

$\qquad = \left[\dfrac{t^{\frac{1}{2}}}{4(\frac{1}{2})} + c\right]_4^{16}$

$\qquad = \left[\tfrac{1}{2}\sqrt{t} + c\right]_4^{16}$

$\qquad = (\tfrac{1}{2}\sqrt{16} + c) - (\tfrac{1}{2}\sqrt{4} + c)$

$\qquad = 2 + c - 1 - c$

$\qquad = 1.$

(c) $\displaystyle\int_4^7 9x^{2\cdot6}dx$

$= \left[\dfrac{9x^{3\cdot6}}{3\cdot6}+c\right]_4^7$

$=[2\cdot5\times7^{3\cdot6}+c]-[2\cdot5\times4^{3\cdot6}+c]$

$=2\cdot5[7^{3\cdot6}-4^{3\cdot6}]$

$\fallingdotseq2\cdot5[1102-147]$

$\fallingdotseq2390.$

$\log 7^{3\cdot6}=3\cdot6\times0\cdot8451$

$=3\cdot042$

$=\log 1102$

$\log 4^{3\cdot6}=3\cdot6\times0\cdot6021$

$=2\cdot168$

$=\log 147.$

In each of the above examples the reader will see that the constant c does not appear in the result, as it disappears when the values of the integral at the upper and lower limits are subtracted. Hence it is not necessary to put in the arbitrary constant when finding a definite integral, but it must be put in when solving any other type of problem by integration, such as the example on page 161.

Exercise XIX.

Integrate :

1. $\displaystyle\int x^{-6}dx.$

2. $\displaystyle\int\sqrt{2x}dx.$

3. $\displaystyle\int 50x^{24}dx.$

4. $\displaystyle\int\dfrac{dx}{x^3}.$

5. $\displaystyle\int\dfrac{dx}{10x^2}.$

6. $\displaystyle\int\dfrac{1\cdot5dx}{x^4}.$

7. $\displaystyle\int\dfrac{2dx}{5x^{\frac{3}{2}}}.$

8. $\displaystyle\int x^{-0\cdot8}dx.$

9. $\displaystyle\int(x^2+2x)dx.$

10. $\displaystyle\int\left(1+\dfrac{1}{x^2}\right)dx.$

11. $\displaystyle\int(2x+2\sqrt{x})dx.$

12. $\displaystyle\int(x-3)^2dx.$

13. $\displaystyle\int(0\cdot04t-0\cdot6t^2)dt.$

14. $\displaystyle\int\left(a+\dfrac{b}{r^2}\right)dr.$

15. $\displaystyle\int 140v^{-1\cdot4}dv.$

16. $\displaystyle\int\tfrac{1}{16}(2-s)ds.$

17. $\displaystyle\int\dfrac{x^3+3}{x^2}dx.$

Evaluate the definite integrals :

18. $\int_1^2 3x\,dx.$ **19.** $\int_4^8 \frac{dx}{\sqrt{x}}.$ **20.** $\int_0^1 12x^7\,dx.$

21. $\int_{-2}^1 x^2\,dx.$ **22.** $\int_3^4 \frac{6}{x^4}\,dx.$ **23.** $\int_{10}^{20} v^{-1\cdot4}\,dv.$

24. $\int_{\frac{1}{2}}^1 h^{2\cdot5}\,dh.$ **25.** $\int_0^a \left(\frac{Wbx}{a+b}\right)^2 dx.$ **26.** $\int_0^{\frac{1}{2}l} w\left(\frac{l}{2}-x\right)dx.$

27. $\int_{H_1}^{H_2} H^{-\frac{3}{2}}\,dH.$ **28.** $\int_{-9}^9 (3\cdot95 - 0\cdot0122y^2)\,dy.$

29. $\int_R^\infty \frac{q}{r^2}\,dr.$ **30.** $\frac{3}{2\pi r^3}\int_0^r \pi(r^2-x^2)\,dx.$ **31.** $\int_0^H (Hh^{\frac{1}{2}} - h^{\frac{3}{2}})\,dh.$

32. At time t sec. a body is at a distance x ft. from a point O in a straight line. If its velocity is $(2t+3)$ ft./sec., show that $x = \int (2t+3)\,dt + C.$ Hence find x. If the body is at O when $t=0$, find the value of C and the position of the body when $t=4$.

33. If in Question 32, $x=2$ when $t=0$, find the value of C and the position of the body when $t=4$.

34. A body moving in a straight line has an acceleration $16t$ ft./sec.^{2} at time t sec. If its velocity is 4 ft./sec. at $t=1$, find its velocity after t sec.

35. If the gradient of the graph of y against x is $x-1$ at the point whose abscissa is x, express y as an integral. Hence show that, whatever the value of C, the graph of $y = \frac{1}{2}x^2 - x + C$ has the given gradient. Find the equation of the particular curve which passes through the point $(1, 1)$.

36. If $\frac{dM}{dx} = S$, find M when $S = \frac{1}{2}wl - wx$ and $M=0$ at $x=0$. What is the maximum value of M ?

37. The acceleration of a body decreases uniformly from 2 ft./sec.^{2} to $\frac{1}{2}$ ft./sec.^{2} in 4 sec. If the velocity at the beginning of this interval is 3 ft./sec., find the velocity t sec. later and calculate its value when $t=4$.

Area under a curve

We shall show that $\int_a^b y\,dx$ equals the area bounded by the graph of y, the axis of x and the ordinates at $x=a$ and $x=b$; this area is called "the area under the graph of y from $x=a$ to $x=b$."

Let $$\int y\,dx=z, \quad \text{i.e.} \quad \frac{dz}{dx}=y.$$

If the graph of z is a straight line as in Fig. 86, the derivative y is constant and hence the derived curve of the graph

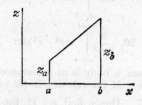

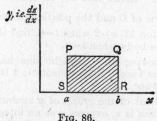

FIG. 86.

of z is a horizontal straight line; this is shown in the lower half of Fig. 86. Hence, if the values of z at $x=a$ and $x=b$ are z_a and z_b,

$z_b - z_a =$ increase of $z =$ increase of $x \times$ gradient of line

$= (b-a) \times$ ordinate of derived curve

$=$ area of shaded rectangle $PQRS$

$=$ area under the derived curve from $x=a$ to b.

Now suppose that the graph of z is a polygon inscribed in a curve as shown in the upper half of Fig. 87. Along each side of the polygon $\dfrac{dz}{dx}$ is constant and so the derived curve, i.e. the graph of y, consists of a number of horizontal straight lines as shown in the lower half of Fig. 87. Hence

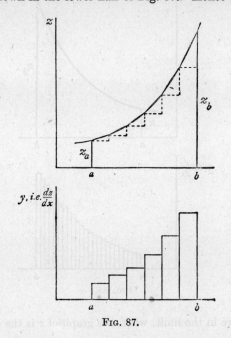

FIG. 87.

$z_b - z_a =$ sum of the increments of z along the sides of the polygon

  = sum of the areas of the rectangles under the graph of y

  = area under the derived curve from $x = a$ to b.

If we make the lengths of the sides of the polygon all tend to zero, the inscribed polygon approaches the curve and

6*

the graph of y approaches its derived curve. In Fig. 88 the polygon has four times the number of sides that it has in Fig. 87 and the sides are so close to the curve that the polygon and curve cannot be distinguished in the drawing.

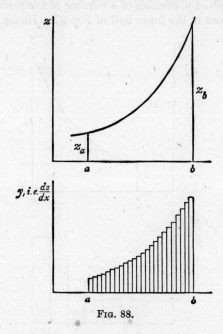

FIG. 88.

Therefore in the limit, when the graph of z is the curve,

$z_b - z_a$ = area under the derived curve from $x = a$ to b

= area under the graph of y from $x = a$ to b.

But $z_b - z_a = \int_a^b y\,dx$,

$\therefore \int_a^b y\,dx$ = area under the graph of y from $x = a$ to b.

Examples.—Find (a) the area under the graph of $y = x^3$ from $x = 1$ to 2; (b) the area under the graph of $y = \dfrac{1}{t^2}$ from $t = 3$ to 5.

These areas are shown in Fig. 89, (a) and (b).

(a) Area $= \displaystyle\int_1^2 x^3 dx = \left[\frac{x^4}{4}\right]_1^2 = \frac{2^4}{4} - \frac{1^4}{4} = 3\frac{3}{4}.$

(b) Area $= \displaystyle\int_3^5 \frac{dt}{t^2} = \left[-\frac{1}{t}\right]_3^5 = -\frac{1}{5} - \left(-\frac{1}{3}\right) = \frac{2}{15}.$

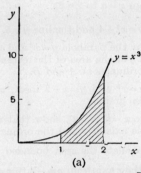 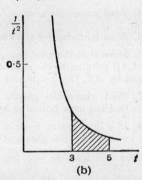

(a)   (b)

FIG. 89.

Exercise XX.

Sketch roughly the boundary of each of the following areas and calculate each area by integration. Check your answers to Questions 1 and 2 by some other method.

1. Area under $y = x$ from $x = 0$ to $x = a$.

2. Area under $y = 2x$ from $x = 1$ to $x = 3$.

3. Area under $y = 4 - x^2$, (a) from $x = 1$ to $x = 2$, (b) from $x = -2$ to $x = 2$.

4. Area under $y = x^3$ from $x = a$ to $x = b$.

5. Area under $y = \sqrt{x}$ from $x = 2$ to $x = 3$.

6. Area bounded by the curve $y^2 = x$ and the lines $x = 2$ and $x = 3$.

7. Area under $y = \dfrac{1}{x^m}$ from $x = p$ to $x = q$.

8. Area under $y = x^{\frac{2}{3}}$ from $x = 0$ to $x = 1$.

9. Area under $y = x^{0.6}$ from $x = 2$ to $x = 3$.

10. Area under $y = \dfrac{1}{x^3}$ from $x = \frac{1}{2}$ to $x = 2$.

11. Area under $p = 8v^{-1.2}$ from $v = 1$ to $v = 5$.

12. Area under $z = r(a - r)$ from $r = 0$ to $r = a$.

13. Area under $s = b^2 y - y^3$ from $y = 0$ to $y = b$.

14. Area under $y = \sqrt{ax} - \dfrac{a^{\frac{3}{2}}}{\sqrt{x}}$ from $x = a$ to $x = 2a$.

15. Area bounded by the curve $y = x^2 + 4$ and the line $y = 5$.

16. Show that the area bounded by the parabola $y = x^2$ and any chord AB parallel to the axis of x is $\frac{2}{3}$ of the area of the rectangle formed by AB, the x axis and the ordinates at A and B.

17. Find where the graphs of $y = x^2$ and $y = x + 2$ meet, and hence find the area bounded by these graphs.

18. If y is negative from $x = a$ to $x = b$ $(b > a)$, show that the area bounded by the graph of y, the axis of x and the ordinates at $x = a$ and $x = b$ is $-\displaystyle\int_a^b y\,dx$. Calculate the area bounded by the curve $y = x^2 - a^2$ and the part of the x axis from $x = -a$ to $x = a$.

Definite integral as a sum

Let the area under the graph of y from $x = a$ to $x = b$ be divided by ordinates into strips of equal width δx and let the lengths of the ordinates starting from the left be y_1, y_2, y_3, etc., as in Fig. 90. Then the area under the steps from D to C formed by the dotted lines

$$= y_1 \cdot \delta x + y_2 \cdot \delta x + \ldots + y_n \cdot \delta x.$$

This may be written shortly $\displaystyle\sum_a^b y \cdot \delta x$; here Σ is the capital sigma of the Greek alphabet and stands for " the sum of all the values of."

As δx approaches zero the area under the steps approaches the area under the curve DC, which we have seen is equal to $\int_a^b y dx$.

$$\therefore \int_a^b y dx = \lim_{\delta x \to 0} \sum_a^b y \delta x,$$

where the right-hand side is read as " the limiting value as δx approaches 0 of the sum of all the terms like $y . \delta x$ from $x = a$ to $x = b$." The integral sign $\int$ is an elongated S, standing for " sum " as Σ does, but with the difference that $\int_a^b y dx$ implies

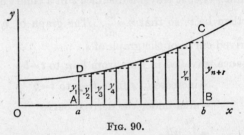

Fig. 90.

that after finding the sum of the products $y . \delta x$ we make δx approach zero and find the limiting value of the sum.

The importance of the above result is that many quantities such as distances moved, volumes, work, moments, etc., can be found by dividing them up into small parts as the area has been divided above. We then find the limiting value of the sum of these small parts by means of a definite integral. In this chapter several applications of this type follow, but a greater variety of examples will be found in Chapter IX.

We have said that areas, volumes, distances, etc., can be expressed as definite integrals because they are the limiting value of sums. Archimedes (287–212 B.C.) and other Greek mathematicians found areas by finding the limiting values of such sums by algebra.* Calculus was not used until its invention by Newton and Leibniz 2000 years later. Galileo (1564–1642) showed that the distance travelled by a body is equal to the area under the velocity-time graph and Cavalieri (1598–1647), a pupil of Galileo, by using methods similar to those of Archimedes, found the area under the curve $y = x^n$ and calculated volumes and the positions of centres of gravity.

Distance moved by a body whose velocity is known in terms of the time

Suppose the body starts from a point O and moves in a straight line. Let it travel a distance s in a time t and let its velocity then be v, so that $v = \dfrac{ds}{dt}$. The graph of v against t is the derived curve of the graph of s.

∴ distance travelled in time from $t = a$ to $t = b$

$$= \text{increase of } s \text{ from } t = a \text{ to } t = b$$

$$= \text{area under the derived curve}$$

$$= \int_a^b v\,dt.$$

Because of the importance of this result we shall show how the definite integral comes from the limit of a sum.

Suppose the body moves from A to B in the time from $t = a$ to $t = b$. Let its velocity have the values v_1, v_2, v_3 . . . at equal intervals of time δt. Fig. 91 (a) shows the positions of the body when it has these velocities ; these positions are not at equal distances, but the body takes the same time δt to go from any one position to the next. Fig. 91 (b) shows the velocity-time graph which has ordinates of lengths v_1, v_2, . . . at equal intervals δt from $t = a$ to b.

If during each interval the velocity remained constant at

---

* The method used by Archimedes is shown in the Appendix, p. 337.

the value it had at the beginning of the interval the distance moved would be

$$v_1 . \delta t + v_2 . \delta t + \ . \ . \ . \ + v_n . \delta t.$$

In Fig. 91 this is the area under the horizontal dotted lines. If δt is made smaller and smaller this sum approaches

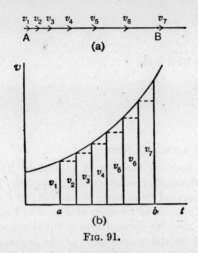

FIG. 91.

a limiting value equal to the distance moved, viz. AB. But the limiting value of the sum is $\int_a^b v dt$.

$$\therefore \ AB = \int_a^b v dt = \text{area under } v, t \text{ graph from } t=a \text{ to } t=b.$$

[Using the sigma notation we should write

$$AB = \lim_{\delta t \to 0} \sum_{t=a}^{t=b} v . \delta t = \int_a^b v dt.]$$

Example.—The velocity of a body after t sec. is v ft./sec. where $v = 0 \cdot 15 t + 0 \cdot 005 t^2$. Find the distance it travels in the second half minute.

The distance travelled is the distance from $t=30$ to $t=60$

$$= \int_{30}^{60} v\,dt = \int_{30}^{60} (0 \cdot 15t + 0 \cdot 005t^2)\,dt$$

$$= \left[\frac{0 \cdot 15t^2}{2} + \frac{0 \cdot 005t^3}{3} \right]_{30}^{60}$$

$$= \frac{0 \cdot 15 \times 3600}{2} + \frac{0 \cdot 005 \times 216{,}000}{3} - \left[\frac{0 \cdot 15 \times 900}{2} + \frac{0 \cdot 005 \times 27{,}000}{3} \right]$$

$$= 270 + 360 - 67 \cdot 5 - 45$$

$$= 630 - 112 \cdot 5$$

$$= 517 \cdot 5 \text{ ft.}$$

Work done by a variable force

Suppose a body is moving in a straight line under the action of a force along the line. When the body has moved a distance x measured from some fixed point in the line let the force in the direction of increase of x be F. Let the interval from $x=a$ to $x=b$ be divided into n equal space intervals of length δx and let the values of F at the beginnings of these intervals be F_1, F_2, . . . Then, if the force were constant in each interval instead of variable, the total work done by the force would be

$$F_1 \,.\, \delta x + F_2 \,.\, \delta x + \ldots + F_n \,.\, \delta x.$$

The exact amount of work is the limiting value of this sum as δx approaches 0 which is $\displaystyle\int_a^b F\,dx$.

Motion of a body in a straight line under a force varying in any way

By Newton's laws of motion the acceleration of a body is proportional to the force applied. Hence, if a force F acts on a body of weight W, the acceleration of the body is given by

$$\frac{\text{acceleration}}{g} = \frac{F}{W}$$

$$\therefore F = \frac{W}{g} \times \text{(acceleration)}.$$

But if the velocity of the body is v its acceleration is $\dfrac{dv}{dt}$. This can be written in another way

$$\frac{dv}{dt} = \frac{dv}{dx} \cdot \frac{dx}{dt} = \frac{dv}{dx} \cdot v = \frac{d(\frac{1}{2}v^2)}{dv} \cdot \frac{dv}{dx}.$$

$$\therefore \frac{dv}{dt} = \frac{d(\frac{1}{2}v^2)}{dx}.$$

Hence $\quad F = \dfrac{W}{g} \dfrac{d(\frac{1}{2}v^2)}{dx} = \dfrac{d\left(\frac{1}{2}\dfrac{W}{g}v^2\right)}{dx}$

$$\therefore \int_a^b F dx = \text{increase of } \tfrac{1}{2}\frac{W}{g}v^2 \text{ from } x=a \text{ to } x=b$$

$$= \text{increase of kinetic energy of the body.}$$

Example.—A body of weight 2 lb. hangs in equilibrium at the end of a spring which stretches $\frac{1}{2}$ in. per lb. wt. It is then given a velocity of 10 ft./sec. vertically downwards. What will be its velocity when it has moved 3 in. ? Find also how far the body will fall before it begins to move upwards.

In equilibrium the spring is extended 1 in. When it has extended x in. further its tension is $2(x+1)$ lb. wt. and hence

downward force on body = weight − tension = $2 - 2(x+1)$
$$= -2x \text{ lb. wt.}$$

While the body is moving 3 in. downwards the amount of work done by this force is

$$\int_0^3 (-2x)dx = -\left[x^2\right]_0^3 = -9 + 0 = -9 \text{ in. lb. wt.}$$

The initial velocity is 120 in./sec. Therefore, if the final velocity is v in./sec., the increase of kinetic energy (which is, of course, actually a decrease) is

$$\left(\tfrac{1}{2}\frac{2}{g}v^2 - \tfrac{1}{2}\frac{2}{g}\,.\,120^2\right)$$ in. lb. wt. (where $g = 32 \times 12$ since the unit of length is 1 inch).

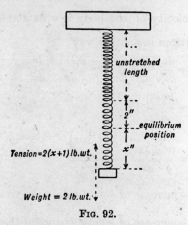

unstretched length

2″

equilibrium position

x''

Tension = 2(x + 1) lb. wt.

Weight = 2 lb. wt.

FIG. 92.

Equating this increase of kinetic energy to the work done

$$\frac{v^2}{12 \times 32} - \frac{120^2}{12 \times 32} = -9$$

$$\therefore v^2 = 120^2 - 9\,.\,12\,.\,32 = 12^2\,.\,76$$

$$\therefore v = 12\sqrt{76}$$

$$\therefore \text{velocity} = 12\sqrt{76}\ \text{in./sec.} = 8\cdot72\ \text{ft./sec.}$$

Let the body start to move upwards when it has moved x in. Then the work done by the forces while it is moving this distance is

$$\int_0^x (-2x)dx = -\left[x^2\right]_0^x = -x^2 \text{ in. lb. wt.}$$

Since the final velocity is zero the increase in kinetic energy is

$$-\tfrac{1}{2}\frac{2}{g} \cdot 120^2 = -\frac{120^2}{12 \times 32} = -\frac{75}{2} \text{ in. lb. wt.}$$

Equating the work done to the increase of kinetic energy

$$-x^2 = -\frac{75}{2}$$

Hence the body falls $\sqrt{\dfrac{75}{2}} \backsimeq 6\cdot12$ in. before it begins to move upwards.

Note on the expression of distance, work, etc., as definite integrals

The argument in each of the applications of integration that we have considered so far has been the same and is typical of the process involved in a large number of practical applications where we have to make summations which involve variable quantities and lead to integration. Instead of writing out the whole argument each time we therefore usually condense it and write in practice :

The distance moved in a short time $\delta t \backsimeq v \cdot \delta t$.

$\therefore$ total distance moved from $t = a$ to $t = b$ is $\displaystyle\int_a^b v \, dt$

or

The work done by a force F when the body moves a short distance $\delta x \backsimeq F \cdot \delta x$.

$\therefore$ total work done when body moves from $x = a$ to $x = b$ is $\displaystyle\int_a^b F \, dx$.

Work done by an expanding gas

When the volume of the gas is v let a small area δS of the surface enclosing the gas be moved outwards a small distance h perpendicular to δS. Let the resulting increase in the volume of the gas be δv. Then $\delta v = h \cdot \delta S$. If the pressure of the gas is p when the volume is v, the force on the area δS is $p \cdot \delta S$ and this remains nearly constant while the gas expands δv. Hence the work done by the gas while it is expanding δv is nearly $p\delta S \cdot h$ which equals $p\delta v$. Therefore

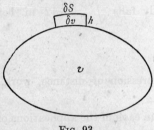

FIG. 93.

the total work done as the gas expands from a volume a to a volume $b = \int_a^b p\,dv$.

Example.—During the compression stroke of a gas engine the mixture of gas and air is compressed from a volume 12 ft.^{3} to a volume 4·6 ft.^{3}, the initial pressure being 15 lb. wt./in.^{2}. If the relation between the pressure p lb. wt./in.^{2} and the volume v ft.^{3} is $pv^{1\cdot4} = k$, where k is constant, find k and find the work done in compressing the gas.

Since $p = 15$ when $v = 12$, $k = 15 \times 12^{1\cdot4}$.

$\therefore \log k = \log 15 + 1\cdot4 \log 12$

$\therefore k = 486\cdot4$.

$\therefore pv^{1\cdot4} = 486\cdot4$.

No.	Log.
15	1·1761
$12^{1\cdot4}$	$1\cdot4 \times 1\cdot0792 = 1\cdot5109$
486·4	2·6870

Work done during compression

$$= \int_{4\cdot6}^{12} p\,dv = \int_{4\cdot6}^{12} 486\cdot4 v^{-1\cdot4}\,dv$$

$$= \left[-\frac{486\cdot4}{0\cdot4} v^{-0\cdot4} \right]_{4\cdot6}^{12}$$

$$= \frac{486\cdot4}{0\cdot4}(-12^{-0\cdot4} + 4\cdot6^{-0\cdot4})$$

$$= \frac{486\cdot4}{0\cdot4}(-0\cdot3701 + 0\cdot5431)$$

$$= \frac{486\cdot4}{0\cdot4}(0\cdot1730)$$

$$= 210\cdot4$$

$\log 4\cdot6^{-0\cdot4} = -0\cdot4 \times 0\cdot6628$

$\qquad = -0\cdot2651$

$\qquad = \bar{1}\cdot7349$

$\qquad = \log 0\cdot5431$

$\log 12^{-0\cdot4} = -0\cdot4 \times 1\cdot0792$

$\qquad = -0\cdot4317$

$\qquad = \bar{1}\cdot5683$

$\qquad = \log 0\cdot3701$

Since p is in lb. wt./in.^{2} and v in ft.^{3} this amount of work is in $\dfrac{\text{lb. wt.}}{\text{in.}^2} \times \text{ft.}^3$

$\therefore$ work done $= 210\cdot4 \dfrac{\text{lb. wt.}}{\text{in.}^2} \cdot \text{ft.}^3$

$\qquad = 210\cdot4 \times 12^2 \dfrac{\text{lb. wt}}{\text{ft.}^2} \cdot \text{ft.}^3$

$\qquad = 30300$ ft. lb. wt.

No.	Log.
486·4	2·6870
0·1730	$\bar{1}$·2380
	1·9250
0·4	$\bar{1}$·6021
210·4	2·3229

The volume of a solid

Suppose the required volume divided up into thin slices by planes perpendicular to a line Ox at equal intervals δx (see Fig. 94). Then the volume between two consecutive planes is approximately $A \cdot \delta x$ where A is the area of the cross-section by one of them. The total volume from $x = a$ to $x = b$ is the limiting value of the sum of terms like $A \cdot \delta x$ which is $\displaystyle\int_{a}^{b} A\,dx$.

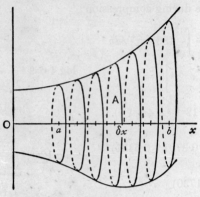

FIG. 94.

Example.—Prove that the volume of a sphere of radius r is $\frac{4}{3}\pi r^3$ and that the volume of a zone of a sphere is $\frac{1}{6}\pi h\{3(r_1{}^2 + r_2{}^2) + h^2\}$, where h is the distance between the parallel plane faces and r_1, r_2 are the radii of the faces.

Take an axis Ox through the centre O and let y be the radius of a cross-section at a distance x from O (Fig. 95). Then, by Pythagoras' theorem, $y^2 = r^2 - x^2$.

Hence the area of this crosss-section

$$= \pi y^2 = \pi(r^2 - x^2).$$

Therefore the volume of the hemisphere from $x = 0$ to $x = r$ is

$$\int_0^r \pi(r^2 - x^2)dx$$

$$\pi \int_0^r (r^2 - x^2)dx$$

$$= \pi \left[r^2 x - \tfrac{1}{3}x^3 \right]_0^r$$

$$= \pi(r^3 - \tfrac{1}{3}r^3) - (0 - 0)$$

$$= \tfrac{2}{3}\pi r^3.$$

Hence the volume of the whole sphere is $\frac{4}{3}\pi r^3$.

To find the volume of a zone, let the plane faces be given by $x = h_1$ and $x = h_2$ (Fig. 96). Then its volume is

$$\int_{h_1}^{h_2} \pi(r^2 - x^2)dx = \pi\left[r^2x - \frac{x^3}{3}\right]_{h_1}^{h_2}$$

$$= \pi\left\{r^2(h_2 - h_1) - \frac{h_2^3 - h_1^3}{3}\right\}$$

$$= \pi(h_2 - h_1)\left\{r^2 - \frac{h_2^2 + h_1h_2 + h_1^2}{3}\right\}$$

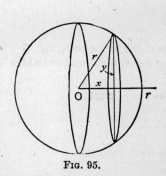

FIG. 95.

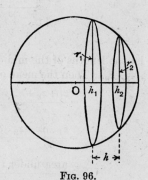

FIG. 96.

But $\qquad h_2 - h_1 = h \quad$ and $\quad r^2 = r_1^2 + h_1^2 = r_2^2 + h_2^2.$

$$\therefore 2(h_2^2 + h_1h_2 + h_1^2) = 3h_1^2 + 3h_2^2 - (h_2 - h_1)^2$$

$$= 3r^2 - 3r_1^2 + 3r^2 - 3r_2^2 - h^2$$

$$= 6r^2 - 3r_1^2 - 3r_2^2 - h^2$$

$\therefore$ volume of zone $= \pi h\left\{r^2 - \dfrac{6r^2 - 3r_1^2 - 3r_2^2 - h^2}{6}\right\}$

$$= \frac{\pi h}{6}\{3(r_1^2 + r_2^2) + h^2\}$$

Mean value

Let the area under the graph of y from $x=a$ to $x=b$ be divided into n strips by ordinates at equal intervals δx, and

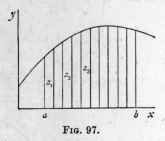

Fig. 97.

let the lengths of the mid-ordinates of the strips be $z_1, z_2, \ldots$ $\ldots z_n$. Then the mean or average value of the mid-ordinates

$$= \frac{z_1 + z_2 + \ldots + z_n}{n}$$

$$= \frac{z_1 . \delta x + z_2 . \delta x + \ldots + z_n . \delta x}{n . \delta x}$$

$$\simeq \frac{\text{area under the graph from } x=a \text{ to } b}{b-a}$$

Hence the ratio of the area under the graph to the base $b-a$ is the limiting value of the mean of the ordinates as n is made larger and larger. We therefore call the ratio " the mean ordinate of the graph from $x=a$ to $x=b$ "; hence the mean value of y from $x=a$ to $x=b$

$$\frac{\text{area under graph of } y \text{ from } x=a \text{ to } b}{b-a} = \frac{\int_a^b y \, dx.}{b-a}$$

Example.—(a) A force $6\sqrt{x}$ lb. wt. acts on a body while it moves from $x=0$ to $x=4$ ft. Find the mean value of the force with respect to x. (b) It can be shown that with this force the distance x ft. moved in t sec. by a body weighing 32 lb. is given by $x = \frac{1}{4}t^4$. Use this equation to express the force in terms of t and find the mean value of the force with respect to t while the body moves from $x = 0$ to $x = 4$.

(a) Mean value of the force with respect to x

$$= \frac{1}{4} \int_0^4 6\sqrt{x}\ dx = \frac{6}{4}\left[\frac{2}{3}x^{\frac{3}{2}}\right]_0^4 = 8 \text{ lb. wt.}$$

(b) If $x = \frac{1}{4}t^4$ the force is $6\sqrt{\frac{1}{4}t^4}$, i.e. $3t^2$ lb. wt. Also when $x = 4$, $t = \sqrt[4]{16} = 2$ and when $x = 0$, $t = 0$. Hence mean value of the force with respect to t

$$= \frac{1}{2} \int_0^2 3t^2 dt = \frac{1}{2}\left[t^3\right]_0^2 = 4 \text{ lb. wt.}$$

Note.—If $x = \frac{1}{4}t^4$, $\dot{x} = t^3$ and $\ddot{x} = 3t^2$, which equals $6\sqrt{x}$. The force on the body is proportional to the acceleration $\ddot{x}$. It is therefore $3t^2$ or $6\sqrt{x}$ lb. wt. for a body which weighs 32 lb.

The area under a parabola between two ordinates in terms of those ordinates and the mid-ordinate

Let y_1, y_2, y_3 be the ordinates of the parabola $y = ax^2 + bx + c$ at $x = -h$, 0 and h respectively. Then $y_1 = ah^2 - bh + c$, $y_2 = c$, $y_3 = ah^2 + bh + c$.

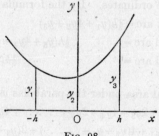

Fig. 98.

The area under the parabola from $x = -h$ to $x = h$ is

$$\int_{-h}^{h} (ax^2 + bx + c)dx$$

$$= \left[\frac{ax^3}{3} + \frac{bx^2}{2} + cx \right]_{-h}^{h}$$

$$= \left(\frac{ah^3}{3} + \frac{bh^2}{2} + ch \right) - \left(-\frac{ah^3}{3} + \frac{bh^2}{2} - ch \right)$$

$$= \frac{2ah^3}{3} + 2ch$$

$$= \tfrac{1}{3}h(2ah^2 + 6c).$$

But $y_1 + y_3 = 2ah^2 + 2c$ and $y_2 = c.$

$\therefore$ $2ah^2 + 6c = y_1 + y_2 + 4y_2$

$\therefore$ area $= \tfrac{1}{3}h(y_1 + y_3 + 4y_2) = \tfrac{1}{3}h(y_1 + 4y_2 + y_3).$

Since this result involves only the width of the strips and the lengths of the ordinates it is independent of the position of the origin.

Simpson's rule for approximating to the area under a curve

This rule has been stated and used in Parts I and II.   To prove it we suppose that the area under a curve from $x = a$ to $x = b$ is divided into an even number, $2n$, of strips by ordinates at equal intervals h, of lengths y_1, y_2, y_3 . . . y_{2n}, y_{2n+1}. Then suppose the curve replaced by a series of parabolic arcs so that each arc passes through the tops of three consecutive ordinates.   By the formula proved above

Area under 1st arc $= \tfrac{1}{3}h(y_1 + 4y_2 + y_3)$

Area under 2nd arc $=$ $\qquad\quad \tfrac{1}{3}h(y_3 + 4y_4 + y_5)$

Area under 3rd arc $=$ $\qquad\qquad\qquad \tfrac{1}{3}h(y_5 + 4y_6 + y_7)$

and so on.

Hence the total area under the parabolas is

$\tfrac{1}{3}h(y_1 + 4y_2 + 2y_3 + 4y_4 + 2y_5 + \ . \ . \ . \ + 4y_{2n} + y_{2n+1})$

$= \tfrac{1}{3}h\{y_1 + y_{2n+1} + 4(y_2 + y_4 + \ . \ . \ . \ ) + 2(y_3 + y_5 + \ . \ . \ . \ )\}.$

Hence the area under the parabolas between the ordinates y_1 and y_{2n+1} is

$\frac{1}{3}$ (width of strip) × [sum of first and last ordinates + twice the sum of the other odd ordinates + four times the sum of the even ordinates].

This formula is called Simpson's rule.

We have seen on page 173 that the area under a curve is the limit of the area under the steps from D to C in Fig. 90. It can also be shown that the area under the curve is the limit of the sum of the areas under the parabolic arcs as h approaches zero and n becomes larger and larger. Hence, by taking sufficient ordinates, the above formula gives a good approximation to the area under a curve.

Any quantity which can be expressed as a definite integral is numerically equal to an area and so can be found approximately by Simpson's rule.

Simpson's rule can be used to find the area bounded by a closed curve. $y_1, y_2, \ldots$ are then the widths of the area at equal intervals h. It is applied below to find the area of an indicator diagram.

Indicator diagram

When the crank of an engine makes a complete revolution the gas in the cylinder expands while the piston is moving forwards and is compressed on the return stroke. During the expansion stroke the p, v graph is a curve like ABC in Fig. 99, and during the compression stroke it is a curve like CDA. The diagram formed by these curves is called an "indicator diagram." The work done by the gas pressure during the expansion stroke is the area $ABCNM$ under the curve ABC, and the work done by it during the compression stroke is "minus the area $ADCNM$ under the curve ADC." Hence the total work done during one revolution of the engine equals

area $ABCNM$ − area $ADCNM$ = area bounded by $ABCD$.

Fig. 99 shows a typical indicator diagram divided into 8 strips by ordinates at intervals of 0·07 ft.³ for v. It is found by measurement that the heights of the diagram at these

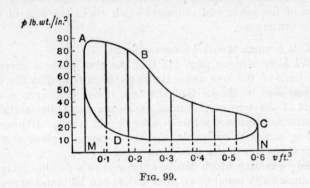

FIG. 99.

intervals are 23, 67, 68, 56, 36, 29, 23, 20, 0 lb.wt./in². Hence by Simpson's rule

$$\text{work done} = \tfrac{1}{3} \times 0{\cdot}07 \text{ ft.}^3 \times \{23 + 0 + 4(67 + 56 + 29 + 20) \\ + 2(68 + 36 + 23)\} \text{ lb. wt./in.}^2.$$

$$= \tfrac{1}{3} \times 0{\cdot}07 \text{ ft.}^3 \{965 \times 144\} \text{ lb. wt./ft.}^2$$

$$\eqsim 3240 \text{ ft. lb. wt.}$$

Exercise XXI.

1. A body has a velocity $(2 + 3t)$ ft./sec. after t sec. How far does it move in the first 4 sec. ? How far does it move in the 6th sec. ?

2. When a train is travelling at 30 m.p.h. steam is shut off and the brakes are applied. The speed of the train, v m.p.h., after t sec. is given by :

t ..	0	5	10	15	20	25	30	35	40
v ..	30	24	19·5	16	13·6	11·7	10	8·5	7

Find by Simpson's rule how far the train moves in the 40 sec. Hence find its average speed during this time.

3. If a body has a velocity $(36 - t^2)$ ft./sec. after t sec., find how far it moves in 6 sec. from $t = 0$. Also find its average velocity during this time.

4. By dividing the area bounded by a curve, the y axis and the lines $y = y_1$, $y = y_2$ into thin strips by lines parallel to the x axis at intervals equal to δy, show that this area is $\int_{y_1}^{y_2} x\,dy$. Hence find the area bounded by the curve $x = y^2$, the y axis and the lines $y = 1$ and $y = 4$.

5. Express the area bounded by the line $y = 2x + 1$, the y axis and the lines $y = 2$ and $y = 6$ as a definite integral and hence find this area. Check your answer by using the formula for the area of a trapezium.

6. Find the area in the first quadrant bounded by $y = \dfrac{1}{x^2}$, the y axis and the lines $y = 4$ and $y = 9$.

7. Find the work done on a body by a force, which is $6x$ lb. wt. when the body has moved x ft., as the body moves from $x = 0$ to $x = 5$.

8. A body moves from $x = 0$ to $x = 6$ ft. under the action of a force which diminishes uniformly with the distance from 4 lb. wt. at $x = 0$ to 1 lb. wt. at $x = 6$. Show by a figure the area which is equal to the work done by the force. Find this area by integration and also by using the formula for the area of a trapezium.

9. Find the work done in stretching a spring from a natural length of 10 in. to a length of 15 in. if a force of 6 lb. wt. extends the spring to a length of 12 in.

10. When a bar 4 ft. long is stretched it is found that a force of 6 tons wt. stretches it $0 \cdot 008$ in. Assuming that the tension of the bar is proportional to its extension, show that the tension when the bar is stretched x in. is $750x$ tons wt. Hence find the work in ft. lb. wt. which is done in stretching the bar $0 \cdot 008$ in.

11. Explain in your own words why the work done by a force F which moves a body in a straight line from $x = 0$ to $x = a$ is $\int_0^a F\,dx$. A cylinder of weight 10 lb. and 9 in. long is floating in water with its axis vertical and 6 in. immersed. Show that the force required to hold it down x in. further is $\dfrac{5x}{3}$ lb. wt., and hence find the work that has to be done to immerse it completely.

12. A body of weight 50 lb. starts with a velocity of 3 ft./sec. and it is acted on by a force $4x$ lb. wt. when it has moved x ft. Find the work done by the force while the body moves 4 ft. Hence find the velocity of the body when it has moved this distance.

13. A body of weight $\frac{1}{2}$ ton is moving at 20 ft./sec. It is slowed down by a varying force F lb. wt. whose value when the body has moved x ft. is given by :

x	0	10	20	30	40	50	60
F	59	50	43	37	37	39	45

Use Simpson's rule to find the work done by the force and, hence find the velocity of the body when it has moved 60 ft. What is the average force acting on the body during its motion ?

14. The area bounded by $y = 2x$, the x axis and the line $x = 5$ is rotated about the x axis. Find the volume so generated.

15. Find the volume swept out by revolving the area bounded by the line $y = 1 - x$ and the axes about the axis of x.

16. Find the area under the curve $y = \sqrt{x}$ from $x = 0$ to 2 and also the volume obtained by revolving this area about Ox.

17. Find the volume obtained by revolving the part of the circle $x^2 + y^2 = 4$ between $x = -1$ and $x = 1$ about the x axis.

18. Draw the curve $y^2 = 4ax$. Find the volume of the solid obtained by rotating the part of this curve from $x = 0$ to a about the axis Ox.

19. Prove the formula for the volume of a cone by integration.

20. Find by integration the volume of the part of a sphere of radius 10 in. which lies between two parallel planes at 2 in. and 6 in. from the centre and on the same side of it.

21. A frustum of a cone is 6 in. long and its end radii are 2 in. and 5 in. respectively. Show that the area of a cross-section at x in. from the smaller end is $\pi(2 + \frac{1}{2}x)^2$ in.^{2}, and hence find the volume of the frustum.

22. Show that the volume of a frustum of a cone obtained by revolving the area under the line $y = x \tan \alpha$ from $x = a$ to $x = b$ about the axis of x is $\int_{a}^{b} \pi x^2 \tan^2 \alpha \, dx$. Hence show that the volume of the frustum is $\frac{1}{3}\pi h(R_1^2 + R_1 R_2 + R_2^2)$, where R_1 and R_2 are the end radii of the frustum and h is its length. What is the mean cross-sectional area of the frustum ?

23. Draw the curve $y = x^2$ from $x = -2$ to $x = 2$. Explain in your own words how you would find the volume obtained by revolving the area bounded by this curve and the line $y = 4$ about the axis of y. Express this volume as the limiting value of a sum and hence find it.

24. Find the volume swept out by revolving about the y axis the area bounded by $y = \dfrac{2}{x}$, the y axis and the lines $y = 1$ and $y = 2$.

25. Find the volumes swept out by revolving the ellipse $\dfrac{x^2}{a^2} + \dfrac{y^2}{b^2} = 1$, (i) about the x axis, (ii) about the y axis.

26. The lengths in inches of the ordinates of a curve at equal intervals of $\frac{1}{2}$ in. from $x = 0$ to 3 are given by :

x	0	$\frac{1}{2}$	1	$1\frac{1}{2}$	2	$2\frac{1}{2}$	3
y	3	3·26	3·60	4·09	4·80	5·81	6·20

Find the area under this curve by Simpson's rule. Also make a table of the values of y^2 and hence find the volume swept out when the area is rotated about the x axis. State the mean value of the ordinates of the curve from $x = 0$ to 3 and also the mean area of a cross-section of the solid by a plane perpendicular to Ox.

27. Find the mean value of the ordinate of the curve $y = 6x - x^2$ from $x = 0$ to 6.

28. The force on a body when it is x ft. from a fixed point is $\frac{2}{3}x^{\frac{1}{3}}$ lb. wt. Find the work done by the force in moving the body 8 ft. and hence find the mean value of the force (i.e. distance–mean).

29. If in Question 28 the distance x ft. is given in terms of the time t by $x = \frac{1}{27}t^3$, express the force in terms of t and find the time–mean of the force while the body moves 8 ft.

30. A body moves with a constant acceleration f ft./sec.² It starts with a velocity u ft./sec. at $t = 0$. Show that it moves $(ut + \frac{1}{2}ft^2)$ ft. in t sec.

31. Calculate the lengths of the ordinates of $y = (5 - x)(x + 1)$ at $x = 0$, $\frac{1}{2}$, . . . 3. Hence find the area under the graph from $x = 0$ to $x = 3$ by Simpson's rule. Also find the area by integration.

32. Find the area under the curve $y = \dfrac{1}{x^2}$ from $x = 1$ to 3 by using Simpson's rule with four strips, and also find the same area by integration.

33. A cylinder closed by a piston at one end contains gas of volume v ft.^{3} and pressure p lb. wt./ft.^{2} If the gas pushes the piston so that the volume of the gas increases by δv ft.^{3}., show that the work done by the gas is $p \cdot \delta v$ ft. lb. wt. nearly. What is the total amount of work done as the gas expands from a volume v_1 ft.^{3} to a volume v_2 ft.^{3} ? Evaluate it if $pv^{1\cdot3} = 500$, $v_1 = 20$, $v_2 = 30$.

34. The figure is an indicator diagram in which the pressure of the gas is plotted vertically and the volume horizontally. Find the work done by the gas during a complete cycle of the engine.

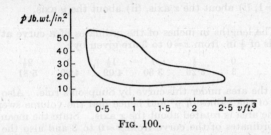

Fig. 100.

35. If A is the cross-section of a pyramid or cone at a distance x from its vertex measured perpendicular to its base, show that A is proportional to x^2, i.e. the graph of A against x^2 is a parabola. Deduce by Simpson's rule that, if A_1, A_2, A_3 are the cross-sections at intervals h of x, the volume between A_1 and A_3 is $\frac{1}{3}h(A_1 + 4A_2 + A_3)$ exactly.

36. When water flows over a sluice a ft. wide the velocity of the water at a depth x ft. is given approximately by $\sqrt{2gx}$ ft./sec. Show that the total volume which flows over the sluice per sec. is $a \int_0^b \sqrt{2gx}\, dx$ cu.ft., where b is the depth of the water. Evaluate this integral.

37. If two small spheres at r cm. apart have charges e and e' coulombs, the force with which they repel each other is $\dfrac{9 \times 10^{18} ee'}{r^2}$ dynes. Show that the work done in bringing the spheres from a distance a apart to a distance b $(a > b)$ is $9 \times 10^{18} ee'\left(\dfrac{1}{b} - \dfrac{1}{a}\right)$ ergs. Calculate this if $e = e' = 10^{-9}$, $a = 20$, $b = 10$

CHAPTER VIII

DIFFERENTIATION AND INTEGRATION OF TRIGONOMETRIC FUNCTIONS

The limiting value of $\dfrac{\sin (\theta \text{ radians})}{\theta}$ as θ approaches 0

It was shown in Part II that, when θ is small, $\dfrac{\sin \theta^c}{\theta}$ is very nearly 1. We shall now show that $\lim\limits_{\theta \to 0} \dfrac{\sin \theta^c}{\theta} = 1$.

Let $\widehat{AOP}$ be an acute angle θ radians subtended by an arc AP of a circle of radius r and centre O.

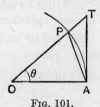

Fig. 101.

Let the tangent at A to the circle meet OP produced in T. Then

Area of triangle $AOP = \frac{1}{2}OA \cdot OP \sin \theta^c = \frac{1}{2}r^2 \sin \theta^c$,

Area of sector $\quad AOP = \frac{1}{2}r^2\theta$,

Area of triangle $AOT = \frac{1}{2}OA \cdot AT = \frac{1}{2}r^2 \tan \theta^c$.

Now area of triangle $AOP <$ area of sector $AOP <$ area of triangle AOT.

$$\therefore \tfrac{1}{2}r^2 \sin \theta^c < \tfrac{1}{2}r^2\theta < \tfrac{1}{2}r^2 \tan \theta^c.$$
$$\therefore \sin \theta^c < \theta < \tan \theta^c.$$

Dividing by sin θ^c

$$1 < \frac{\theta}{\sin \theta^c} < \frac{1}{\cos \theta^c}$$

Now, as θ approaches 0, $\cos \theta^c$ tends to the value 1, and hence also $\dfrac{1}{\cos \theta^c}$ tends to 1. Thus $\dfrac{\theta}{\sin \theta^c}$ lies between 1 and a quantity which tends to 1 as θ approaches zero, it must therefore itself tend to 1.

$$\therefore \quad \lim_{\theta \to 0} \frac{\theta}{\sin \theta^c} = 1.$$

$$\therefore \quad \lim_{\theta \to 0} \frac{\sin \theta^c}{\theta} = 1.$$

This limit implies that, when θ is small,

$$\frac{\sin \theta^c}{\theta} \simeq 1, \quad \text{i.e.} \quad \sin \theta^c \simeq \theta.$$

When θ is small, $\cos \theta^c \simeq 1$, but by using the approximation to $\sin \theta^c$ we can obtain a closer approximation to $\cos \theta^c$.

$\cos \theta^c = 1 - 2 \sin^2 \frac{1}{2}\theta^c$ and $\sin \frac{1}{2}\theta^c \simeq \frac{1}{2}\theta^c$, since $\frac{1}{2}\theta$ is small.

$\therefore \cos \theta^c \simeq 1 - 2(\frac{1}{2}\theta)^2 = 1 - \frac{1}{2}\theta^2.$

To find an approximate value of $\tan \theta^c$ when θ is small,

$$\lim_{\theta \to 0} \frac{\tan \theta^c}{\theta} = \lim_{\theta \to 0} \frac{\sin \theta^c}{\theta} \cdot \frac{1}{\cos \theta^c} = 1 \times 1 = 1.$$

Hence, when θ is small, $\tan \theta^c \simeq \theta$.

It can be shown by methods beyond this book that closer approximations for $\sin \theta^c$ and $\tan \theta^c$ are

$$\sin \theta^c \simeq \theta - \tfrac{1}{6}\theta^3 \quad \text{and} \quad \tan \theta^c \simeq \theta + \tfrac{1}{3}\theta^3.$$

Differential coefficients of sin x and cos x

In differential and integral calculus $\sin x$ is always taken to mean $\sin x^c$ unless the angle is specifically stated to be in degrees; similarly for the other trigonometric ratios.

We have seen on page 126 that

$$f'(x) = \lim_{h \to 0} \frac{f(x+h) - f(x-h)}{2h}.$$

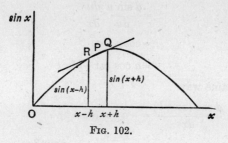

Fig. 102.

Hence if $f(x) = \sin x$,

$$f'(x) = \lim_{h \to 0} \frac{\sin(x+h) - \sin(x-h)}{2h}$$

$$= \lim_{h \to 0} \frac{\sin x \cos h + \cos x \sin h - (\sin x \cos h - \cos x \sin h)}{2h}$$

$$= \lim_{h \to 0} \frac{2 \cos x \sin h}{2h}$$

$$= \cos x \cdot \lim_{h \to 0} \frac{\sin h}{h}$$

$$= \cos x, \quad \text{since} \quad \lim_{h \to 0} \frac{\sin h}{h} = 1.$$

$$\therefore \frac{d(\sin x)}{dx} = \cos x.$$

The student should prove in a similar manner that

$$\frac{d(\cos x)}{dx} = -\sin x$$

Differential coefficients of sin $(ax + b)$ and cos $(ax + b)$

$$\frac{d \sin (ax+b)}{dx} = \frac{d \sin u}{dx}, \text{ where } u = ax + b$$

$$= \frac{d \sin u}{du} \frac{du}{dx}$$

$$= \cos u \cdot a.$$

$$= a \cos (ax + b).$$

In the same way

$$\frac{d \cos (ax+b)}{dx} = -a \sin (ax + b).$$

Examples.—Find the values of (a) $\dfrac{d \sin 3x}{dx}$, (b) $\dfrac{d (\cos^2 x)}{dx}$,

(c) $\dfrac{d \{5 \cos (420t + 24)\}}{dt}$.

(a) $\dfrac{d \sin 3x}{dx} = 3 \cos 3x$ by the rule for differentiating $\sin (ax + b)$ above.

(b) $\dfrac{d (\cos^2 x)}{dx} = \dfrac{du^2}{dx}$. where $u = \cos x$,

$$= \frac{du^2}{du} \cdot \frac{du}{dx}$$

$$= 2u \cdot (-\sin x) = -2 \sin x \cos x.$$

(c) $\dfrac{d \{5 \cos (420t + 24)\}}{dt} = 5(-420) \sin (420t + 24)$

$$= -2100 \sin (420t + 24).$$

Example.—A point moves with simple harmonic motion of period $\dfrac{2\pi}{n}$ so that its displacement x from a point O after time t is given by $x = a \sin (nt + \alpha)$; show that the acceleration of the point is proportional to x and that it is always directed towards O. Show also that the period of a complete oscillation is $2\pi\sqrt{\dfrac{\text{displacement}}{\text{acceleration}}}$.

$$x = a \sin (nt + \alpha)$$

$$\therefore \frac{dx}{dt} = an \cos (nt + \alpha)$$

$$\therefore \frac{d^2x}{dt^2} = -an^2 \sin (nt + \alpha) = -n^2 x.$$

This equation shows that the acceleration is n^2 times the displacement and that it is towards the point O, for when x is positive $\dfrac{d^2x}{dt^2}$ is negative, i.e. the acceleration is to the left and therefore towards $x = 0$, and when x is negative $\dfrac{d^2x}{dt^2}$ is positive, i.e. the acceleration is to the right which is again towards $x = 0$.

$$n^2 = -\frac{\dfrac{d^2x}{dt^2}}{x} = \frac{\text{magnitude of acceleration}}{\text{magnitude of displacement}};$$

hence, disregarding signs, $n = \sqrt{\dfrac{\text{acceleration}}{\text{displacement}}}$.

$$\therefore \text{Period} = \frac{2\pi}{n} = 2\pi \sqrt{\frac{\text{displacement}}{\text{acceleration}}}.$$

Example.—The voltage v required to produce a current i amp. in a circuit containing a resistance R ohms and an inductance L henrys is given by

$$v = Ri + L\frac{di}{dt}.$$

If $i = I_m \sin \omega t$ gives the current in terms of the time, find v and express it in the form $ZI_m \sin (\omega t + \alpha)$.

Since $\quad i = I_m \sin \omega t, \quad \dfrac{di}{dt} = I_m \omega \cos \omega t.$

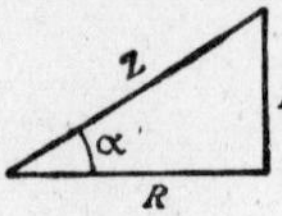

$$\therefore \ v = RI_m \sin \omega t + LI_m \omega \cos \omega t$$
$$= I_m(R \sin \omega t + L\omega \cos \omega t)$$
$$= ZI_m \sin (\omega t + \alpha)$$

FIG. 103.

where $Z = \sqrt{R^2 + L^2 \omega^2}$ and $\tan \alpha = \dfrac{L\omega}{R}.$

Differential coefficients of sec x and cosec x

Let $\qquad y = \sec x = \dfrac{1}{\cos x}$ and put $\cos x = u.$

Then $\qquad y = \dfrac{1}{u}.$

$$\therefore \ \frac{dy}{du} = -\frac{1}{u^2}, \ \frac{du}{dx} = -\sin x.$$

$$\therefore \ \frac{dy}{dx} = \frac{dy}{du} \cdot \frac{du}{dx} = \left(-\frac{1}{u^2}\right)(-\sin x) = \frac{\sin x}{\cos^2 x}.$$

$$\therefore \ \frac{d \sec x}{dx} = \frac{1}{\cos x} \cdot \frac{\sin x}{\cos x} = \sec x \tan x.$$

In the same way, by writing $\operatorname{cosec} x = 1/\sin x,$

$$\frac{d \operatorname{cosec} x}{dx} = -\operatorname{cosec} x \cot x.$$

Exercise XXII.

1. Find $\lim\limits_{\theta \to 0} \dfrac{\sin 2\theta^c}{\theta}.$

2. If a pendulum of length l makes small oscillations, its angular acceleration $\dfrac{d^2\theta}{dt^2}$ when it makes an angle θ^c with the vertical is given by $\dfrac{d^2\theta}{dt^2} = -\dfrac{g}{l} \sin \theta.$ What is the percentage error in taking $\dfrac{d^2\theta}{dt^2} = -\dfrac{g\theta}{l}$ when $\theta^c = 5$ degrees ?   [$\sin 5° = 0{\cdot}08716.$]

3. Use the approximation $\cos \theta^c \simeq 1 - \frac{1}{2}\theta^2$ to find $\cos 20°$ and compare the answer with that found from tables.

4. Show that $\dfrac{\tan (x+h) - \tan x}{h} = \left(\dfrac{\sin h}{h}\right)\dfrac{1}{\cos (x+h) \cos x}$.

Hence, by making h approach 0, show that the differential coefficient of $\tan x$ is $\sec^2 x$.

5. From a table of sines find $\sin 0 \cdot 99^c$ and $\sin 1 \cdot 01^c$, and hence find approximately the value of $\dfrac{d \sin x}{dx}$ when $x = 1$. Compare your answer with $\cos 1^c$.

6. What is the differential coefficient of $\sin (\omega x + \alpha)$ with respect to x ? Find the value $\dfrac{d \sin x^0}{dx}$ by writing $x^0 = \dfrac{\pi x}{180}$ radians.

Find the differential coefficients with respect to x of :

7. $3 \sin x - 4 \cos x$. **8.** $\sin 8x$. **9.** $\frac{1}{6} \cos 3x$.

10. $3 \sin (2x + 5)$. **11.** $\cos (\frac{1}{6}\pi - x)$. **12.** $6 \sin \frac{2}{3}x$.

13. $\sin 2\pi nx$. **14.** $\cos^2 x$. **15.** $4 \sin \frac{1}{2}x$.

16. $\sqrt{\sin x}$. **17.** $\sin x - \frac{1}{6} \sin 3x$. **18.** $\operatorname{cosec} 2x$.

19. $0 \cdot 8 \cos 2x + 0 \cdot 1 \cos 4x$. **20.** $\frac{1}{20} \cos (100x - 5)$. **21.** $\dfrac{1}{\sin^2 x}$.

22. $(2 + 3 \cos x)^2$. **23.** $\sin^5 x$. **24.** $\sin^2 x - 2 \cos^2 x$.

25. $\dfrac{1}{5 + 4 \sin x}$ [put $5 + 4 \sin x = u$]. **26.** $\sec^2 x$ [put $\sec x = u$].

27. $\dfrac{1 + \cos^2 x}{\cos x}$ [write in form $\sec x + \cos x$]. **28.** $\cos^2 5x$.

Find the values of :

29. $\dfrac{d}{dt}(15 \cos 100\pi t)$. **30.** $\dfrac{d(a \sin \omega t)}{dt}$. **31.** $\dfrac{d}{dt}\{c \cos (nt - \beta)\}$.

32. $\dfrac{d}{d\theta}(\frac{1}{2} \sin 2\theta)$. **33.** $\dfrac{d \sin^2 \phi}{d\phi}$. **34.** $\dfrac{d \sec \lambda}{d\lambda}$.

35. $\dfrac{d}{dt}\{10^{-5}(\cos 200t - 0 \cdot 25 \cos 600t)\}$. **36.** $\dfrac{d \cos (\alpha - \phi)}{d\phi}$.

37. $\dfrac{d}{dt}(\sin 2\pi ft + \frac{1}{3} \sin 6\pi ft)$. **38.** $\dfrac{d \operatorname{cosec}^2 \theta}{d\theta}$.

39. The displacement s in. of a point executing simple harmonic motion is given by $s = 3 \cos 2t$ after t sec. Find the velocity and acceleration of the point after t sec. State their maximum values and show that the acceleration is equal to $-4s$ in./sec.²

40. A radius vector OP of a circle of radius 6 in. starts from the position OA and rotates at a rate of 2 rev. per sec. ; PN is drawn perpendicular to OA. Find the lengths of PN and of the chord AP when OP has rotated for t sec., and hence find the rates at which these lengths are increasing. Calculate these rates to the nearest $\frac{1}{10}$ in. per sec. when t is (a) 0·1, (b) 0·2.

41. The voltage required to give a current i amp. through an inductance L henrys is $L\dfrac{di}{dt}$. What is the greatest voltage required if $L = 10^{-5}$ and the current is a sine-wave of maximum value 12 and frequency 50 ?

42. The displacement x in. of the slide valve of an engine running at 250 r.p.m. is given by $x = 1·04 \cos \theta + 1·51 \sin \theta$, where $\theta = \dfrac{250 \times 2\pi t}{60}$. Find the velocity and acceleration of the slide valve in terms of t.

43. From the graph of $\sin x$ find for what values of x its differential coefficient is positive and for what values it is negative. Verify your answers from the actual differential coefficient.

44. Prove that as t increases from 0 to 2π, $\sin t + \sqrt{3} \cos t$ increases between $t = 0$ and $t = \frac{1}{6}\pi$, decreases between $t = \frac{1}{6}\pi$ and $t = \frac{7}{6}\pi$ and increases between $t = \frac{7}{6}\pi$ and $t = 2\pi$. Find the maximum and minimum values of the expression.

45. The flux ϕ through a single turn coil is given by

$$\phi = 10^6(\cos 314t + 0·1 \cos 628t).$$

If the E.M.F., e volts, induced by the current is given by $e = -10^{-8}\dfrac{d\phi}{dt}$, find e.

46. Find the maximum and minimum values of $3 \sin x + 4 \cos x$.

47. An electric current is i amp. where

$$i = 15 \sin 20\pi t + 30 \cos 20\pi t.$$

Show that i is a maximum when $20\pi t = \alpha + 2n\pi$, where n is a whole number and $\alpha = \tan^{-1}\frac{1}{2}$ (the acute angle). Calculate the smallest positive value of t for which i is a maximum and also the maximum value of i to 3 sig. fig.

48. Show that the acceleration of a particle moving in a circle of radius r with uniform velocity v is v^2/r towards the centre. [Hint. Let the velocity be v and the radius of the circle be r. Let P and Q be two positions of the particle such that $\widehat{POQ}=\theta$. Then the length of the arc $PQ=r\theta$ and the time taken to go from P to Q is $\dfrac{r\theta}{v}$. The component of the velocity at Q in the direction PO is $v\sin\theta$. This is the change of velocity in the direction of PO in time $\dfrac{r\theta}{v}$. Hence the average acceleration in this time is $(v\sin\theta)\div\left(\dfrac{r\theta}{v}\right)=\dfrac{v^2}{r}\left(\dfrac{\sin\theta}{\theta}\right)$. The acceleration along PO at the instant when the particle is at P is the limiting value of this average acceleration as θ approaches 0. Show that this is $\dfrac{v^2}{r}$ and also show that if the angular velocity of OP is ω the acceleration of P along PO is $r\omega^2$.]

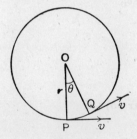

FIG. 104.

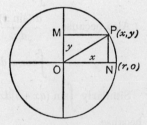

FIG. 105.

49. If a particle P starts from the point $(r,\ 0)$ and moves round a circle of centre O and radius r with uniform angular velocity ω, show that after time t its co-ordinates are $x=r\cos\omega t$ and $y=r\sin\omega t$. Deduce that it has component accelerations $-\omega^2 x$, $-\omega^2 y$ parallel to the axes and show that these have a resultant $r\omega^2$ along PO (Fig. 105).

50. The voltage required to give a current i amp. through a resistance R ohms and an inductance L henrys placed in series is given by $v=Ri+L\dfrac{di}{dt}$. If $i=0\cdot01\sin 300t$ and $R=700$, $L=3\cdot5$, find the voltage in terms of t and calculate (a) its maximum value, (b) the angle of lag of the current.

7*

51. In a motor engine the distance x in. of the piston head from the crank-pin is given approximately by

$$x = 5 \cdot 08 + 1 \cdot 5 \cos \frac{200\pi t}{3} - 0 \cdot 94 \cos \frac{400\pi t}{3}.$$

Find the velocity in ft./sec. and acceleration in ft./sec.² of the piston head and calculate their values at $t = \dfrac{3}{400}$.

52. If $x = A \cos 2\pi ft + B \sin 2\pi ft$ where A, B, f are constants, prove that $\dfrac{d^2x}{dt^2} + 4\pi^2 f^2 x = 0$, whatever the values of A and B.

Integrals of sin x and cos x

Since $\qquad \dfrac{d(\cos x)}{dx} = -\sin x, \quad \dfrac{d(-\cos x)}{dx} = \sin x.$

$$\therefore \quad \int \sin x \, dx = -\cos x + c,$$

Also because $\qquad \dfrac{d(\sin x)}{dx} = \cos x,$

$$\int \cos x \, dx = \sin x + c.$$

Similarly $\displaystyle\int \sin(ax+b)dx = -\frac{1}{a}\cos(ax+b) + c,$

because

$$\frac{d\left\{-\dfrac{1}{a}\cos(ax+b)\right\}}{dx} = -\frac{1}{a}\{-a\sin(ax+b)\} = \sin(ax+b).$$

In the same way

$$\int \cos(ax+b)dx = \frac{1}{a}\sin(ax+b) + c.$$

Example.—Find the values of $(a) \displaystyle\int_0^\pi \sin x \, dx, \quad (b) \displaystyle\int_0^{\frac{1}{4}\pi} \cos 2x \, dx,$

$(c) \displaystyle\int_{-\frac{1}{2}\pi}^{\frac{1}{2}\pi} \sin\left(\tfrac{1}{3}t + \tfrac{1}{4}\pi\right)dt.$

(a)
$$\int_0^\pi \sin x dx = \left[-\cos x \right]_0^\pi = [-\cos \pi] - [-\cos 0]$$
$$= [1] - [-1] = 2.$$

Thus the mean value of $\sin x$ from $x = 0$ to π is $\dfrac{2}{\pi} \backsimeq 0.64$.

(b)
$$\int_0^{\frac{1}{4}\pi} \cos 2x dx = \left[\tfrac{1}{2} \sin 2x \right]_0^{\frac{1}{4}\pi}$$
$$= \tfrac{1}{2} \sin \tfrac{1}{2}\pi - \tfrac{1}{2} \sin 0$$
$$= \tfrac{1}{2} \cdot 1 - 0 = \tfrac{1}{2}.$$

(c)
$$\int_{-\frac{1}{2}\pi}^{\frac{1}{2}\pi} \sin \left(\tfrac{1}{3}t + \tfrac{1}{4}\pi \right) dt = \left[-\frac{1}{\frac{1}{3}} \cos \left(\tfrac{1}{3}t + \tfrac{1}{4}\pi \right) \right]_{-\frac{1}{2}\pi}^{\frac{1}{2}\pi}$$
$$= -3 \cos \left(\tfrac{1}{6}\pi + \tfrac{1}{4}\pi \right) - \left\{ -3 \cos \left(-\tfrac{1}{6}\pi + \tfrac{1}{4}\pi \right) \right\}$$
$$= -3 \cos \frac{5\pi}{12} + 3 \cos \frac{\pi}{12}$$
$$= -3 \cos 75° + 3 \cos 15°$$
$$\backsimeq 2.12.$$

Example.—If q coulombs is the charge on a plate of a condenser and i amp. (coulombs per sec.) is the current flowing into the plate, $\dfrac{dq}{dt} = i$. If $i = I_m \sin \omega t$ and the charge on the plate is zero at $t = 0$, find q in terms of t.

Since
$$\frac{dq}{dt} = i = I_m \sin \omega t,$$

$$q = \int I_m \sin \omega t \, dt$$

$$= -\frac{I_m}{\omega} \cos \omega t + c.$$

But $q = 0$ at $t = 0$.

$$\therefore 0 = -\frac{I_m}{\omega} \cos 0 + c = -\frac{I_m}{\omega} + c.$$

$$\therefore c = \frac{I_m}{\omega}.$$

$$\therefore q = -\frac{I_m}{\omega} \cos \omega t + \frac{I_m}{\omega} = \frac{I_m}{\omega} (1 - \cos \omega t).$$

Integrals of $\sin^2 x$ and $\cos^2 x$

Since $2 \sin^2 x = 1 - \cos 2x,$

$$\int \sin^2 x \, dx = \int \tfrac{1}{2}(1 - \cos 2x) dx$$

$$= \int \tfrac{1}{2} dx - \int \tfrac{1}{2} \cos 2x dx$$

$$= \tfrac{1}{2}x - \tfrac{1}{4} \sin 2x + c.$$

Similarly

$$\int \cos^2 x \, dx = \int \tfrac{1}{2}(1 + \cos 2x) dx$$

$$= \tfrac{1}{2}x + \tfrac{1}{4} \sin 2x + c.$$

Mean values of $\sin^2 x$ and $\cos^2 x$

The mean value of $\sin^2 x$ from $x = 0$ to π

$$= \frac{1}{\pi} \int_0^\pi \sin^2 x \, dx$$

$$= \frac{1}{\pi} \left[\tfrac{1}{2}x - \tfrac{1}{4} \sin 2x \right]_0^\pi$$

$$= \frac{1}{\pi} [(\tfrac{1}{2}\pi - 0) - (0 - 0)]$$

$$= \tfrac{1}{2}.$$

In the same way the mean value of $\cos^2 x$ from $x = 0$ to π is $\tfrac{1}{2}$.

These results can also be deduced from the fact that the graphs of $\sin^2 x$ and $\cos^2 x$ are of the same shape, as shown in

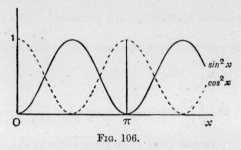

FIG. 106.

Fig. 106, and hence from Fig. 106 we see that the areas under them from $x = 0$ to π are the same ; in other words,

$$\int_0^\pi \sin^2 x \, dx = \int_0^\pi \cos^2 x \, dx.$$

But $\sin^2 x + \cos^2 x = 1$;

$$\therefore \int_0^\pi \sin^2 x \, dx + \int_0^\pi \cos^2 x \, dx = \int_0^\pi 1 \, dx = \pi.$$

$$\therefore 2\int_0^\pi \sin^2 x \, dx = \pi.$$

$$\therefore \int_0^\pi \sin^2 x \, dx = \tfrac{1}{2}\pi.$$

Virtual, or root-mean-square, value of an alternating current or voltage

The virtual value of an alternating current is the value of the steady current which produces the same heating effect as the alternating current when passed through a given resistance for one period.

Suppose the alternating current is i amp. of period T and the virtual current I amp. Then, when the current i passes through a resistance R ohms, heat is produced at a rate Ri^2

watts, i.e. Ri^2 joules per sec. Therefore the heat produced in a short time δt sec. is approximately $Ri^2\delta t$ joules, and hence,

$$\text{heat produced by current } i \text{ in a period} = \int_0^T Ri^2dt \text{ joules.}$$

A steady current I produces heat RI^2T joules in a period.

$$\therefore RI^2T = \int_0^T Ri^2dt.$$

$$\therefore I^2 = \frac{1}{T}\int_0^T i^2dt = \text{mean value of } i^2 \text{ over a period.}$$

$$\therefore \text{ virtual value } I = \sqrt{\text{mean value of } i^2}.$$

This is the reason for calling I the root-mean-square value or " R.M.S. value."

Examples.—Find the virtual value of i, (i) when $i = I_m \sin \omega t$, (ii) when i is given by the graph in Fig. 107.

(i) If $i = I_m \sin \omega t$,

$$\text{mean value of } i^2 = \frac{1}{2\pi/\omega} \int_0^{2\pi/\omega} I_m^2 \sin^2 \omega t \, dt$$

$$= \frac{I_m^2}{2\pi/\omega} \int_0^{2\pi/\omega} \tfrac{1}{2}(1 - \cos 2\omega t)dt$$

$$= \frac{I_m^2}{2\pi/\omega} \left[\tfrac{1}{2}t - \frac{1}{4\omega} \sin 2\omega t \right]_0^{2\pi/\omega}$$

$$= \frac{I_m^2}{2\pi/\omega} \cdot \frac{\pi}{\omega}$$

$$\therefore I = \sqrt{\tfrac{1}{2}I_m^2} = \frac{I_m}{\sqrt{2}}.$$

(ii) If the current is given by the graph in Fig. 107, then $i = I_m \cdot \dfrac{2\omega t}{\pi}$, from $t = 0$ to $\dfrac{\pi}{2\omega}$. Since the numerical values of i are the same in each quarter period, mean value of i^2 over a period = mean value over $\frac{1}{4}$ period

$$= \frac{2\omega}{\pi} \int_0^{\pi/2\omega} \left(\frac{I_m 2\omega t}{\pi} \right)^2 dt$$

$$= \frac{2\omega}{\pi} \cdot \frac{I_m^2 4\omega^2}{\pi^2} \left[\frac{t^3}{3} \right]_0^{\pi/2\omega}$$

$$= \frac{2\omega}{\pi} \cdot \frac{I_m^2 4\omega^2}{\pi^2} \cdot \frac{\pi^3}{24\omega^3}$$

$$= \frac{I_m^2}{3}.$$

$$\therefore I = \sqrt{\frac{I_m^2}{3}} = \frac{I_m}{\sqrt{3}}.$$

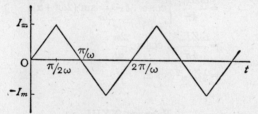

F$_{\text{IG}}$. 107.

$$\int \sin mx \sin nx \, dx, \text{ etc.}$$

In all cases where the integrand is the product of two sines, of two cosines or a sine and a cosine the integral can be evaluated by expressing the integrand as a sum or difference. For example,

$$\int \sin mx \sin nx \, dx = \int \frac{1}{2} \{ \cos (m-n)x - \cos (m+n)x \} dx$$

$$= \frac{1}{2} \left[\frac{\sin (m-n)x}{m-n} - \frac{\sin (m+n)x}{m+n} \right] + C,$$

provided that m is not equal to n.

Example.—The current i amp. in a wire and the potential difference v volts between its ends are given by $i = I_m \sin \omega t$ and $v = ZI_m \sin (\omega t + \alpha)$ respectively. Find the mean value, over a period, of vi, the power used.

$$\text{Mean value} = \frac{\displaystyle\int_0^{2\pi/\omega} vi \, dt}{2\pi/\omega}$$

$$= \frac{\omega}{2\pi} \int_0^{2\pi/\omega} I_m \sin \omega t \, . \, ZI_m \sin (\omega t + \alpha) dt$$

$$= \frac{\omega ZI_m{}^2}{2\pi} \int_0^{2\pi/\omega} \tfrac{1}{2}\{\cos \alpha - \cos (2\omega t + \alpha)\} dt$$

$$= \frac{\omega ZI_m{}^2}{4\pi} \left[\cos \alpha \, . \, t - \frac{1}{2\omega} \sin (2\omega t + \alpha) \right]_0^{2\pi/\omega}$$

$$= \frac{\omega ZI_m{}^2}{4\pi} \, . \, \cos \alpha \, . \, \frac{2\pi}{\omega}$$

$$= \tfrac{1}{2} ZI_m{}^2 \cos \alpha.$$

Exercise XXIII.

Find the following integrals :

1. $\displaystyle\int \sin 2x \, dx.$ **2.** $\displaystyle\int \cos \tfrac{1}{2}x \, dx.$

3. $\displaystyle\int \sin (2\pi ft + \alpha) dt.$ **4.** $\displaystyle\int \cos (\omega t - \beta) dt.$

5. $\displaystyle\int (2 \sin 3x - \cos 4x) dx.$ **6.** $\displaystyle\int \cos 1 \cdot 6\theta \, d\theta.$

7. $\displaystyle\int (2 + 3 \sin x) dx.$ **8.** $\displaystyle\int (a + b \sin \omega t + c \cos \omega t) dt.$

9. $\displaystyle\int \tfrac{1}{2}(1 - \cos 2\phi) d\phi.$ **10.** $\displaystyle\int \sin^2 \theta \, d\theta.$ **11.** $\displaystyle\int \cos^2 2x \, dx.$

12. $\displaystyle\int (1 + \sin x)^2 dx.$ **13.** $\displaystyle\int \sin^2 \omega t \, dt.$ **14.** $\displaystyle\int \cos^2 (\omega t + \alpha) dt.$

15. $\int 2 \cos^2 \frac{1}{2}\phi \, d\phi.$

16. $\int \sin 2x \cos 3x \, dx.$

17. $\int 2 \sin 2\omega t \cos \omega t \, dt.$

18. $\int \cos 2\theta \cos 6\theta \, d\theta.$

Evaluate :

19. $\int_0^\pi \sin x \, dx.$

20. $\int_{-\frac{1}{2}\pi}^{\frac{1}{2}\pi} 3 \cos x \, dx.$

21. $\int_0^{\frac{1}{4}\pi} 4 \cos 2x \, dx.$

22. $\int_0^{\frac{1}{6}\pi} \sin 2x \, dx.$

23. $\int_{\frac{1}{3}\pi}^{\frac{2}{3}\pi} 2 \sin x \, dx.$

24. $\int_0^1 \cos x \, dx.$

25. $\int_0^{\pi/2\omega} a \cos \omega t \, dt.$

26. $\int_0^{\frac{1}{2}\pi} \sin^2 \theta \, d\theta.$

27. $\int_{\frac{1}{4}\pi}^{\frac{3}{4}\pi} \cos^2 x \, dx.$

28. $\int_0^\pi \sin x \sin 2x \, dx.$

29. $\int_0^{\frac{1}{2}\pi} \cos 2x \cos 3x \, dx.$

30. $\int_0^{\pi/2\omega} 4 \sin \omega t \cos \omega t \, dt.$

31. Find the mean value of $\cos x$ from $x=0$ to $x=\frac{1}{4}\pi$.

32. A current i is given by $i=I_m \sin \omega t$. Find the mean value of i over the half period from $t=0$ to $t=\pi/\omega$. The *form factor* of the current is the ratio of its mean value over a half period to its root mean square value ; find the form factor.

33. Show that the mean value of $\sin^2 nx$ over a period is independent of the value of n.

34. If $i=I_m \sin \omega t$, $v=ZI_m \cos \omega t$, find the mean value of vi over a period $2\pi/\omega$.

35. If $i=I_m \cos \omega t$, $v=ZI_m \cos (\omega t + \alpha)$, find the mean value of vi over a period.

36. If the acceleration of a body is $-4 \sin 2t$ ft./sec.² after t sec. and its velocity is 6 ft./sec. at $t=0$, find its velocity in terms of t.

37. When an electromotive force $E_m \sin \omega t$ is applied to a coil of inductance L and negligible resistance the current i is given by $L\dfrac{di}{dt}=E_m \sin \omega t$. Find the general expression for i in terms of t and choose the arbitrary constant so that $i=0$ at $t=0$.

38. The value of a current i amp. is given by the graph in Fig. 108. Find the mean value of i from $t = 0$ to π. Also find the R.M.S. value of i over the same interval.

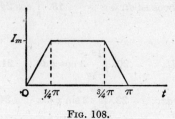

FIG. 108.

39. If $i = I_m \sin(\omega t + \alpha)$, find its R.M.S. value over a period $2\pi/\omega$.

40. The work done per stroke of an engine is $\displaystyle\int_0^{\pi} T\,d\theta$ ft. lb. wt. If $T = 7850 \sin\theta + 1500 \sin 2\theta$, find the work done per stroke.

CHAPTER IX

APPLICATIONS OF INTEGRATION

Suppose that bodies of weights w_1, w_2, w_3 . . . are placed with their centres of gravity in a horizontal plane at distances x_1, x_2, x_3 . . . from a line Oy in the plane. Let G be the centre of gravity of all the bodies together and let its distance from Oy be $\bar{x}$. Then the weights w_1, w_2, w_3, . . . acting vertically downwards have a resultant $w_1 + w_2 + w_3 + \ldots$ acting vertically downwards through G. Hence, taking moments about Oy,

$$(w_1 + w_2 + w_3 + \ldots)\bar{x} = w_1 x_1 + w_2 x_2 + w_3 x_3 + \ldots$$

or
$$(\Sigma w)\bar{x} = \Sigma wx.$$

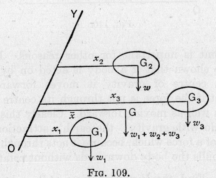

FIG. 109.

If the total weight of the bodies is W, $\Sigma w = W$;

$$\therefore \; W\bar{x} = \Sigma wx.$$

In the same way, if the centres of gravity are at distances

211

y_1, y_2, y_3 . . . from a perpendicular line Ox and G is at a distance $\bar{y}$ from Ox,

$$W\bar{y} = \Sigma wy.$$

Fig. 110 shows the plan of the centres of gravity in the horizontal plane Oxy.

The two formulæ above give the co-ordinates of the centre of gravity G when the co-ordinates (x_1, y_1), etc. of the centres of gravity of the separate bodies are known. The name " centre of gravity " means that G is the point through which the resultant weight due to the gravitation of the earth acts,

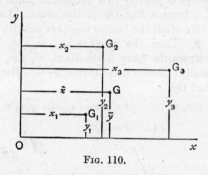

FIG. 110.

but this point is important for other reasons. It can, for instance, be shown that if a body is acted on by any force through its centre of gravity it moves forward without rotation, but if the force is not through its centre of gravity it rotates as well as moving forward. Clearly this effect has nothing to do with gravity ; the earth's attraction is just a special case of a force which, because it acts through the centre of gravity, pulls the body downwards without rotating it.

Example.—Find the distances from AB and AC of the centre of gravity of the thin metal sheet, of uniform thickness and density, shown in Fig. 111.

By symmetry the centre of gravity of the sheet of metal will be half-way through the thickness of the sheet, so we may suppose that Fig. 111 is a section half-way through the sheet. Divide the sheet into three rectangles as shown in Fig. 111. The weights of these rectangular parts are proportional to their areas, which are 144, 16 and 48 sq. in. respectively, and act at G_1, G_2, G_3, the centres of the rectangles. The resultant weight is proportional to the total area $144 + 16 + 48$, which is 208 sq. in. Suppose the centre of gravity G is at a distance $\bar{x}$ in. from AC and $\bar{y}$ in. from AB. Taking moments about AB we get

$$208\bar{x} = 144 \times 4 + 16 \times 9 + 48 \times 16$$

$$\therefore\ 13\bar{x} = 36 + 9 + 48 = 93$$

$$\therefore\ \bar{x} = 7\tfrac{2}{13}.$$

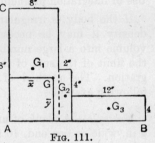

Fig. 111.

Similarly by taking moments about AB we get

$$208\bar{y} = 144 \times 9 + 16 \times 4 + 48 \times 2$$

$$\therefore\ 13\bar{y} = 81 + 4 + 16 = 101.$$

$$\therefore\ \bar{y} = 7\tfrac{10}{13}.$$

Thus the centre of gravity is half-way through the plate at $7\tfrac{2}{13}$ in. from AC and $7\tfrac{10}{13}$ in. from AB.

Centroid

In the above example the weights are proportional to areas. If we replace the weights w_1, w_2, . . . in the formula $(\Sigma w)\bar{x} = \Sigma(wx)$ by areas a_1, a_2, . . . we get

$$(\Sigma a)\bar{x} = \Sigma(a x), \text{ or } A\bar{x} = \Sigma(ax),$$

where $A = \Sigma a$ and x, y are the distances of the centroid of a from the axes. Similarly $A\bar{y} = \Sigma(ay)$.

The point $(\bar{x}, \bar{y})$ found from these formulæ is called the centroid of the whole area A. The product ax is called the moment of the area a about Oy.

In the same way, if we replace the weights w_1, w_2, . . . by volumes v_1, v_2, . . . we get

$$V\bar{x} = \Sigma(vx) \text{ and } V\bar{y} = \Sigma(vy),$$

where $V = \Sigma v$.

The point given by these formulæ is called the centroid of the whole volume V. It is the same as the centre of gravity of the bodies if they are all of the same density.

Use of integration in finding centres of gravity or centroids

If the body is irregular in shape or of varying width or density it may be necessary to divide the body, area or volume into a large number of small parts and then to find the limit of the sum of the moments of these parts by integration. The method of doing this is illustrated by the following examples.

Example.—A plank of uniform density is 14 ft. long. It is 4 in. wide at one end, 10 in. wide at the other end and it is 2 in. thick. Find its centre of gravity.

The centre of gravity is 1 in. through the plank from the centroid G of a face $PQRS$. Let G be at a distance $\bar{x}$ from PQ. By symmetry G will be on the line joining the middle points of PQ and RS. $PQRS$ is a trapezium and hence its area is $14\left(\dfrac{4+10}{2 \times 12}\right)$, i.e. $\dfrac{49}{6}$ sq. ft.

Suppose $PQRS$ is divided into a number of thin strips of width δx ft. by lines parallel to PQ. The width of the plank at x ft. from PQ is $\frac{1}{12}\left(4 + \dfrac{3x}{7}\right)$ ft. because the plank widens $\frac{3}{7}$ in. per foot of length. Hence the area of the strip from x to $x + \delta x$ is approximately $\frac{1}{12}\left(4 + \dfrac{3x}{7}\right)\delta x$. ft.² and its moment about PQ is approximately $\frac{1}{12}x\left(4 + \dfrac{3x}{7}\right)\delta x$. ft.³

Therefore the total moment of all the strips about PQ is approximately $\sum\limits_{0}^{14} \frac{1}{12}x\left(4+\frac{3x}{7}\right)\delta x$, and hence the exact moment of the area $PQRS$ about PQ is the limit of this sum as δx

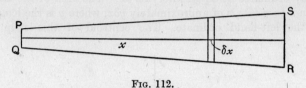

Fig. 112.

approaches 0 which is $\displaystyle\int_{0}^{14} \frac{1}{12}x\left(4+\frac{3x}{7}\right)dx.$ But this moment is also (area of $PQRS$) $\times \bar{x}$ which equals $\dfrac{49}{6}\bar{x}.$

$$\therefore \frac{49}{6}\bar{x} = \int_{0}^{14} \frac{1}{12}x\left(4+\frac{3x}{7}\right)dx$$

$$= \frac{1}{12}\int_{0}^{14}\left(4x+\frac{3x^2}{7}\right)dx$$

$$= \frac{1}{12}\left[2x^2+\frac{x^3}{7}\right]_{0}^{14}$$

$$= \frac{1}{12}\left[2 \cdot 14^2+\frac{14^3}{7}\right]$$

$$= \frac{14^2}{3}.$$

$$\therefore \bar{x} = \frac{6}{49}\cdot\frac{14^2}{3} = 8.$$

Therefore the centre of gravity is 8 ft. from the end PQ, half-way through the plank.

Example.—Find the centroid of the area of the upper half of the ellipse $\dfrac{x^2}{a^2}+\dfrac{y^2}{b^2}=1.$

By symmetry the centroid G lies on Oy. The area of the half ellipse is $\frac{1}{2}\pi ab$ and hence, if $OG = \bar{y}$, the moment of the area about Ox is $\frac{1}{2}\pi ab \cdot \bar{y}$.

Suppose that the area is divided into thin strips of width δx by ordinates at equal intervals δx. The area of the strip from x to $x + \delta x$ is of approximately $y\delta x$, where y is the length of the left-hand ordinate. The centroid of this strip is

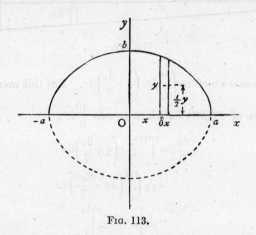

FIG. 113.

approximately at a distance $\frac{1}{2}y$ from Ox and so the moment of the area of this strip about Ox is approximately $\frac{1}{2}y(y\delta x)$ which is $\frac{1}{2}y^2\delta x$. Hence the total moment of the area of the half ellipse about Ox is $\int_{-a}^{a} \frac{1}{2}y^2dx$, the limits of this summation being $-a$ and a because the strips start at $x = -a$ and end at $x = a$. But we have already seen that the moment is $\frac{1}{2}\pi ab\bar{y}$,

$$\therefore \frac{1}{2}\pi ab\bar{y} = \int_{-a}^{a} \frac{1}{2}y^2dx$$

Now $\qquad \dfrac{x^2}{a^2} + \dfrac{y^2}{b^2} = 1$ whence $y^2 = b^2\left(1 - \dfrac{x^2}{a^2}\right)$.

$$\therefore \tfrac{1}{2}\pi ab\bar{y} = \int_{-a}^{a} \tfrac{1}{2}b^2\left(1 - \frac{x^2}{a^2}\right)dx$$

$$= \tfrac{1}{2}b^2\left[x - \frac{x^3}{3a^2}\right]_{-a}^{a}$$

$$= \tfrac{1}{2}b^2\left(a - \frac{a}{3}\right) - \tfrac{1}{2}b^2\left(-a + \frac{a}{3}\right)$$

$$= \tfrac{2}{3}ab^2$$

$$\therefore \bar{y} = \frac{4b}{3\pi}.$$

Example.—Prove that the centroid of a solid hemisphere of radius r is at a distance $\tfrac{3}{8}r$ from the centre of the plane face.

Take the centre O as origin and the axis Ox perpendicular to the plane face. Suppose that the hemisphere is divided into thin slices of thickness δx by planes perpendicular to Ox. The volume of a slice of radius y between the planes at distances x and $x + \delta x$ from O is approximately $\pi y^2 \delta x$. Since the centroid of the slice is on Ox, at a distance from O, which is approximately equal to x, the moment of the volume of the slice about Oy is approximately $\pi xy^2\delta x$. Hence the moment of the whole volume of the hemisphere is $\int_0^r \pi xy^2 dx$. But, if the centroid G is at a distance $\bar{x}$ from O, the moment of the whole volume $\tfrac{2}{3}\pi r^3$ about Oy is $\tfrac{2}{3}\pi r^3\bar{x}$.

$$\therefore \tfrac{2}{3}\pi r^3\bar{x} = \int_0^r \pi xy^2 dx$$

$$= \int_0^r \pi x(r^2 - x^2)dx, \text{ since } x^2 + y^2 = r^2,$$

$$= \int_0^r \pi(xr^2 - x^3)dx$$

$$= \pi\left[\frac{x^2r^2}{2} - \frac{x^4}{4}\right]_0^r$$

$$= \tfrac{1}{4}\pi r^4.$$

$$\therefore \bar{x} = \frac{\tfrac{1}{4}\pi r^4}{\tfrac{2}{3}\pi r^3} = \tfrac{3}{8}r.$$

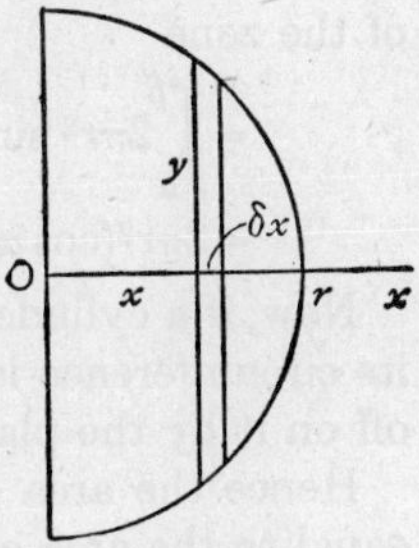

Fig. 114.

Area of the surface of a zone of a sphere

We shall show that the area of the surface of a zone of a sphere is equal to the area of the surface cut off by the planes bounding the zone on a cylinder which has its axis perpendicular to these planes and touches the sphere.

Let Ox be perpendicular to the planes AB, CD bounding the zone, and let it cut the planes in M and N. Let the radii OP, OQ make angles θ^c and $(\theta + \delta\theta)^c$ with Ox. Then the length of the arc PQ is $r\delta\theta$ and, since the ordinate of P is $r \sin \theta$, the length of the ribbon obtained by revolving this arc about Ox is $2\pi r \sin \theta$. Hence the area of this ribbon is approximately $2\pi r \sin \theta (r\delta\theta)$, i.e. $2\pi r^2 \sin \theta \, \delta\theta$. Therefore, if

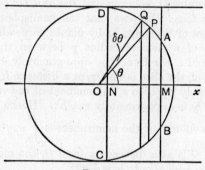

Fig. 115.

OA, OD make angles α and β with Ox, the area of the surface of the zone

$$= \int_\alpha^\beta 2\pi r^2 \sin \theta \, d\theta = \left[-2\pi r^2 \cos \theta \right]_\alpha^\beta$$
$$= 2\pi r^2 (\cos \alpha - \cos \beta) = 2\pi r(OM - ON) = 2\pi r \cdot NM$$

Now, if a cylinder with its axis along Ox touches the sphere, its circumference is $2\pi r$ and NM is the width of the zone cut off on it by the planes AB and CD.

Hence the area of the surface of the zone of the sphere is equal to the area cut off on the circumscribing cylinder.

In particular,

area of surface of a sphere $= 2\pi r \times 2r = 4\pi r^2$.

Pappus' theorems

I. If a plane area A is revolved round an axis in its plane, which does not intersect the area, the volume swept out is equal to A multiplied by the length of the path traced out by the centroid of the area.

Suppose the area A divided up into very small areas a. Let y be the distance of the centroid of a from this axis. Then, since a is very small, the volume swept out when it revolves round the axis is very nearly equal to that of a cylinder of cross-section a and length $2\pi y$.

$\therefore$ volume swept out by $a \simeq 2\pi y a$.

Hence the total volume swept out by $A \simeq \Sigma 2\pi y a$, the sum being taken for all the small areas which make up A. But, as we have seen on page 213,

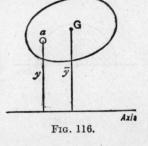

$$A\bar{y} = (\Sigma a)\bar{y} = \Sigma y a.$$

$$\therefore \; \Sigma 2\pi y a = 2\pi A \bar{y}.$$

Fig. 116.

Since the approximation to the volume becomes more and more accurate the smaller a is taken, the volume is exactly equal to $2\pi A \bar{y}$, which is equal to $A \times 2\pi \bar{y}$ or A multiplied by the length of the path of the centroid G.

Example.—Show that the centroid of the area of a semi-circle of radius r is at a distance $\dfrac{4r}{3\pi}$ from the centre (Fig. 117).

Suppose that the semicircle is the part of the circle of centre O and radius r which is above the x axis, and that the centroid is at a distance $\bar{y}$ from the origin along the y axis. When the semicircular area is revolved about Ox it sweeps out the volume of a sphere of radius r, which is $\frac{4}{3}\pi r^3$. Therefore, by Pappus' theorem,

$$\tfrac{1}{2}\pi r^2 \times 2\pi\bar{y} = \tfrac{4}{3}\pi r^3$$

$$\bar{y} = \frac{4r}{3\pi}.$$

II. If a plane arc of length l is revolved round an axis in its plane, which does not cut the arc, the area of the surface swept out is equal to l multiplied by the length of the path traced out by the centroid of the arc.

The proof of this theorem is similar to that given above. Divide the arc into small pieces of length s, and suppose the

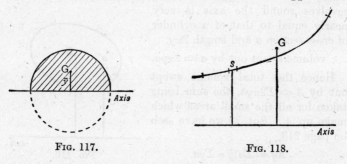

FIG. 117.   FIG. 118.

centroid of s is at distance y from the axis (Fig. 118). Then the area of the surface swept out when s is revolved is nearly $2\pi ys$.

∴ total area of the surface swept out by $l \backsimeq \Sigma 2\pi ys$

$$= 2\pi\Sigma ys$$
$$= 2\pi(\Sigma s)\bar{y}$$
$$= 2\pi l\bar{y}.$$

As the small pieces of arc are made shorter and shorter this equation becomes more and more accurate and ultimately exact.

∴ area of surface $= l \times 2\pi\bar{y} = l$ multiplied by the length of the path of the centroid G.

Example.—A square $ABCD$ of side a revolves about a line parallel to AB at a distance b from the centre of the square. Find the volume swept out by the area of the square and the area of the surface swept out by its perimeter (Fig. 119).

$$\text{Volume} = \text{area of square} \times \text{path of centre}$$

$$= a^2 \times 2\pi b$$

$$= 2\pi a^2 b.$$

$$\text{Surface} = \text{length of perimeter} \times \text{path of centre}$$

$$= 4a \times 2\pi b = 8\pi a b.$$

Example.—Find the centre of gravity of a thin wire in the shape of a semicircle (Fig. 120).

If the semicircle is revolved round its bounding diameter it sweeps out a spherical surface which has an area $4\pi r^2$.

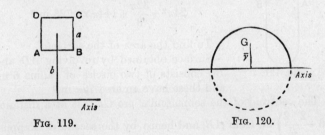

FIG. 119.   FIG. 120.

Hence, if the centre of gravity of the wire is at a distance $\bar{y}$ from the centre,

$$4\pi r^2 = \text{length of arc} \times \text{the length of the path of } G$$

$$= \pi r \times 2\pi \bar{y}$$

$$\therefore \bar{y} = \frac{2r}{\pi}.$$

Example.—The surface of a solid is obtained by revolving the curve in Fig. 121 about the axis of symmetry AB. Find the volume of the solid and the area of its surface.

To find the volume.

Volume obtained by revolving the rectangle $ABCD$ is the volume of a cylinder of radius 6 in. and height 4 in., which is $\pi \cdot 6^2 \cdot 4$ in.^{3}

The centroid of the semicircle CDE is at a distance $\left(6 + \dfrac{4 \cdot 2}{3\pi}\right)$ in. from AB, and hence by the first of Pappus' theorems the volume swept out by the semicircle is

$$\text{area} \times \text{length of path of centroid} = \frac{\pi \cdot 2^2}{2}\left\{2\pi\left(6 + \frac{8}{3\pi}\right)\right\}$$

$$= \left(24\pi^2 + \frac{32\pi}{3}\right) \text{ in.}^3$$

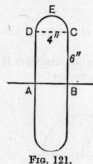

FIG. 121.

Therefore the total volume of the solid is

$$24\pi^2 + \frac{32\pi}{3} + 144\pi \doteqdot 723 \text{ in.}^3$$

To find the area of the surface.

Surface obtained by revolving AD and BC consists of two circles of radius 6 in. and these have an area 72π in.^{2}

The centroid of the semicircular arc CED is at a distance $\left(6 + \dfrac{2 \cdot 2}{\pi}\right)$ in. from AB, and hence by the second of Pappus' theorems the area of the surface swept out by the arc CED is

$$\text{arc} \times \text{length of path of centroid} = 2\pi\left\{2\pi\left(6 + \frac{4}{\pi}\right)\right\} \text{ in.}^2$$

Therefore the total area of the surface of the solid is

$$72\pi + 24\pi^2 + 16\pi = 88\pi + 24\pi^2 \doteqdot 513 \text{ in.}^2$$

Pressure of a liquid

Example.—A trough has a parabolic section 4 ft. wide at the top and 4 ft. deep. If it is full of water weighing 62·5 lb. per cu. ft., find the thrust on an end.

If the equation of a parabolic section is $y = ax^2$, $y = 4$ when $x = 2$,

$$\therefore \ 4 = 4a, \text{ i.e. } a = 1.$$

Therefore the equation is $y = x^2$.

Now, if w lb. wt. is the weight per cu. ft. of water, the pressure at a height y ft. above the bottom is $w(4 - y)$ and hence the thrust on a strip of length $2x$ and width δy is approximately $w(4 - y)2x\delta y$. Therefore the thrust on an end is

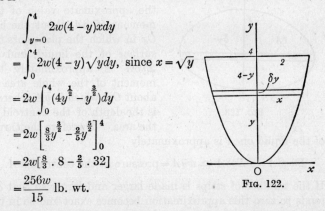

$$\int_{y=0}^{4} 2w(4 - y)x \, dy$$

$$= \int_{0}^{4} 2w(4 - y)\sqrt{y} \, dy, \text{ since } x = \sqrt{y}$$

$$= 2w \int_{0}^{4} (4y^{\frac{1}{2}} - y^{\frac{3}{2}}) \, dy$$

$$= 2w \left[\frac{8}{3} y^{\frac{3}{2}} - \frac{2}{5} y^{\frac{5}{2}} \right]_{0}^{4}$$

$$= 2w [\frac{8}{3} \cdot 8 - \frac{2}{5} \cdot 32]$$

$$= \frac{256w}{15} \text{ lb. wt.}$$

Fig. 122.

Since $w = 62 \cdot 5$ the thrust on an end is approximately 1067 lb. wt.

In this and in succeeding problems the air pressure has been neglected. Thus the result obtained above is really the resultant thrust on the end of the trough, i.e. the difference of the thrust of the liquid on the inside and the air on the outside.

Total liquid thrust on a plane area

We shall show that the thrust of a liquid on a plane area immersed in it equals the product of the area and the pressure at the centroid of the area.

Fig. 123 shows a plane area A immersed vertically in a liquid. Suppose it divided into thin strips by lines parallel to the surface of the liquid, and let the area of the strip between the lines at depths y and $y + \delta y$ be δA. Then, if the weight per unit volume of the liquid is w, the pressure at the upper edge of δA is wy and hence the thrust on δA is $wy\delta A$ approximately. Therefore the thrust on the whole area A

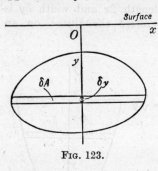

FIG. 123.

is approximately $\Sigma wy\delta A$, the summation being taken to include every strip. But $y\delta A$ is the approximate value of the moment of δA about the line Ox in which the plane cuts the surface of the liquid, and so $\Sigma y\delta A$ is approximately the moment of the whole area A about Ox, which is $\bar{y}A$, where $\bar{y}$ is the depth of the centroid of the area. Therefore the thrust of the liquid on A is approximately

$$\Sigma wy\delta A = w\Sigma y\delta A \backsimeq w\bar{y}A = \text{pressure at the centroid} \times A.$$

If the number of strips is made larger and larger so that δA tends to zero this approximation becomes exact and so in the limit

Thrust of liquid on a vertical plane area = pressure at centroid × area

This result is also true when the plane is not vertical, but in that case the distances y and $\bar{y}$ are measured vertically from the surface of the liquid.

Example.—A tank on a petrol lorry is in the form of an elliptic cylinder. The horizontal axis of the ellipse is 6 ft. long and the vertical axis is 4 ft. long. Find the thrust on an end of the tank (a) when it is full, (b) when it is half full of petrol weighing 52 lb./ft.[3]

(*a*) When the tank is full the centroid is 2 ft. below the surface of the liquid.

$$\therefore \text{ thrust on end} = 52 . 2 . \text{ (area of ellipse)}$$
$$= 104 . \pi . 2 . 3.$$
$$\fallingdotseq 1960 \text{ lb. wt.}$$

(*b*) When the tank is half full the centroid is $\dfrac{3 . 2}{4\pi}$ ft. beneath the surface of the liquid (see example on page 215).

$$\therefore \text{ thrust on end} = \frac{52 . 6}{4\pi}(\tfrac{1}{2} \text{ area of ellipse})$$
$$= \frac{52 . 6}{4\pi} . 3\pi$$
$$= 234 \text{ lb. wt.}$$

Centre of pressure

The point at which the resultant liquid thrust on a plane area acts is called the centre of pressure. Its vertical depth can be found by dividing the area into thin strips by horizontal lines and adding the moments of the thrusts on these strips about the line in which the plane cuts the surface of the liquid. The method is shown in the following example.

Example.—A sluice gate is a rectangle 4 ft. deep and 3 ft. wide. When the water is 2 ft. above the top of the gate on one side and below the bottom of the gate on the other, find the centre of pressure on the gate.

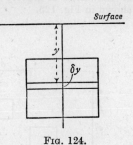

Fig. 124.

The pressure at a depth y beneath the surface of the liquid is wy where w is the weight per unit volume of the liquid, and hence the thrust on the part of the gate between depths y and $y + \delta y$ is approximately $wy . 3\delta y$.

8

The moment of this thrust about the line in which the plane of the rectangle cuts the surface of the liquid is $3wy^2\delta y$, and hence the moment of the total thrust on the gate about this line (which we call the surface line) is

$$\int_{2}^{6} 3wy^2 dy = \left[wy^3\right]_{2}^{6} = 208w \text{ lb. wt. ft.}$$

But the total thrust on the gate

$$= \text{area} \times \text{pressure at centroid}$$

$$= 12 \times 4w = 48w \text{ lb. wt.}$$

If this thrust acts at a distance y_p beneath the surface line, its moment about this line is $48wy_p$ lb. wt. ft.

$$\therefore 48wy_p = 208w$$

$$\therefore y_p = \frac{208}{48} = 4\tfrac{1}{3} \text{ ft.}$$

Thus the resultant thrust acts at a point on the vertical line through the centre of the rectangle at a point $2\tfrac{1}{3}$ ft. below the top of the rectangle.

Exercise XXIV

1. Use the formula $(\Sigma w)\bar{x} = \Sigma(wx)$ to find the distance from A of the centre of gravity of the thin plate of uniform thickness shown in Fig. 125.

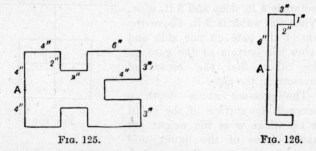

FIG. 125.   FIG. 126.

2. Fig. 126 shows the cross-section of a flywheel. Find the distance of its centre of gravity from A.

3. A metal plate is in the shape of an isosceles triangle of sides 5, 5 and 6 in. It is of uniform density and 4 in. thick. Find its centre of gravity.

4. Find the centroid of the area bounded by the lines $y = 2x$, $y = -2x$ and the line $x = 6$.

5. Find the centroid of the area bounded by the curves $y = \frac{1}{100}x^2$, $y = -\frac{1}{100}x^2$ and the line $x = 20$.

6. Find both co-ordinates of the centroid of the area bounded by the curve $ly = x^2$, the x axis and the line $x = l$.

7. Show that the moment of the area $ABCD$ in Fig. 127 about

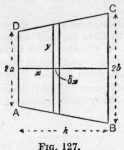

Fig. 127.

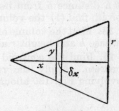

Fig. 128.

AD is the limiting value of the sum $\sum\limits_{0}^{h} \left\{ 2ax + \dfrac{2(b-a)x^2}{h} \right\} \delta x$ as δx approaches 0. Hence show that the centroid of the area is at a distance $\dfrac{2(a+2b)}{3(a+b)}$ from AD.

8. A cone of uniform density and weight W has height h and base radius r. Suppose that the axis of the cone is horizontal and that the cone is divided into thin slices of thickness δx by planes parallel to its base (Fig. 128). Hence show that the moment of the weight of the cone about a horizontal line through the vertex parallel to the base of the cone is the limiting value of $\sum\limits_{0}^{h} \dfrac{3Wx^2\delta x}{h^3}$ as δx approaches 0. Express this limit as an integral, and hence show that the centre of gravity of the cone is at a distance $\frac{3}{4}h$ from the vertex.

9. Use the result in Question 8 to find the centre of gravity of the solid obtained by rotating the area in Fig. 129 about AB.

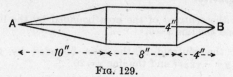

FIG. 129.

10. Find the centroid of the smaller segment cut off from a sphere of radius 8 in. by a plane 4 in. from the centre.

11. Sketch the graph of the equation $y = 1 - x^2$, and show that the centroid of the area bounded by the curve and the x axis lies on Oy and find its distance from O.

12. If a circle of radius a is revolved about an axis in its plane at a distance h from its centre so as to form an anchor ring or toroid, find (1) the volume of the ring, (2) the area of its surface.

13. Find the volume of a cone by rotating a right-angled triangle of base h and height r about the base and using Pappus' theorem.

14. Find the centroid of a semicircular area by using Pappus' theorem. Apply the result to find the volume obtained by revolving Fig. 130 about AB.

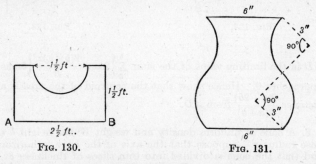

FIG. 130.   FIG. 131.

15. A V-shaped groove 2 in. wide and 3 in. deep is cut round a solid cylinder of radius 8 in. Find the volume of material removed and the area of the surface of the groove.

16. Fig. 131 shows the cross-section of a vase, the curved sides being formed by two equal arcs each subtending 90° at the centre of a circle of radius 3 in. Find the area of the curved surface of the vase.

17. Find the volume obtained by revolving the area under $y = \sin x$ from $x = 0$ to π about the x axis. Hence find the centroid of the area.

18. Show that if an area A is revolved about an axis in its plane (not intersecting A) through an angle θ radians, the volume swept out equals the area multiplied by the length of the path of the centroid of the area.

19. An arc AB of a circle of radius r subtends an angle $2\alpha^c$ at the centre. If this arc is revolved round the diameter of the circle which is parallel to the chord AB, show that the area of the zone of a sphere which is swept out by the arc is $4\pi r^2 \sin \alpha$. Hence, by using Pappus' theorem, show that the centroid of the arc AB is at a distance $\dfrac{r \sin \alpha}{\alpha}$ from the centre of the circle.

20. The end of a trough is an isosceles triangle with a base 10 in. and height 12 in. If the trough is full of water weighing 62·5 lb. wt./ft.³, find the thrust on an end of the trough by integration.

21. A cylindrical boiler is h ft. long and of r ft. radius. If its axis is horizontal, find the thrust on an end when it is full of liquid of weight w lb. per cu. ft. Find also the thrust on the base when the axis of the cylinder is vertical.

22. Show that the centre of pressure on a vertical rectangular area a ft. wide, b feet deep, when the upper edge is in the surface of the liquid, is at a depth $\frac{2}{3} b$.

23. Find the depth of the centre of pressure of a liquid on a vertical rectangular area 8 ft. wide, 3 ft. deep, when the upper edge is 4 ft. beneath the surface.

24. Find the centre of pressure on a vertical isosceles triangle with its base horizontal (i) with its vertex, (ii) with its base in the surface of the liquid.

Moments of inertia

If an exceedingly small body of weight w is rotating in a circle of radius r with angular velocity ω about an axis, its velocity is $r\omega$, and hence its kinetic energy is $\frac{1}{2}\dfrac{w}{g}(r\omega)^2$, i.e. $\frac{1}{2}\omega^2 \cdot \dfrac{w}{g}r^2$.

It follows that if a number of exceedingly small bodies of weights w_1, w_2, . . . are rigidly connected together by light rods, and the whole system rotates about an axis with angular velocity ω, the total kinetic energy is

$$\tfrac{1}{2}\omega^2 \cdot \frac{w_1 r_1^2}{g} + \tfrac{1}{2}\omega^2 \cdot \frac{w_2 r_2^2}{g} + \dots$$

where r_1, r_2, $\dots$ are the distances of the bodies from the axis (Fig. 133). This sum can be written

$$\tfrac{1}{2}\omega^2\left(\frac{w_1 r_1^2}{g} + \frac{w_2 r_2^2}{g} + \dots\right) = \tfrac{1}{2}\omega^2 \cdot \Sigma\frac{wr^2}{g}.$$

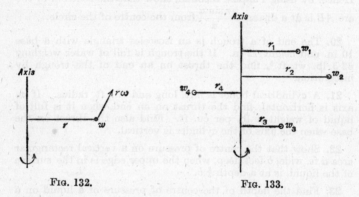

FIG. 132.   FIG. 133.

$\Sigma\dfrac{wr^2}{g}$ is called the moment of inertia of the system about the axis and is denoted by I. The larger the value of I the greater is the amount of work that has to be done to give the system an angular velocity ω, and so I measures the tendency of the body to resist being given a rotational velocity, i.e. it measures the rotational inertia of the body.

If all the bodies were concentrated at a distance k from the axis they would all have a velocity $k\omega$, and their kinetic energy would then be

$$\tfrac{1}{2}\omega^2\left(\frac{w_1 k^2}{g} + \frac{w_2 k^2}{g} + \dots\right) = \tfrac{1}{2}\omega^2 \cdot \frac{(\Sigma w)k^2}{g}.$$

This is the same as the actual kinetic energy if

$$\frac{(\Sigma w)k^2}{g} = I = \frac{\Sigma(wr^2)}{g}$$

i.e. if $(\Sigma w)k^2 = \Sigma(wr^2)$.

k is called the radius of gyration of the system of bodies about the axis. If the total weight of the system, Σw, is denoted by W,

kinetic energy of the system $= \frac{1}{2}I\omega^2$, where

$$I = \frac{W}{g}k^2 = \frac{\Sigma(wr^2)}{g}.$$

Example.—Two bodies of 6 and 4 lb. wt. are joined by a light rod 5 ft. long. If the rod rotates about an axis at right angles to it through a point 2 ft. from the heavier body, find the moment of inertia and the radius of gyration of the system about the axis.

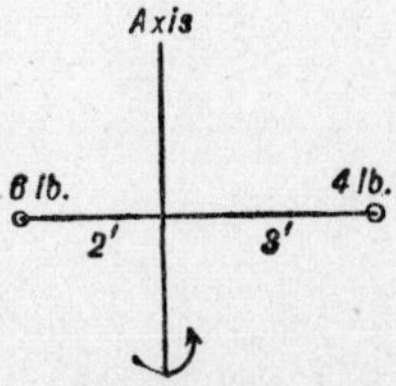

Since the 6 lb. is 2 ft. from the axis and the 4 lb. is 3 ft. from the axis

$$\Sigma wr^2 = 6 \times 2^2 + 4 \times 3^2 = 60.$$

FIG. 134.

Hence using ft., lb. wt. and sec. as units $I = \dfrac{\Sigma wr^2}{g} = \dfrac{60}{32} = 1\frac{7}{8}$.

Since $\Sigma w = 6 + 4 = 10$,

$$10k^2 = 60, \text{ and therefore } k = \sqrt{6} \backsimeq 2\cdot45 \text{ ft.}$$

The moment of inertia of a continuous body is found by dividing it up into a number of small parts for each of which wr^2 can be found approximately; then Wk^2 is the limiting value of Σwr^2 as the weight of each part tends to zero and the number of parts tends to infinity.

Moment of inertia of a thin rod

Suppose a thin rod of length l and weight W is rotating about an axis through one end perpendicular to the rod. Suppose the rod divided into very small parts. The part between distances x and $x + \delta x$ from the axis is of weight $\dfrac{W\delta x}{l}$ and every point of it is approximately at a distance x from the axis. Hence for this part

$$wr^2 \eqsim \frac{W\delta x}{l} \cdot x^2 = \frac{Wx^2\delta x}{l}.$$

Therefore

$$Wk^2 = \Sigma wr^2 \eqsim \Sigma \frac{Wx^2\delta x}{l},$$

and hence by making δx approach 0,

$$Wk^2 = \int_0^l \frac{Wx^2}{l}dx$$

$$= \left[\frac{Wx^3}{3l}\right]_0^l$$

$$= \frac{Wl^2}{3}$$

$$\therefore k^2 = \frac{l^2}{3}, \text{ and } I = \frac{Wk^2}{g} = \frac{Wl^2}{3g}.$$

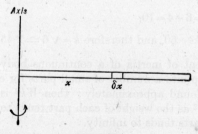

Fig. 135.

Thin rectangular plate rotating about an edge

Let the plate have a weight W and let the edges perpendicular to the axis have length a and the other edges length b. Suppose the plate divided into thin strips by lines parallel to the axis. The strip between the lines at distances x and $x+\delta x$ from the axis is of weight $\frac{W\delta x}{a}$ and every part of it is approximately at a distance x from the axis. Hence, as in the case of the straight rod (p. 232),

$$Wk^2 = \int_0^a \frac{Wx^2}{a}\,dx = \frac{Wa^2}{3}$$

$$\therefore k^2 = \frac{a^2}{3} \text{ and } I = \frac{Wa^2}{3g}.$$

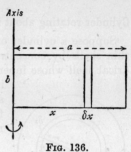

FIG. 136.

Thin rectangular plate rotating about an axis through its centre parallel to an edge

In this case Wk^2 is the limiting value of the sum of terms like $\frac{Wx^2}{a}\delta x$ between the limits $-\tfrac{1}{2}a$ and $\tfrac{1}{2}a$ instead of between the limits 0 and a.

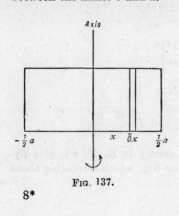

FIG. 137.

$$\therefore Wk^2 = \int_{-\frac{1}{2}a}^{\frac{1}{2}a} \frac{Wx^2}{a}\,dx$$

$$= \left[\frac{Wx^3}{3a}\right]_{-\frac{1}{2}a}^{\frac{1}{2}a}$$

$$= \frac{Wa^2}{24} - \left(-\frac{Wa^2}{24}\right)$$

$$= \frac{Wa^2}{12}.$$

$$\therefore k^2 = \frac{a^2}{12} \text{ and } I = \frac{W}{g}\cdot\frac{a^2}{12}$$

8*

Alternatively we can say that the rectangle is the sum of two rectangles of sides $\frac{1}{2}a$ and b, each rotating about an edge and each having a weight $\frac{1}{2}W$.

$$\therefore I = 2\left[\frac{(\frac{1}{2}W)}{g} \cdot \frac{(\frac{1}{2}a)^2}{3}\right] = \frac{W}{g} \cdot \frac{a^2}{12}.$$

Cylinder rotating about its own axis

Suppose a cylinder of radius a and weight W divided into thin shells by concentric cylinders. The weight of a cylindrical shell whose inner radius is r and outer radius is $r + \delta r$

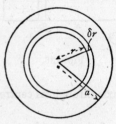

FIG. 138.

is proportional to the area of its cross-section, which is nearly $2\pi r \cdot \delta r$. Therefore the weight of this part is approximately

$$\frac{2\pi r \cdot \delta r}{\pi a^2} \cdot W, \text{ i.e. } \frac{2Wr \cdot \delta r}{a^2}.$$

Hence for the whole of the shells making up the cylinder

$$\Sigma wr^2 \simeq \Sigma \frac{2Wr^3 \delta r}{a^2}.$$

Wk^2 is the limiting value of this sum as δr approaches zero.

$$\therefore Wk^2 = \int_0^a \frac{2Wr^3 dr}{a^2}$$

$$= \left[\frac{Wr^4}{2a^2}\right]_0^a$$

$$= \frac{Wa^2}{2}.$$

$$\therefore k^2 = \frac{1}{2}a^2 \text{ and } I = \frac{W}{g} \cdot \frac{a^2}{2}.$$

Example.—Find the kinetic energy in ft. lb. wt. of a flywheel of weight 100 lb. and radius 6 in. which is rotating about its axis at 4 rev. per sec.

Using ft., lb. wt. and sec. as units

radius of flywheel $= \frac{1}{2}$

$$\therefore I = \frac{W}{g}k^2 = \frac{W}{g} \cdot \frac{a^2}{2} = \frac{100}{32} \cdot \frac{\frac{1}{4}}{2} = \frac{25}{64}.$$

Angular velocity $\omega = 8\pi$ (rad. per sec.)

$$\therefore \text{kinetic energy} = \frac{1}{2}I\omega^2$$

$$= \frac{1}{2} \cdot \frac{25}{64} \cdot 64\pi^2$$

$$= \frac{25\pi^2}{2}$$

$$\simeq 123 \text{ ft. lb. wt.}$$

Second moment of area

Let a thin plate of area A be divided up into a number of exceedingly small parts and let δA be the area of a part at a distance r from a fixed axis. Then, if the plate is of uniform weight per unit area, the weights of the whole plate and of the part with area δA are proportional to A and δA respectively. Hence Ak^2 is the limiting value of $\Sigma r^2 \delta A$ as the area of each part tends to zero. This is called the second moment of the area about the axis. It is often loosely called the moment of inertia of the area about the axis.

Example.—A beam has a width b and depth d; find the second moment of area of its cross-section about a line parallel to a side of length b through the centre of the cross-section.

About this line $k^2 = \frac{d^2}{12}$ (see page 233).

$\therefore$ second moment of area about the line

$$= \text{area} \times k^2 = bd \cdot \frac{d^2}{12}$$

$$= \frac{bd^3}{12}.$$

The parallel axes theorem

This theorem states that, if k_g is the radius of gyration of a body about any axis through its centroid and k is the radius of gyration about a parallel axis at a distance l from the first one, then

$$k^2 = k_g{}^2 + l^2.$$

A proof of this theorem for a body of any shape is beyond the scope of this book, but a proof is given below for the case of a plane area when both the axes lie in the plane.

Let δA be the area of a small part of the whole area A and let its algebraical distances from the axis through the centroid

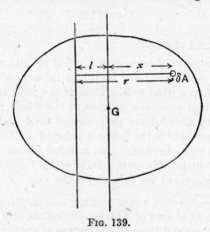

Fig. 139.

and the other axis be x and r respectively. Then $r = x + l$ for all positions of δA and hence

$$\Sigma r^2 \delta A = \Sigma (x + l)^2 \delta A$$
$$= \Sigma (x^2 + 2lx + l^2) \delta A$$
$$= \Sigma x^2 \delta A + 2l \Sigma x \delta A + l^2 \Sigma \delta A.$$

Now $\Sigma \delta A = A$, and, if we make δA tend to zero, the sums $\Sigma r^2 \delta A$ and $\Sigma x^2 \delta A$ tend to $k^2 A$ and $k_g{}^2 A$ respectively; also

$\Sigma x \delta A$ tends to $A\bar{x}$, which is zero because x is measured from an axis through the centroid. Therefore in the limit

$$Ak^2 = Ak_g{}^2 + Al^2,$$

whence
$$k^2 = k_g{}^2 + l^2.$$

Note.—It is often useful, especially when using the parallel axes theorem, to denote the radius of gyration about an axis AB by k_{AB}.

Example.—Find the second moment of area of the beam section in Fig. 140 about AB.

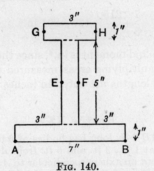

FIG. 140.

Divide the figure into three rectangles by the dotted lines. Then, for the lower rectangle, $k^2{}_{AB} = \frac{1}{3}$ in.^{2}

$\therefore$ 2nd moment of area about AB
$$= \text{area of rectangle} \times k^2{}_{AB} = \tfrac{7}{3} \text{ in.}^4$$

For the middle rectangle, $k^2{}_{EF} = \dfrac{5^2}{12}$ in.^{2}, where EF is the axis through its centroid parallel to AB. Hence, by the parallel axes theorem, since EF is $3\frac{1}{2}$ in. from AB,

$$k^2{}_{AB} = \frac{5^2}{12} + \left(\frac{7}{2}\right)^2 = \frac{25 + 147}{12} = \frac{172}{12} = \frac{43}{3} \text{ in.}^2$$

$\therefore$ 2nd moment of area about $AB = \dfrac{5 \times 43}{3} = \dfrac{215}{3}$ in.^{4}

For the upper rectangle $k^2{}_{GH} = \frac{1}{12}$ in.^{2}, where GH is the axis through its centroid parallel to AB. Hence, by the parallel axes theorem, since GH is $6\frac{1}{2}$ in. from AB,

$$k^2{}_{AB} = \frac{1}{12} + \left(\frac{13}{2}\right)^2 = \frac{1 + 507}{12} = \frac{508}{12} = \frac{127}{3} \text{ in.}^2$$

$\therefore$ 2nd moment of area about $AB = \dfrac{3 \times 127}{3} = 127$ in.^{4}.

Adding the 2nd moments of the three rectangles we find that the 2nd moment of area of the whole figure about AB is

$$\frac{7}{3} + \frac{215}{3} + 127 = 201 \text{ in.}^4.$$

The unit of the 2nd moment is in.^{4}, since these 2nd moments are obtained by multiplying areas measured in square inches by the squares of lengths measured in inches.

Exercise XXV

1. A light rod AB 6 ft. long has bodies of 6 lb., 2 lb. and 1 lb. weight fixed to it at 1 ft., 3 ft. and 6 ft. from A respectively. If the rod rotates about an axis perpendicular to AB through A, find the radius of gyration of the system of bodies about it. (The bodies may be assumed to be concentrated at the given points.)

2. Show that the moment of inertia of a thin rod of length l and weight W rotating about an axis perpendicular to it through a point $\frac{1}{4}l$ from one end is $\displaystyle\int_{-\frac{1}{4}l}^{\frac{3}{4}l} \frac{Wx^2 \cdot dx}{gl}$. Evaluate this integral.

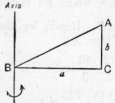

3. The figure shows a thin triangular plate. If it rotates about an axis through B parallel to AC, show that

$$k^2 = \int_0^a \frac{2x^3 dx}{a^2} \text{ and hence find } k^2.$$

Fig. 141.

4. Show by direct integration that the moment of inertia of a hollow cylinder of weight W, internal radius r and external radius R is $\frac{1}{2}\frac{W}{g}(R^2+r^2)$. Also deduce this result from the formula for the moment of inertia of a solid cylinder.

5. Use the result of Question 4 to find the radius of gyration of the rim of a flywheel about the axis of the flywheel if the inner radius of the rim is 10 in. and the outer radius is 12 in. If the rim of the flywheel weighs 80 lb., find its kinetic energy when it is rotating at 40 r.p.m.

6. A door is 6 ft. high, 4 ft. wide and 2 in. thick. Find the radius of gyration of the door about its hinges by integration, neglecting the thickness of the door. Compare your answer with that obtained by using the formula for the radius of gyration of a rectangle on page 233. If the material of which the door is made weighs 90 lb. per cu. ft., find its kinetic energy when it is rotating at a rate of $\frac{1}{4}$ rev. per sec.

7. What is the radius of gyration of a disc flywheel of radius a about its axis of rotation ? A disc flywheel has a diameter of 16 in. and is 3 in. thick, and it is made of cast iron weighing 0·26 lb. per cub. in. The speed of rotation of the flywheel is reduced from 20 to 10 rev. per sec. in $\frac{1}{2}$ min. At what average horse-power is the flywheel doing work during this time ?

8. Show that the second moment of area of a rectangle of sides b and d about an axis in its plane parallel to a side of length b at a distance l from the centre is $\int_{l-\frac{1}{2}d}^{l+\frac{1}{2}d} bx^2dx$. Hence show that the second moment of area is $bd(\frac{1}{12}d^2+l^2)$.

9. By using the formula on page 235 for the second moment of area of a rectangle about a side, find the second moment of

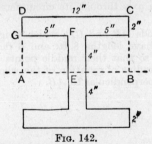

FIG. 142.

area of the I section in Fig. 142 about the axis AB through its centroid. [Take half the I section as the rectangle $ABCD$ – twice the rectangle $AEFG$.]

10. Prove the result in Question 8 by using the parallel axes theorem.

11. Find the second moment of area of the figure in Fig. 143 about the axis AB. Find the radius of gyration of the figure about this axis, and also about a parallel axis through the centroid of the figure.

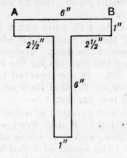

FIG. 143.

12. Find by integration the second moment of area of an isosceles triangle, which has a base a and height h, about a line through the vertex parallel to the base. Use the parallel axes theorem to deduce the second moment of area of the triangle about a line through its centroid parallel to the base.

13. Assuming that the parallel axes theorem is true for a body of any shape, find the radius of gyration of a circular disc of radius a about an axis through its circumference perpendicular to the disc.

14. Two thin rods AB and CD, which weigh 6 lb. and 4 lb. respectively and have lengths 8 ft. and 6 ft. respectively, are clamped together so that their middle points are opposite each other. Find the radius of gyration of the whole body about an axis through AB perpendicular to AB.

CHAPTER X

LOGARITHMIC AND EXPONENTIAL FUNCTIONS

Differentiation of $\log_{10} x$

We have already differentiated x^n (where n is a constant), $\sin x$ and $\cos x$. The next most commonly occurring function

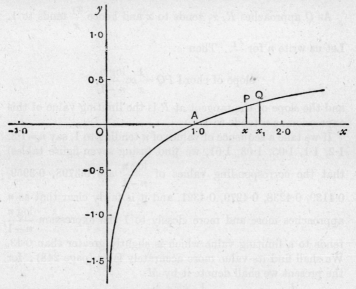

Fig. 144.

in elementary mathematics is $\log_{10} x$. Its graph is shown in Fig. 144.

241

If P is a point whose abscissa is x, the differential coefficient of $\log_{10} x$ is the slope of the tangent to the graph at P.

Let Q be a neighbouring point on the graph; call its abscissa x_1.

$$\text{Slope of chord } PQ = \frac{\text{increase in } y}{\text{increase in } x}$$

$$= \frac{\log x_1 - \log x}{x_1 - x}$$

$$= \frac{\log \dfrac{x_1}{x}}{x\left(\dfrac{x_1}{x} - 1\right)}$$

As Q approaches P, x_1 tends to x and hence $\dfrac{x_1}{x}$ tends to 1.

Let us write n for $\dfrac{x_1}{x}$. Then

$$\text{slope of chord } PQ = \frac{1}{x} \times \frac{\log n}{n-1},$$

and the slope of the tangent at P is the limiting value of this expression as n tends to 1.

If we take a sequence of values of n tending to 1, say $n = 1 \cdot 3$, $1 \cdot 2$, $1 \cdot 1$, $1 \cdot 05$, $1 \cdot 03$, $1 \cdot 01$, we find (using seven-figure tables) that the corresponding values of $\dfrac{\log n}{n-1}$ are $0 \cdot 3798$, $0 \cdot 3959$, $0 \cdot 4139$, $0 \cdot 4238$, $0 \cdot 4279$, $0 \cdot 4321$, and it is fairly clear that as n approaches more and more closely to 1 the expression $\dfrac{\log n}{n-1}$ tends to a limiting value which is slightly greater than $0 \cdot 43$. We shall find its value more accurately later (page 248); for the present we shall denote it by M.

Thus $\dfrac{d}{dx}(\log_{10} x) = M \times \dfrac{1}{x}$, where $M \simeq 0 \cdot 43$.

Note.—Putting $x = 1$ we see that M is the slope of the tangent at the point A.

Differentiation of $\log_a x$ where a is any base

Since $\qquad \log_a x = \dfrac{\log_{10} x}{\log_{10} a}$ (see Part II, page 94)

and $\log_{10} a$ is constant,

$$\frac{d}{dx}(\log_a x) = \frac{1}{\log_{10} a} \cdot \frac{d}{dx}(\log_{10} x)$$

$$= \frac{M}{\log_{10} a} \times \frac{1}{x}.$$

The number e.   Natural logarithms

In the formula for $\dfrac{d}{dx}(\log_a x)$ there is an awkward numerical factor $\dfrac{M}{\log_{10} a}$. This factor will be equal to 1, however, if we choose the number a so that $\log_{10} a = M$, that is, if

$$a = \text{antilog}_{10}\, M \simeq \text{antilog}_{10}\, 0\cdot43 \simeq 2\cdot7.$$

This number is always denoted by e. A more accurate value for e is $2\cdot7183$ (see page 247).

Thus $\qquad\qquad \dfrac{d}{dx}(\log_e x) = \dfrac{1}{x}$

It is evident that this number e is the most convenient base for logarithms when using calculus; it is more convenient than the base 10, since every time that we differentiate $\log_{10} x$ the factor $0\cdot43$ occurs.

Logarithms to the base e are called *natural logarithms* or *Napierian logarithms* after Napier, the originator of logarithms. (For historical note, see Part II, page 78.)

In calculus and in all more advanced mathematics it is customary always to use natural logarithms, and when no base is indicated it will in future be understood that the base is e, except, of course, in purely arithmetical calculations when it is still most convenient to use common logarithms.

Integration of $\dfrac{1}{x}$

Since
$$\frac{d}{dx}(\log_e x) = \frac{1}{x},$$

$$\int \frac{1}{x} dx = \log_e x + C,$$

where C is an arbitrary constant (or constant of integration).

We have seen earlier (page 163) that $\int x^n dx = \dfrac{x^{n+1}}{n+1} + C$ for all values of n except $n = -1$. The integral in the exceptional case is now given by the above, viz. :

$$\int x^{-1} dx = \log_e x + C.$$

Example.—The pressure p lb. wt. per sq. ft. and volume v cu. ft. of a gas, which is kept at a constant temperature, are connected by the relation $pv = $ constant (Boyle's Law). Find the work done by the gas in expanding from 2 cu. ft. to 6 cu. ft., given that $p = 250$ when $v = 3$.

$$pv = \text{constant} = C, \text{ say.}$$

Since $p = 250$ when $v = 3$, $C = 250 \times 3 = 750$. $\therefore p = 750/v$.

$$\begin{aligned}
\text{Work done} &= \int_2^6 p\,dv \\
&= \int_2^6 \frac{750}{v} dv \\
&= 750 \int_2^6 \frac{1}{v} dv \\
&= 750 \left[\log_e v \right]_2^6 \\
&= 750(\log_e 6 - \log_e 2) \\
&= 750 \log_e \tfrac{6}{2} = 750 \log_e 3 \\
&\simeq 750 \times 1 \cdot 0986 \\
&\simeq 824 \cdot 0 \text{ ft. lb. wt.}
\end{aligned}$$

Differentiation of e^x

Let $$y = e^x$$

Then $$x = \log_e y$$

$$\therefore \frac{dx}{dy} = \frac{1}{y}$$

$$\therefore \frac{dy}{dx} = \frac{1}{\dfrac{dx}{dy}} = y = e^x$$

Hence $$\frac{d}{dx}(e^x) = e^x$$

Differentiation of e^{kx}, where k is a constant

If $$y = e^{kx}$$

we can write $$y = e^u \quad \text{where} \quad u = kx.$$

$$\therefore \frac{dy}{du} = e^u \quad \text{and} \quad \frac{du}{dx} = k.$$

$$\therefore \frac{dy}{dx} = \frac{dy}{du} \times \frac{du}{dx} = e^u \cdot k = k e^{kx}$$

Hence $$\frac{d}{dx}(e^{kx}) = k e^{kx}.$$

Differentiation of a^x, where a is a constant

Since $a = e^{\log_e a}$ (by the definition of a logarithm)

$$a^x = e^{x \log_e a}$$

Thus, putting $\log_e a$ for k in the previous paragraph, we have

$$\frac{d}{dx}(a^x) = \log_e a \cdot e^{x \log_e a} = a^x \log_e a.$$

A function such as a^x in which a is constant and x is variable is called an exponential function because the variable x occurs as an exponent or index. The special function e^x is of such importance in mathematics that it is usually referred to as *the exponential function*. We have seen above that any exponential function a^x can be expressed in the form e^{kx} where $k \equiv \log_e a$.

The graphs of some exponential functions have been illustrated in Chapter III.

The student must observe carefully the difference between a^x, in which a constant is raised to a variable power, and x^a in which a variable is raised to a constant power.

$$\frac{d}{dx}(x^a) = ax^{a-1} \; ; \qquad \frac{d}{dx}(a^x) = a^x \log_e a.$$

For example,

$$\frac{d}{dx}(x^3) = 3x^2 \text{ and } \frac{d}{dx}(3^x) = 3^x \log_e 3 = 1 \cdot 0986 \times 3^x.$$

Series for e^x

It can be shown that e^x can be expanded in a series of powers of x. Assuming this, it is easy to find the series. Let

$$e^x = a_0 + a_1 x + a_2 x^2 + a_3 x^3 + a_4 x^4 + \ldots,$$

where the coefficients $a_0, a_1, a_2, a_3, \ldots$ are constants. Then

$$\frac{d}{dx}(e^x) = a_1 + 2a_2 x + 3a_3 x^2 + 4a_4 x^3 + \ldots .$$

But since $\frac{d}{dx}(e^x) = e^x$, these two series must be identical, and

hence, on equating coefficients of like powers of x,

$$a_1 = a_0, \; 2a_2 = a_1, \; 3a_3 = a_2, \; 4a_4 = a_3, \text{ etc.}$$

$\therefore a_1 = a_0, \; a_2 = \frac{1}{2}a_1 = \frac{1}{2}a_0, \; a_3 = \frac{1}{3}a_2 = \frac{1}{3} \cdot \frac{1}{2}a_0, \; a_4 = \frac{1}{4}a_3 = \frac{1}{4} \cdot \frac{1}{3} \cdot \frac{1}{2}a_0,$ etc.

Putting $x = 0$ in the first series, we find $a_0 = e^0 = 1$.

$$\therefore \; a_1 = 1, \; a_2 = \frac{1}{2}, \; a_3 = \frac{1}{2 \times 3}, \; a_4 = \frac{1}{2 \times 3 \times 4}, \text{ etc.}$$

Using factorial notation (see page 48)

$$a_0 = 1, \; a_1 = 1, \; a_2 = \frac{1}{2!}, \; a_3 = \frac{1}{3!}, \; a_4 = \frac{1}{4!}, \text{ etc.}$$

Hence

$$e^x = 1 + x + \frac{x^2}{2!} + \frac{x^3}{3!} + \frac{x^4}{4!} + \frac{x^5}{5!} + \ldots$$

Calculation of e

Putting $x = 1$ in the series for e^x, we have

$$e = 1 + 1 + \frac{1}{2!} + \frac{1}{3!} + \frac{1}{4!} + \frac{1}{5!} + \ldots$$

The terms decrease as we proceed and by taking sufficient terms we can calculate e to any degree of accuracy we require. Moreover the terms decrease very rapidly, so that not many terms are required to give a fairly good approximation.

For example, to calculate e to six significant figures,

$$1 = 1$$

$$1 = 1$$

$$\frac{1}{2!} = 0 \cdot 5$$

$$\frac{1}{3!} = \frac{1}{3} \times \frac{1}{2!} = 0 \cdot 166667$$

$$\frac{1}{4!} = \frac{1}{4} \times \frac{1}{3!} = 0 \cdot 041667$$

$$\frac{1}{5!} = \frac{1}{5} \times \frac{1}{4!} = 0 \cdot 008333$$

$$\frac{1}{6!} = \frac{1}{6} \times \frac{1}{5!} = 0 \cdot 001389$$

$$\frac{1}{7!} = \frac{1}{7} \times \frac{1}{6!} = 0 \cdot 000198$$

$$\frac{1}{8!} = \frac{1}{8} \times \frac{1}{7!} = 0 \cdot 000025$$

$$\frac{1}{9!} = \frac{1}{9} \times \frac{1}{8!} = 0 \cdot 000003$$

$$2 \cdot 71828(2)$$

$\therefore e = 2 \cdot 71828$ to six significant figures.

From this the number M (page 242) can be found more accurately. For $M = \log_{10} e$, and taking e as 2·718 we find $M \simeq 0\cdot4343$.

The exponential (or natural) law of growth

If $y = Ce^{kx}$, where k and C are constants,

$$\frac{dy}{dx} = C \cdot ke^{kx} = k \cdot Ce^{kx} = ky \; ;$$

that is, the rate of increase of y is proportional to y itself. This law of growth is extremely important because it occurs so frequently in mechanics, physics, chemistry, engineering and other sciences. We call it the exponential law, or natural law, of growth.

As a simple example, if we have two rods of the same metal, one twice as long as the other, the longer rod will expand twice as much per unit rise of temperature as the shorter one ; i.e. the rate of increase of the length of a rod with respect to the temperature is proportional to the length of the rod. Other examples of the same law of growth are given in the next paragraph.

Since the law of compound interest is an exponential law (see Exercise VIII, Question 9) the natural law of growth is sometimes called the compound interest law.

The equation $\dfrac{dy}{dx} = ky$, where k is a constant

We saw in the previous paragraph that every exponential function obeys the natural law of growth. We shall now prove the converse, which is still more important ; namely, that any function which obeys the natural law of growth is an exponential function, i.e. a function of the type Ce^{kx}, in which C and k are constants, k being the constant of proportionality in the law of growth.

If
$$\frac{dy}{dx} = ky,$$

then
$$\frac{dx}{dy} = \frac{1}{ky}$$

$$\therefore x = \int \frac{1}{ky} dy$$

$$= \frac{1}{k} \int \frac{1}{y} dy$$

$$\therefore kx = \int \frac{1}{y} dy$$

$$= \log y + C,$$

where C is a constant of integration.

If $y = y_0$ when $x = 0$,

$$0 = \log y_0 + C$$

$$\therefore C = -\log y_0$$

$$\therefore kx = \log y - \log y_0$$

$$= \log \frac{y}{y_0}$$

$$\therefore \frac{y}{y_0} = e^{kx}$$

$$\therefore y = y_0 e^{kx}$$

Examples.—(1) *Expansion of a rod.*

If l is the length of a rod at temperature $\theta°$ C. and α is its coefficient of linear expansion, the increase δl in the length when the temperature rises by $\delta\theta°$ is given by

$$\delta l \simeq \alpha l \delta \theta$$

$$\therefore \frac{\delta l}{\delta \theta} \simeq \alpha l$$

and
$$\frac{dl}{d\theta} = \alpha l.$$

This equation is of the type $\dfrac{dy}{dx} = ky$ with θ, l, α in place of x, y, k respectively. Its solution is therefore

$$l = l_0 e^{\alpha\theta},$$

where l_0 is the length of the rod at $0°$ C.

Putting in the series for $e^{\alpha\theta}$

$$l = l_0 \left(1 + \alpha\theta + \frac{\alpha^2\theta^2}{2!} + \frac{\alpha^3\theta^3}{3!} + \ \ldots\ \right).$$

Since α is usually very small, we have as a first approximation

$$l \simeq l_0(1 + \alpha\theta).$$

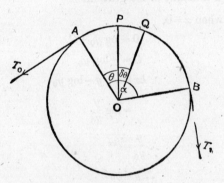

Fig. 145.

(2) *Newton's law of cooling.*

Newton's law states that the rate of cooling of a hot body is proportional to the excess of its temperature above that of its surroundings.

If the excess of temperature at time t is $\theta°$, the rate of cooling is $-\dfrac{d\theta}{dt}$. Hence

$$-\frac{d\theta}{dt} = k\theta$$

where k is a positive constant.

$$\therefore \frac{d\theta}{dt} = -k\theta$$

$$\therefore \theta = \theta_0 e^{-kt},$$

where θ_0 is the excess of temperature when $t = 0$.

(3) *Tension in a belt round a rough pulley or cylinder.*

If a belt is in contact with a fixed rough pulley or cylinder along an arc AB (Fig. 145) and is about to slip in the direction

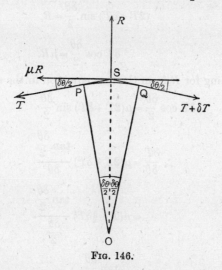

Fɪɢ. 146.

from A to B, the tension is greater at B than at A since friction acts in the direction opposite to that in which the rope tends to slip. Let $\widehat{AOP} = \theta$, $\widehat{AOQ} = \theta + \delta\theta$ and let the tensions at P and Q be T and $T + \delta T$ respectively. The element PQ is drawn enlarged in Fig. 146 and the forces acting on the element are marked. If S is the point of intersection of the tangents at P and Q, i.e. of the lines of action of the forces T and $T + \delta T$, the resultant reaction of the pulley on the element must act through S, and in limiting equilibrium its components are R and μR as shown. Resolving along OS and perpendicular to OS we get the two equations :

$$(T + \delta T) \sin \frac{\delta\theta}{2} + T \sin \frac{\delta\theta}{2} = R,$$

$$(T + \delta T) \cos \frac{\delta\theta}{2} - T \cos \frac{\delta\theta}{2} = \mu R ;$$

i.e.
$$(2T + \delta T) \sin \frac{\delta\theta}{2} = R,$$

$$\delta T \cos \frac{\delta\theta}{2} = \mu R.$$

Substituting for R from the first equation in the second.

$$\delta T \cos \frac{\delta\theta}{2} = \mu(2T + \delta T) \sin \frac{\delta\theta}{2}$$

$$\therefore \frac{\delta T}{\delta\theta} = \mu(2T + \delta T) \frac{\tan \dfrac{\delta\theta}{2}}{\delta\theta}$$

$$= \mu(T + \tfrac{1}{2}\delta T) \frac{\tan \dfrac{\delta\theta}{2}}{\dfrac{\delta\theta}{2}} \cdot$$

As $\delta\theta \to 0$ so does $\dfrac{\delta\theta}{2}$, and $\dfrac{\tan \dfrac{\delta\theta}{2}}{\dfrac{\delta\theta}{2}} \to 1$; also $\delta T \to 0$.

$$\therefore \frac{dT}{d\theta} = \mu T.$$

Hence
$$T = T_0 e^{\mu\theta},$$

where T_0 is the tension when $\theta = 0$, i.e. the tension at A.

If T_1 is the tension at B and the angle of lap (i.e. AOB) is α,

$$T_1 = T_0 e^{\mu a} \quad \text{i.e.} \quad \frac{T_1}{T_0} = e^{\mu a}.$$

Taking a numerical example, if a rope is wrapped once round a cylinder, and the coefficient of friction is 0·25, the ratio of the tensions at the two ends is $e^{0\cdot25 \times 2\pi} = e^{1\cdot5708} \frown 4\cdot81$.

(4) *Discharge of a condenser.*

Suppose a condenser of capacity C farads carries an initial charge of q_0 coulombs on its positive plate and is allowed to discharge through a wire of resistance R ohms connecting the plates. If the charge t sec. later is q coulombs, the current at that instant, which is the rate at which the positive plate loses its charge to the negative plate, is $-\dfrac{dq}{dt}$ amp. Hence

$$-R\frac{dq}{dt} = \frac{q}{C}$$

$$\therefore \frac{dq}{dt} = -\frac{q}{CR}.$$

This is an equation of the type $\dfrac{dq}{dt} = kq$ where $k = -\dfrac{1}{CR}$. Hence

$$q = q_0 e^{-\frac{t}{CR}}.$$

(5) *Decay of current in an inductive circuit.*

The current i amp. in a circuit of resistance R ohms and inductance L henrys satisfies the equation

$$L\frac{di}{dt} + Ri = E,$$

where E volts is the e.m.f. applied to the circuit.

If the e.m.f. is cut off (if, for example, it is supplied by a battery which is short-circuited) the equation for the current is

$$L\frac{di}{dt} + Ri = 0$$

$$\frac{di}{dt} = -\frac{Ri}{L}$$

$$\therefore \ i = i_0 e^{-\frac{Rt}{L}},$$

where i_0 is the current at the instant when the e.m.f. is cut off.

(6) *Variation in atmospheric pressure with height.*

If p is the pressure and ρ the density of the air at a height x above the ground, then by considering the equilibrium of a small vertical column of air of length δx and small cross-sectional area A (Fig. 147) we have the equation

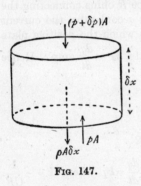

$$(p + \delta p)A + \rho A \delta x = pA$$

$$\therefore \ \delta p \cdot A = -\rho A \delta x$$

$$\therefore \ \frac{\delta p}{\delta x} = -\rho,$$

and, going to the limit,

$$\frac{dp}{dx} = -\rho.$$

Fig. 147.

If the temperature is assumed constant for different heights then, by Boyle's law,

$$\frac{p}{\rho} = \text{constant} = c, \text{ say.}$$

Hence

$$\frac{dp}{dx} = -\frac{p}{c}$$

$$\therefore \ p = p_0 e^{-\frac{x}{c}},$$

where p_0 is the pressure at ground level.

If ρ_0 is the density at ground level, $c = \dfrac{p_0}{\rho_0}$

$$\therefore p = p_0 e^{-\frac{\rho_0}{p_0}x}.$$

We can use this formula also to find the height when the pressure is known.   For

$$\frac{p}{p_0} = e^{-\frac{x}{c}}$$

$$\therefore \log \frac{p}{p_0} = -\frac{x}{c}$$

$$\therefore x = -c \log \frac{p}{p_0} = c \log \frac{p_0}{p} = \frac{p_0}{\rho_0} \log \frac{p_0}{p}.$$

Some standard integrals

(1) If $y = \log (ax + b)$ we can write

$$y = \log u \quad \text{where} \quad u = ax + b.$$

Then $\qquad \dfrac{dy}{du} = \dfrac{1}{u} \quad \text{and} \quad \dfrac{du}{dx} = a$

$$\therefore \frac{dy}{dx} = \frac{dy}{du} \cdot \frac{du}{dx} = \frac{1}{u} \times a = \frac{a}{ax + b}$$

$$\therefore \int \frac{1}{ax + b} dx = \frac{1}{a} \log (ax + b) + C.$$

(2) If $y = \log \sin x$ then

$$y = \log u \quad \text{where} \quad u = \sin x.$$

$$\therefore \frac{dy}{du} = \frac{1}{u} \quad \text{and} \quad \frac{du}{dx} = \cos x,$$

$$\therefore \frac{dy}{dx} = \frac{dy}{du} \cdot \frac{du}{dx} = \frac{1}{u} \cdot \cos x = \frac{\cos x}{\sin x} = \cot x$$

$$\therefore \int \cot x \, dx = \log \sin x + C.$$

(3) Similarly, by writing log cos x as log u where $u = \cos x$, we have

$$\frac{d}{dx}(\log \cos x) = \frac{d}{dx}(\log u) = \frac{d}{du}(\log u) \cdot \frac{du}{dx} = \frac{1}{u} \times (-\sin x)$$

$$= -\frac{\sin x}{\cos x} = -\tan x$$

$$\therefore \int \tan x \, dx = -\log \cos x + C.$$

Equations of the type $\frac{dy}{dx} = ay + b$, where a and b are constants

(1) *Velocity of chemical reactions.*

Wilhelmy's law, for certain types of chemical reaction, states that the velocity of the reaction (i.e. the rate at which the reacting substance is being transformed) is proportional to the concentration of the substance (i.e. the amount which has not been transformed).

If a is the initial concentration and x is the amount transformed in time t, the amount which has not been transformed is $a - x$.

$$\therefore \frac{dx}{dt} = k(a - x),$$

where k is a constant.

$$\therefore \frac{dt}{dx} = \frac{1}{k(a - x)}$$

$$\therefore t = \frac{1}{k}\int \frac{1}{a - x} \, dx$$

$$\therefore kt = \int \frac{1}{a - x} \, dx$$

$$= -\log(a - x) + C.$$

Since $x = 0$ when $t = 0$

$$0 = -\log a + C$$

$$\therefore C = \log a$$

$$\therefore kt = -\log (a - x) + \log a$$

$$= \log \frac{a}{a - x}$$

$$\therefore \frac{a}{a - x} = e^{kt}$$

$$\therefore \frac{a - x}{a} = e^{-kt}$$

$$\therefore x = a(1 - e^{-kt}).$$

(2) *Growth of current in an inductive circuit.*
The equation for the current (p. 253) is

$$L\frac{di}{dt} + Ri = E.$$

If the e.m.f. E is constant, we can write the equation as

$$L\frac{di}{dt} = E - Ri$$

$$\frac{dt}{di} = \frac{L}{E - Ri}$$

$$t = L \int \frac{1}{E - Ri} di$$

$$= -\frac{L}{R} \log (E - Ri) + C.$$

If $i = 0$ when $t = 0$, we find that $C = \frac{L}{R} \log E.$

$$\therefore t = \frac{L}{R} \log \frac{E}{E - Ri}$$

$$\therefore \frac{Rt}{L} = \log \frac{E}{E - Ri}$$

9

$$\therefore \frac{E}{E - Ri} = e^{\frac{Rt}{L}}$$

$$\therefore \frac{E - Ri}{E} = e^{-\frac{Rt}{L}}$$

$$\therefore i = \frac{E}{R}\left(1 - e^{-\frac{Rt}{L}}\right).$$

The graph of i against t is of the shape shown in Fig. 148.

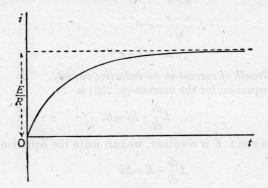

FIG. 148.

As $t \to \infty$, $e^{-\frac{Rt}{L}} \to 0$ and i tends to the steady value $\frac{E}{R}$, which is what the current would be if there were no inductance.

Hyperbolic functions

The functions $\frac{1}{2}(e^x + e^{-x})$ and $\frac{1}{2}(e^x - e^{-x})$ occur in many problems in engineering, as, for instance, in connection with line transmission in telegraphy and in the theory of vibrating beams, and we call them the *hyperbolic cosine* and *hyperbolic sine* of x. The reason for the choice of these names need not be explained here, but the student will discover the connection between these functions and the sine and cosine functions later (see Exercise XXVI, Questions 50, 51, 52). The names are usually abbreviated to cosh x and sinh x (the latter being pronounced as " shine x ").   Thus

$$\cosh x = \frac{e^x + e^{-x}}{2}, \quad \sinh x = \frac{e^x - e^{-x}}{2}.$$

The graphs of these functions are shown in Fig. 149.

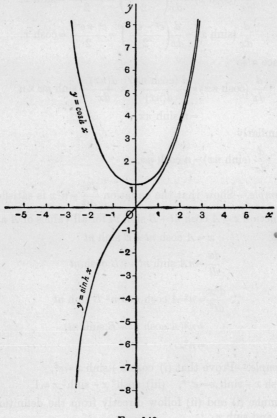

FIG. 149.

The shape of the curve $y = \cosh x$ is that of a hanging chain or string ; the curve is called a *catenary*.

Tables of values of e^x, e^{-x}, $\cosh x$ and $\sinh x$ are printed in many books of mathematical tables.

Differentiation of hyperbolic functions

$$\frac{d}{dx}(\cosh x) = \frac{d}{dx}\left(\frac{e^x + e^{-x}}{2}\right) = \frac{e^x - e^{-x}}{2} = \sinh x.$$

$$\frac{d}{dx}(\sinh x) = \frac{d}{dx}\left(\frac{e^x - e^{-x}}{2}\right) = \frac{e^x + e^{-x}}{2} = \cosh x.$$

Hence also

$$\frac{d}{dx}(\cosh nx) = \frac{d(\cosh nx)}{d(nx)} \times \frac{d(nx)}{dx} = \sinh nx \times n$$

$$= n \sinh nx,$$

and similarly

$$\frac{d}{dx}(\sinh nx) = n \cosh nx.$$

Example.—Show that the equation $\dfrac{d^2x}{dt^2} = n^2x$ is satisfied by the function $x = A \cosh nt + B \sinh nt$ for all values of A and B.

If $$x = A \cosh nt + B \sinh nt$$

$$\frac{dx}{dt} = nA \sinh nt + nB \cosh nt$$

$$\therefore \frac{d^2x}{dt^2} = n^2 A \cosh nt + n^2 B \sinh nt$$

$$= n^2(A \cosh nt + B \sinh nt)$$

$$= n^2x.$$

Example.—Prove that (i) $\cosh x + \sinh x = e^x$, (ii) $\cosh x - \sinh x = e^{-x}$,   (iii) $\cosh^2 x - \sinh^2 x = 1$.

Formulæ (i) and (ii) follow directly from the definitions of $\cosh x$ and $\sinh x$.

Hence $(\cosh x + \sinh x)(\cosh x - \sinh x) = e^x \cdot e^{-x} = e^0 = 1$;

i.e. $\cosh^2 x - \sinh^2 x = 1$.

Example.—Prove that $\cosh^2 x + \sinh^2 x = \cosh 2x$.

$$\cosh^2 x = \left(\frac{e^x + e^{-x}}{2}\right)^2 = \frac{e^{2x} + 2 + e^{-2x}}{4}$$

$$\sinh^2 x = \left(\frac{e^x - e^{-x}}{2}\right)^2 = \frac{e^{2x} - 2 + e^{-2x}}{4}$$

$$\therefore \cosh^2 x + \sinh^2 x = \frac{2(e^{2x} + e^{-2x})}{4}$$

$$= \frac{e^{2x} + e^{-2x}}{2}$$

$$= \cosh 2x.$$

Exercise XXVI

Find the values of :

1. $\dfrac{d}{dx}(e^{3x})$.

2. $\dfrac{d}{dx}(e^{-0.4x})$.

3. $\dfrac{d}{dt}(4e^{2t})$.

4. $\dfrac{d}{d\theta}(10e^{-5\theta})$.

5. $\dfrac{d}{dx}(3e^{1.2x} - 2 \cdot 6e^{0.5x})$.

6. $\dfrac{d}{dx}(10^x)$.

7. $\dfrac{d}{ds}(2^s)$.

8. $\dfrac{d}{dt}(e^{5t+4})$.

9. $\dfrac{d}{dx}(\log 6x)$.

10. $\dfrac{d}{dx}(\log kx)$.

11. $\dfrac{d}{dx}\{\log (3x-2)\}$.

12. $\dfrac{d}{dz}\{\tfrac{1}{2}\log (8z+5)\}$.

13. $\dfrac{d}{dx}(1 \cdot 4e^{-0.2x} + 7 \log x)$.

14. $\dfrac{d}{dt}(9e^{2.1t} + t^2 - 3)$.

15. $\dfrac{d}{dx}(\log x^2)$.

16. $\dfrac{d}{dr}\left\{\log\left(\dfrac{r-1}{r+1}\right)\right\}$.

17. If $y = Ae^{nx} + Be^{-nx}$, prove that $\dfrac{d^2y}{dx^2} = n^2 y$.

18. If $s = Ae^{2t} + Be^{-t}$, prove that $\dfrac{d^2s}{dt^2} - \dfrac{ds}{dt} - 2s = 0$.

19. Find the minimum value of $\dfrac{2}{x} + \log_e x$.

Evaluate :

20. $\displaystyle\int_2^4 \dfrac{1}{x} dx$.

21. $\displaystyle\int_0^2 \dfrac{1}{3x+2} dx$.

22. $\displaystyle\int_0^{0\cdot 6} e^{-2\cdot 5x} dx$.

23. $\displaystyle\int_0^1 e^{2t+3} dt$.

24. $\displaystyle\int_{-1}^2 \dfrac{dx}{2x+5}$.

25. $\displaystyle\int_0^{\frac{\pi}{4}} \tan\theta\, d\theta$.

26. Find the area bounded by the curve $y = e^{-x}$, the y-axis and the positive half of the x-axis.

27. Find the area between the curve $y = \dfrac{1}{4x-1}$, the x-axis and the ordinates at $x = 1$ and $x = 4$.

28. An air-compressor, working at 100 strokes per min., draws in at each stroke 4 cu. ft. of air at a pressure of 15 lb. wt. per sq. in. and delivers it at a pressure of 80 lb. wt. per sq. in.   Find the horse-power of the compressor, assuming there is no rise in temperature during compression.   [1 h.p. = rate of working at 33,000 ft. lb. wt. per min.]

29. Van der Waal's equation connecting the pressure p and the volume v of a given mass of gas at constant temperature is $\left(p + \dfrac{a}{v^2}\right)(v - b) = k$, where a, b and k are constants.   Assuming this relation, find p in terms of v, and show that the work done by a gas in expanding from a volume v_1 to a volume v_2 is

$$a\left(\dfrac{1}{v_2} - \dfrac{1}{v_1}\right) + k \log\left(\dfrac{v_2 - b}{v_1 - b}\right).$$

30. Find y if $\dfrac{dy}{dx} = 3y$ and $y = 2$ when $x = 0$.

31. Find s if $\dfrac{ds}{dt} = -\frac{1}{2}s$ and $s = 0\cdot 45$ when $t = 1$.

32. A rotating flywheel is retarded by a frictional torque proportional to its angular velocity. Write down the equation for the angular velocity. If the wheel starts rotating at 150 r.p.m. and after 10 sec. its speed is 120 r.p.m., what is its speed 1 min. after the start ?

33. If a body is projected vertically upwards and the air resistance is assumed proportional to the velocity v, show that $\dfrac{dv}{dt} = -g - kv$, where k is a constant and g is the acceleration due to gravity. Hence prove that $t = \dfrac{1}{k} \log \left(\dfrac{g + ku}{g + kv} \right)$, where u is the velocity of projection, and find the time taken to reach the highest point.

34. In Question 33 express v in terms of t. By writing v as $\dfrac{ds}{dt}$, where s is the height after time t, prove that

$$s = \frac{1}{k}\left(u + \frac{g}{k}\right)(1 - e^{-kt}) - \frac{gt}{k}.$$

35. The equation for the current in an inductive circuit containing an alternator is $L\dfrac{di}{dt} + Ri = E_m \sin \omega t$. Verify that this equation is satisfied by

$$i = Ae^{-\frac{Rt}{L}} + \frac{E_m}{R^2 + \omega^2 L^2}(R \sin \omega t - \omega L \cos \omega t).$$

36. When a shaft rotates with angular velocity ω the displacement y at a distance x from one end due to centrifugal force is given by the equation $\dfrac{d^4y}{dx^4} = n^4 y$ where $n^4 = \dfrac{w\omega^2}{gEI}$. Show that this equation is satisfied by $y = Ae^{nx} + Be^{-nx} + C \cos nx + D \sin nx$ where A, B, C, D are constants.

37. In a certain type of chemical reaction the quantity x transformed at time t is given by the equation $\dfrac{dx}{dt} = k(a - x)(b - x)$.

Show that $\dfrac{1}{a-x} - \dfrac{1}{b-x} = \dfrac{b-a}{(a-x)(b-x)}$ and hence prove that

$$t = \frac{1}{k(b-a)} \log \left\{ \frac{a(b-x)}{b(a-x)} \right\}. \quad \text{Also express } x \text{ in terms of } t.$$

38. Prove that $\cosh 2x = 2\cosh^2 x - 1 = 1 + 2\sinh^2 x$.

39. Prove that $2\sinh x \cosh x = \sinh 2x$.

40. Verify that $\qquad \cosh(-x) = \cosh x$

and that $\qquad\qquad\qquad \sinh(-x) = -\sinh x$.

Evaluate :

41. $\displaystyle\int_0^1 \sinh x\, dx$. $\qquad\qquad$ **42.** $\displaystyle\int_{-4}^4 \cosh\frac{x}{2}\, dx$.

43. $\displaystyle\int_0^{0\cdot25} \cosh^2 x\, dx$. [Hint. Use Question 38 to express $\cosh^2 x$ in terms of $\cosh 2x$.]

44. Obtain the series for e^{-x} by changing x into $-x$ in the series for e^x, and hence show that

$$\cosh x = 1 + \frac{x^2}{2!} + \frac{x^4}{4!} + \frac{x^6}{6!} + \ldots ,$$

$$\sinh x = x + \frac{x^3}{3!} + \frac{x^5}{5!} + \frac{x^7}{7!} + \ldots$$

45. Use the series in Question 44 to find the value of $\cosh 2$ to 3 significant figures.

46. Verify from the series in Question 44 that $\dfrac{d}{dx}(\sinh x) = \cosh x$

and that $\dfrac{d}{dx}(\cosh x) = \sinh x$.

47. By assuming a series for $\sin x$, viz.

$$\sin x = a_0 + a_1 x + a_2 x^2 + a_3 x^3 + \ldots ,$$

and using the fact that $\dfrac{d^2}{dx^2}(\sin x) = -\sin x$ show that

$$\sin(x \text{ radians}) = x - \frac{x^3}{3!} + \frac{x^5}{5!} - \frac{x^7}{7!} + \ldots$$

[Hint. The coefficients a_0 and a_1 can be found by putting $x = 0$ in the series and its first differential coefficient.]

48. By differentiating the series in Question 47 show that

$$\cos(x \text{ radians}) = 1 - \frac{x^2}{2!} + \frac{x^4}{4!} - \frac{x^6}{6!} + \ldots$$

49. Use the series in Question 47 to find sin 25° to 3 significant figures, and compare with the value given in your tables.

[The student is advised to read pages 280–290, before working the following exercises.]

50. Using the series in Questions 44, 47, 48 show that

$$\cosh jx = \cos (x \text{ radians}) \quad \text{and} \quad \sinh jx = j \sin (x \text{ radians})$$

where $j \equiv \sqrt{-1}$.

51. If the sine and cosine of a complex angle are defined by the series in Questions 47, 48, show that

$$\cos (jx \text{ radians}) = \cosh x \quad \text{and} \quad \sin (jx \text{ radians}) = j \sinh x.$$

52. Verify from the series that

$$\cos x + j \sin x = e^{jx} \quad \text{and} \quad \cos x - j \sin x = e^{-jx},$$

and deduce that

$$\cos x = \frac{e^{jx} + e^{-jx}}{2} \quad \text{and} \quad \sin x = \frac{e^{jx} - e^{-jx}}{2j}.$$

CHAPTER XI

HARDER DIFFERENTIATION AND INTEGRATION

Differentiation of a product

Let $y = uv$ where u and v are functions of x, and let an increase of δx in x cause u, v and y to increase to $u + \delta u$, $v + \delta v$, $y + \delta y$ respectively. Then

$$y + \delta y = (u + \delta u)(v + \delta v)$$

$$= uv + u \cdot \delta v + v \cdot \delta u + \delta u \cdot \delta v.$$

$$\therefore \ \delta y = u \cdot \delta v + v \cdot \delta u + \delta u \cdot \delta v.$$

Hence
$$\frac{\delta y}{\delta x} = \frac{u \cdot \delta v}{\delta x} + \frac{v \cdot \delta u}{\delta x} + \frac{\delta u \cdot \delta v}{\delta x},$$

which may be written

$$\frac{\delta y}{\delta x} = u \cdot \frac{\delta v}{\delta x} + v \cdot \frac{\delta u}{\delta x} + \delta u \cdot \frac{\delta v}{\delta x}.$$

Now let δx approach 0 ; then δu, δv and δy approach 0 and $\dfrac{\delta u}{\delta x}$, $\dfrac{\delta v}{\delta x}$ and $\dfrac{\delta y}{\delta x}$ approach $\dfrac{du}{dx}$, $\dfrac{dv}{dx}$ and $\dfrac{dy}{dx}$ respectively. Hence

$$\frac{dy}{dx} = u \cdot \frac{dv}{dx} + v \cdot \frac{du}{dx} + 0 \cdot \frac{dv}{dx}$$

$$\therefore \ \frac{d(uv)}{dx} = u\frac{dv}{dx} + v\frac{du}{dx}.$$

This is the rule for differentiating a product.

Examples.—Differentiate (*a*) $\sin x \cos x$, (*b*) $x^3 \cos 2x$.

(*a*) Putting $u = \sin x$, $v = \cos x$ in the formula above,

$$\frac{d(\sin x \cos x)}{dx} = \sin x \frac{d \cos x}{dx} + \cos x \frac{d \sin x}{dx}$$

$$= \sin x(-\sin x) + \cos x \cos x$$

$$= \cos^2 x - \sin^2 x.$$

(*b*) Before using the product rule we must know the value of $\dfrac{d \cos 2x}{dx}$. By the rule for differentiating $\cos(ax + b)$

$$\frac{d \cos 2x}{dx} = -2 \sin 2x.$$

Then we have

$$\frac{d(x^3 \cos 2x)}{dx} = x^3 \cdot \frac{d \cos 2x}{dx} + \cos 2x \cdot \frac{dx^3}{dx}$$

$$= x^3(-2 \sin 2x) + \cos 2x \cdot 3x^2$$

$$= 3x^2 \cos 2x - 2x^3 \sin 2x.$$

Differentiation of a quotient

If $y = \dfrac{u}{v}$, then $u = vy$.

Hence by the product rule

$$\frac{du}{dx} = \frac{d(vy)}{dx} = v \frac{dy}{dx} + y \frac{dv}{dx}$$

$$\therefore v \frac{dy}{dx} = \frac{du}{dx} - y \frac{dv}{dx} = \frac{du}{dx} - \frac{u}{v} \frac{dv}{dx}$$

$$= \frac{v \dfrac{du}{dx} - u \dfrac{dv}{dx}}{v}$$

$$\therefore \frac{dy}{dx} = \frac{v \dfrac{du}{dx} - u \dfrac{dv}{dx}}{v^2}.$$

$$\therefore \frac{d}{dx}\left(\frac{u}{v}\right) = \frac{v\dfrac{du}{dx} - u\dfrac{dv}{dx}}{v^2}$$

This formula is called the quotient rule.

Example.—Differentiate $\dfrac{2x-1}{x^2+4}$ and express the answer in its simplest form.

If
$$y = \frac{2x-1}{x^2+4}$$

$$\frac{dy}{dx} = \frac{(x^2+4)\cdot\dfrac{d(2x-1)}{dx} - (2x-1)\cdot\dfrac{d(x^2+4)}{dx}}{(x^2+4)^2}$$

$$= \frac{(x^2+4)2 - (2x-1)2x}{(x^2+4)^2}$$

$$= \frac{2(x^2+4-2x^2+x)}{(x^2+4)^2}$$

$$= \frac{-2(x^2-x-4)}{(x^2+4)^2}.$$

Differential coefficients of tan *x* and cot *x*

If
$$y = \tan x = \frac{\sin x}{\cos x},$$

$$\frac{dy}{dx} = \frac{\cos x\cdot\dfrac{d\sin x}{dx} - \sin x\cdot\dfrac{d\cos x}{dx}}{\cos^2 x}$$

$$= \frac{\cos x\cdot\cos x - \sin x(-\sin x)}{\cos^2 x}$$

$$= \frac{\cos^2 x + \sin^2 x}{\cos^2 x}$$

$$= \frac{1}{\cos^2 x}$$

$$= \sec^2 x.$$

Therefore $$\frac{d \tan x}{dx} = \sec^2 x.$$

In the same way, by writing $\cot x = \dfrac{\cos x}{\sin x}$,

$$\frac{d \cot x}{dx} = - \mathrm{cosec}^2 x.$$

Example.—A ray of light shines from a point A on to a vertical screen at 4 ft. from A. The ray of light rotates in a horizontal plane about a vertical axis through A at 200 r.p.m. If AB is perpendicular to the screen, find the speed at which the mark P, which the ray makes on the screen, is moving 0·04 sec. after it passes B.

Let P be x ft. from B at t sec. after it passes B. Then

$$\widehat{BAP} = \frac{200}{60} \,.\, t \text{ revolutions} = \frac{10t}{3} \times 2\pi \text{ radians} = \frac{20\pi t}{3}.$$

$$\therefore x = 4 \tan \frac{20\pi t}{3}.$$

Now the speed of P is $\dfrac{dx}{dt}$ ft./sec. ;

$$\frac{dx}{dt} = 4 \,.\, \frac{20\pi}{3} \,.\, \sec^2 \frac{20\pi t}{3}$$

$$= \frac{80\pi}{3} \,.\, \sec^2 \frac{20\pi t}{3}.$$

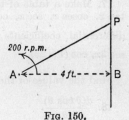

Fig. 150.

When $t = 0·04$

$$\frac{dx}{dt} = \frac{80\pi}{3} \,.\, \sec^2 \left(\frac{20\pi}{3} \times 0·04 \right)$$

$$= \frac{80\pi}{3} \sec^2 \frac{8\pi}{30}$$

$$= \frac{80\pi}{3} \sec^2 48°$$

$$\eqsim 187.$$

$$\therefore \text{ speed is } 187 \text{ ft./sec.}$$

Exercise XXVII

Differentiate with respect to x :

1. $\sqrt{x}\sin x$.   2. $\sin 2x \cos x$.   3. $2x^2 \cos 3x$.

4. $\frac{1}{4}x\sqrt{1+x}$.   5. $\cos ax \cos bx$.   6. $x^2 e^x$.

7. $\dfrac{x}{2x+3}$.   8. $\dfrac{3x-1}{x+5}$.   9. $\dfrac{3x}{x^2+3}$.

10. $\dfrac{\sin x}{x}$.   11. $\dfrac{1+\sin x}{1-\sin x}$.   12. $\dfrac{1-x^2}{1+2x}$.

13. $\dfrac{\log x}{x}$.   14. $e^{2x}\sin x$.   15. $\sqrt{x}\log(1+x)$.

16. By writing $\dfrac{\cos x}{\sin x}$ for $\cot x$, show that $\dfrac{d\cot x}{dx} = -\operatorname{cosec}^2 x$.

Explain by means of the graph of $\cot x$ why its differential coefficient is negative.

17. Make a table of the differential coefficients of $\sin x$, $\cos x$, $\tan x$, $\operatorname{cosec} x$, $\sec x$, $\cot x$. Using this table write down the differential coefficients of $\sin^2 \frac{1}{2}x$, $\cos \dfrac{\pi x}{l}$, $\tan 2r\pi x$, $\operatorname{cosec} 2x$, $\sec 3x$, $\cot(1-2x)$.

Find the values of the following :

18. $\dfrac{d(\theta \cos \theta)}{d\theta}$.   19. $\dfrac{d\{r^{\frac{1}{2}}/(1+r)\}}{dr}$.   20. $\dfrac{d(\phi^2 \sin 2\phi)}{d\phi}$.

21. $\dfrac{d}{dk}\left(\dfrac{k^2-1}{k^2+1}\right)$.   22. $\dfrac{d}{dy}\left(\dfrac{y}{\sqrt{1+y^2}}\right)$.   23. $\dfrac{d}{dm}\left(\dfrac{m-1}{m+1}\right)$.

24. Find the maximum and minimum values of $\dfrac{x^2+1}{x^2+x+1}$ and sketch a rough graph of the expression.

25. Show that $2\sin\phi - \phi$ has a maximum value at $\phi = \frac{1}{3}\pi$ and calculate its value to three significant figures.

26. Show that xe^{-x} has a maximum value $\dfrac{1}{e}$.

Further examples on differentiation

Example.—Find the gradient of the tangent to the ellipse $2x^2 + y^2 = 9$ at the point $(2, 1)$ on the ellipse.

We could do this by first solving the equation for y, which gives $y = \pm \sqrt{9 - 2x^2}$, and then differentiating, but we will use another method here. Since $2x^2 + y^2 = 9$,

$$\frac{d(2x^2 + y^2)}{dx} = \frac{d(9)}{dx} = 0$$

$$\therefore \ 4x + \frac{d(y^2)}{dx} = 0$$

$$\therefore \ 4x + \frac{d(y^2)}{dy} \cdot \frac{dy}{dx} = 0$$

$$\therefore \ 4x + 2y \frac{dy}{dx} = 0$$

$$\therefore \ \frac{dy}{dx} = -\frac{2x}{y}.$$

Hence at the point $(2, 1)$ the gradient of the tangent is -4.

The importance of this method is that we can find $\frac{dy}{dx}$ without first solving for y.

Example.—In a certain engine the angles θ and ϕ which the crank and connecting rod make with the line joining the piston head to the crank axle are related by the equation $\sin \theta = 4 \sin \phi$.

Find the angular velocity, $\dot{\phi}$, of the connecting rod in terms of θ, ϕ and the angular velocity $\dot{\theta}$ of the crank. If the crank rotates at a uniform rate of 2800 r.p.m., find the angular velocities of the connecting rod when θ is (*a*) 15°, (*b*) 75°. Compare the answers with those obtained by an approximate method on page 139.

Differentiating with respect to the time

$$\frac{d(\sin\theta)}{dt} = 4\frac{d(\sin\phi)}{dt}$$

$$\therefore \frac{d(\sin\theta)}{d\theta} \cdot \frac{d\theta}{dt} = 4\frac{d(\sin\phi)}{d\phi} \cdot \frac{d\phi}{dt}$$

$$\therefore \cos\theta \cdot \dot{\theta} = 4\cos\phi \cdot \dot{\phi}.$$

$$\therefore \dot{\phi} = \frac{1}{4}\frac{\cos\theta}{\cos\phi} \cdot \dot{\theta}.$$

When $\qquad\qquad \dot{\theta} = 2800$ r.p.m.,

$$\dot{\phi} = \frac{700\cos\theta}{\cos\phi} \text{ r.p.m.}$$

The calculation of the values of $\dot{\phi}$ when θ is 15° and 75° is set out below.

θ	15°	75°
$\sin\theta$	0·2588	0·9659
$\sin\phi$	0·0647	0·2415
ϕ	3° 43′	13° 59′
$\cos\theta$	0·9659	0·2588
$\cos\phi$	0·9979	0·9704
$\dot{\phi} = \dfrac{700\cos\theta}{\cos\phi}$	678	187

On page 139 we found that these values of $\dot{\phi}$ were 680 and 190 nearly.

Differentiation of x^n for all values of n

If $\qquad\qquad y = x^n,$

$$\log y = n\log x$$

$$\therefore \frac{d(\log y)}{dx} = \frac{n}{x}$$

But

$$\frac{d(\log y)}{dx} = \frac{d(\log y)}{dy}\frac{dy}{dx} = \frac{1}{y}\frac{dy}{dx}$$

$$\therefore \frac{1}{y}\frac{dy}{dx} = \frac{n}{x}$$

$$\therefore \frac{dy}{dx} = \frac{ny}{x} = \frac{nx^n}{x} = nx^{n-1}.$$

Use of dx and dy as symbols

On page 117, $\dfrac{dy}{dx}$ was defined as a symbol for the limiting value of $\dfrac{\delta y}{\delta x}$ as δx approaches zero. In this symbol, dx and dy have no separate identity. We cannot say that dx and dy are what δx and δy become when δx is very, very small because $\dfrac{\delta y}{\delta x}$ is never exactly equal to the differential coefficient however small δx may be. Nevertheless in some processes in differentiation and integration the work is made easier by writing an equation like $\dfrac{dy}{dx} = 2x$ in the form $dy = 2x \cdot dx$, the meaning of this equation being that, if it is divided by dx, it gives the correct value of $\dfrac{dy}{dx}$.

Example.—Find dy (a) if $y = x^n$, (b) if $y = \sin(ax+b)$.

(a) If $y = x^n$, $\dfrac{dy}{dx} = nx^{n-1}$.

$$\therefore dy = nx^{n-1}\, dx.$$

(b) If $y = \sin(ax+b)$, $\dfrac{dy}{dx} = a\cos(ax+b)$.

$$\therefore dy = a\cos(ax+b)dx.$$

If we differentiate $\sin^3 x$ by the method of substitution used on page 152, we proceed as follows:

Put $\qquad u = \sin x$

then $\qquad y = u^3$ and $u = \sin x$

$$\therefore \frac{dy}{du} = 3u^2 \text{ and } \frac{du}{dx} = \cos x$$

$$\therefore \frac{dy}{dx} = \frac{dy}{du} \cdot \frac{du}{dx} = 3u^2 \cdot \cos x = 3\sin^2 x \cdot \cos x.$$

Now instead of writing $\dfrac{dy}{du} = 3u^2$ and $\dfrac{du}{dx} = \cos x$ we could write

$$dy = 3u^2 \ . \ du \text{ and } du = \cos x \ . \ dx \ ;$$

then $\qquad dy = 3u^2 \ . \ \cos x \ dx = 3 \sin^2 x \ . \ \cos x \ dx$

which means the same as $\dfrac{dy}{dx} = 3 \sin^2 x \cos x.$

INTEGRATION

Since $y = \displaystyle\int 2x\,dx$ means that $\dfrac{dy}{dx} = 2x$, it also means that $dy = 2x\,dx.$

Integration by means of a substitution

To integrate $3 \sin^2 x \cos x \, dx$ means the same as to find y if $dy = 3 \sin^2 x \cos x \, dx$. This can be done by means of the same substitution as was used above. We put $u = \sin x$ so that $du = \cos x \, dx$, and merely take the steps above in the reverse order. Thus

$$dy = 3 \sin^2 x \ . \ \cos x \ dx = 3u^2 \ . \ du$$

$$\therefore \ y = u^3 + c.$$

$$= \sin^3 x + c.$$

This is equivalent to writing

$$y = \int 3 \sin^2 x \ . \ \cos x \, dx = \int 3u^2 \ . \ du = u^3 + c = \sin^3 x + c.$$

Example.—Integrate $\displaystyle\int \dfrac{x}{\sqrt{1 + x^2}} \, dx.$

Put $\qquad\qquad u = 1 + x^2$, then $du = 2x\,dx.$

$$\therefore \ \dfrac{x\,dx}{\sqrt{1 + x^2}} = \dfrac{1}{2} \ \dfrac{2x\,dx}{\sqrt{1 + x^2}} = \dfrac{1}{2} \ . \ \dfrac{du}{\sqrt{u}}$$

$$\therefore \int \frac{x\,dx}{\sqrt{1+x^2}} = \int \frac{1}{2}\,\frac{du}{\sqrt{u}}$$

$$= \int \tfrac{1}{2} u^{-\frac{1}{2}}\,du$$

$$= \tfrac{1}{2}\left(\frac{u^{\frac{1}{2}}}{\frac{1}{2}}\right) + c$$

$$= u^{\frac{1}{2}} + c = \sqrt{1+x^2} + c.$$

This example should be compared with the reverse process given on page 152.

Reverting to the product rule $\dfrac{d(uv)}{dx} = u\,\dfrac{dv}{dx} + v\,\dfrac{du}{dx}$, if we multiply by dx, we get $d(uv) = u\,dv + v\,du$.

Thus we have

$$d(x^2 \sin x) = x^2 \,.\, d\sin x + \sin x \,.\, d(x^2)$$

$$= x^2 \,.\, \cos x\,dx + \sin x \,.\, 2x\,dx$$

$$= (x^2 \cos x + 2x \sin x)dx,$$

which means the same as

$$\frac{d(x^2 \sin x)}{dx} = x^2 \cos x + 2x \sin x.$$

The student should practice differentiating a product by both methods, i.e. by finding $\dfrac{d(uv)}{dx}$ and by finding $d(uv)$.

Integration by parts

Since

$$d(uv) = u\,dv + v\,du$$

$$uv = \int (u\,dv + v\,du)$$

$$= \int u\,dv + \int v\,du.$$

$$\therefore \int u\,dv = uv - \int v\,du.$$

This is called the rule for integration by parts.

Example.—Find $\int x \cos x \, dx$.

Here we take u to be x and dv to be $\cos x \, dx$; then

$$du = dx \text{ and } v = \int \cos x \, dx = \sin x. \quad \text{(See footnote *.)}$$

Therefore, substituting in the rule,

$$\int x \cdot \cos x \, dx = x \sin x - \int \sin x \cdot dx$$

$$= x \sin x + \cos x + c.$$

Example.—Find $\int x^2 \log x \, dx$.

Here we cannot take $dv = \log x \, dx$ because we do not know yet the value of $\int \log x \, dx$, so we take $u = \log x$ and $dv = x^2 dx$. Then

$$du = \frac{1}{x} dx \text{ and } v = \int x^2 dx = \frac{x^3}{3}. \quad \text{(See footnote *.)}$$

$$\therefore \int \log x \cdot x^2 dx = \log x \cdot \frac{x^3}{3} - \int \frac{x^3}{3} \cdot \frac{1}{x} dx$$

$$= \frac{x^3}{3} \log x - \int \frac{x^2}{3} dx$$

$$= \frac{x^3}{3} \log x - \frac{x^3}{9} + c.$$

Differential coefficients of $\sin^{-1} x$, $\cos^{-1} x$ and $\tan^{-1} x$ (angles in radians)

If $y = \sin^{-1} x$, $x = \sin y$.

$$\therefore \frac{dx}{dy} = \cos y, \text{ and hence } \frac{dy}{dx} = \frac{1}{\cos y}.$$

---

* The student should verify that the addition of an arbitrary constant here does not affect the final answer.

But $\cos^2 y = 1 - \sin^2 y = 1 - x^2$ and if we take y to be an angle between $-\frac{1}{2}\pi$ and $\frac{1}{2}\pi$, $\cos y$ is positive and therefore

$$\cos y = \sqrt{1 - x^2}.$$

$$\therefore \quad \frac{d \sin^{-1} x}{dx} = \frac{1}{\sqrt{1 - x^2}}.$$

In the same way, by writing $y = \cos^{-1} x$ in the form $x = \cos y$ we find that, if y is an angle between 0 and π,

$$\frac{d \cos^{-1} x}{dx} = -\frac{1}{\sqrt{1 - x^2}}.$$

Also, using the same method, it can be shown that

$$\frac{d \tan^{-1} x}{dx} = \frac{1}{1 + x^2}.$$

$$\int \frac{dx}{\sqrt{1 - x^2}} \quad \text{and} \quad \int \frac{dx}{1 + x^2}.$$

From the above differential coefficients it follows that

$$\int \frac{dx}{\sqrt{1 - x^2}} = \sin^{-1} x + c \; ;$$

$$\int \frac{dx}{1 + x^2} = \tan^{-1} x + c.$$

In these formulæ $\sin^{-1} x$ and $\tan^{-1} x$ are taken to be angles between $-\frac{1}{2}\pi$ and $\frac{1}{2}\pi$.

Example.—Evaluate $\displaystyle\int_0^{\frac{1}{2}} \frac{dx}{\sqrt{1 - x^2}}$

$$\int_0^{\frac{1}{2}} \frac{dx}{\sqrt{1 - x^2}} = \left[\sin^{-1} x \right]_0^{\frac{1}{2}}$$

$$= \sin^{-1} \tfrac{1}{2} - \sin^{-1} 0$$

$$= \tfrac{1}{6}\pi.$$

Exercise XXVIII

Find $\dfrac{dy}{dx}$ from each of the following equations :

1. $y^2 = 1 - x.$ **2.** $x^2 + y^2 = 4.$ **3.** $xy = 100.$

4. $\log y = x.$ **5.** $y^4 = x^3.$ **6.** $\cos y = 2 \cos x.$

7. Find the gradient of the tangent to the hyperbola $x^2 - y^2 = 8$ at the point $(3, 1)$.

8. A rod AB of length 4 in. slides with its ends on two fixed perpendicular lines Ox, Oy. If OA is x in. and OB is y in., $x^2 + y^2 = 16$. Find $\dfrac{dy}{dt}$ from this equation, and hence find the velocity of B if A is moving at 2 in./sec. away from O.

Write down the values of dy when y is :

9. $x^3.$ **10.** $\dfrac{1}{x}.$ **11.** $\log x.$

12. $\sin 2x.$ **13.** $(ax + b)^n.$ **14.** $e^{-x}.$

15. $\dfrac{1}{1+x}.$ **16.** $\tan x.$ **17.** $\sqrt{x}.$

18. If $y = \dfrac{u}{v}$ where u and v are functions of x, what is the value of dy ?

Find y if dy equals :

19. $x^4 dx.$ **20.** $\dfrac{1}{2x} dx.$ **21.** $\cos 4x \, dx.$

22. $e^{2x} dx.$ **23.** $\dfrac{1}{\sqrt{x}} dx.$ **24.** $\dfrac{4}{x^3} dx.$

25. If $dy = 2x(4 + x^2)^{10} dx$, show that $dy = u^{10} du$, where $u = 4 + x^2$, and hence find y.

26. If $dy = \dfrac{\cos x}{\sin^2 x} dx$, show that $dy = \dfrac{du}{u^2}$, where $u = \sin x$, and hence find y.

Evaluate by means of the substitution given :

27. $\displaystyle\int 3x^2(1 + x^3)^5 dx.$ $\{u = 1 + x^3\}$

28. $\displaystyle\int 6 \sin^5 x \cos x \, dx.$ $\{u = \sin x\}$

29. $\int xe^{x^2}dx.$ 　　　　　 $\{u = x^2\}$

Evaluate by means of a substitution .

30. $\int x(4 + x^2)^{10}dx.$ 　　　 **31.** $\int \dfrac{4 \cos x \, dx}{\sin^2 x}.$

32. $\int 10 \sin^4 x \cos x \, dx.$ 　 **33.** $\int 6x\sqrt{1 + x^2} \, dx.$

34. $\int \dfrac{xdx}{x^2 - 1}.$ 　　　　 **35.** $\int \dfrac{4xdx}{(4 - x^2)^2}.$

36. Work out $\int (ax + b)^n dx$ by putting $u = ax + b$, and show that your result agrees with that given on page 153.

Integrate by parts :

37. $\int xe^x dx.$ 　　　　　　 **38.** $\int x \sin x \, dx.$

39. $\int x \log x \, dx.$ 　　　　 **40.** $\int x \cos 2x \, dx.$

41. Find the first moment of the area under the curve $y = e^{-x}$ from $x = 0$ to $x = 1$ about the axis Oy. Also find the co-ordinates of the centroid of this area.

42. Find the co-ordinates of the centroid of the area under $y = \cos x$ from $x = 0$ to $x = \frac{1}{2}\pi.$

43. Differentiate $\sin^{-1} 2x$ with respect to x.

44. Evaluate $\int_0^1 \dfrac{dx}{1 + x^2}.$

45. Show that $\int \dfrac{dx}{\sqrt{a^2 - x^2}} = \sin^{-1} \dfrac{x}{a} + C.$

46. When a point is moving with simple harmonic motion of amplitude a and period n the time is related to the displacement by the equation $\dfrac{dt}{dx} = -\dfrac{1}{n\sqrt{a^2 - x^2}}.$ Find t in terms of x if $x = a$ at $t = 0$.

47. Find $\tan^{-1} 0.95$ and $\tan^{-1} 1.05$. Hence find the approximate value of $\dfrac{d \tan^{-1} x}{dx}$ at $x = 1$. Compare your answer with the value obtained from the formula for the differential coefficient.

CHAPTER XII

COMPLEX NUMBERS

Complex numbers

In Part II (page 72) we saw that there are some quadratic equations whose roots are not ordinary numbers such as we have used hitherto. We shall take two examples of such equations here :

(1) If $x^2 + 4 = 0$

$$x^2 = -4.$$

$$\therefore x = \pm \sqrt{-4} = \pm \sqrt{4}\sqrt{-1} = \pm 2\sqrt{-1}.$$

(2) If $x^2 - 4x + 13 = 0$

$$x^2 - 4x = -13.$$

Completing the square,

$$x^2 - 4x + 4 = -9$$

$$(x-2)^2 = -9$$

$$x - 2 = \pm \sqrt{-9} = \pm \sqrt{9}\sqrt{-1} = \pm 3\sqrt{-1}.$$

$$\therefore x = 2 \pm 3\sqrt{-1}.$$

$\sqrt{-1}$ is not an ordinary number, since the square of every ordinary number is positive. It is often called an " imaginary number," though the name is unfortunate and is a heritage from the early history of such numbers. $\sqrt{-1}$ is usually denoted by i ; but electrical engineers generally use j, since the symbol i is commonly used for current. We shall use j in this chapter. Thus we write the roots of the equation $x^2 - 4x + 13 = 0$ as $2 \pm 3j$. A number such as $a + bj$, where a and b are ordinary (positive or negative) numbers, is called a *complex number.* We call *a* its real part and *bj* its imaginary part. Thus $2+3j$ and $5-3j$ are complex numbers. A number such as $4j$, which has no real part, is called a *purely imaginary number*.

Complex numbers are no more imaginary, in the ordinary sense of the word, than are negative numbers. For just as negative numbers had to be invented in order to subtract, say, 7 from 2, so complex numbers had to be invented in order to find the square root of -4 or of -9. We might put this in another way; just as the negative number -5 had to be invented before we could solve the equation $x+7=2$, so we have to invent the number $\sqrt{-1}$ in order to be able to solve the equation $x^2-4x+13=0$. Any initial prejudice we may have against the number $\sqrt{-1}$ is no more reasonable than that of a person living in the sixteenth century against the number -5, and the student will find that as his familiarity with complex numbers increases any such prejudice will disappear.

Historical note

The adoption into general use of complex numbers, like that of negative numbers, was historically a slow and gradual process. Negative numbers appear to have been first used by Stifel in 1544, though the signs $+$ and $-$ had appeared in writings by Widman in 1489, Riese in 1536 and Recorde in 1540. Stifel himself called them " absurd " numbers and rejected negative roots of an equation. The first to discuss negative roots was Cardan in 1545, but for the next fifty years or more most mathematicians found such roots unintelligible and it was not until the beginning of the seventeenth century that negative numbers began to be used with any confidence.

The idea of complex roots of an equation appears to have occurred to Cardan and to his contemporary Bombelli about 1572 in connection with the solution of cubic equations. Such roots were also discussed by Girard, a Flemish mathematician, in 1629, and by the famous French geometer and philosopher Descartes in 1639. Descartes used the expression " imaginary roots " to distinguish such roots from ordinary—or " real "—roots, but neither he nor his predecessors knew how to interpret these roots and appear to have regarded them with suspicion. The seventeenth and eighteenth centuries saw tremendous progress in many branches of mathematics and mechanics, and mathematicians, while still uncertain about the nature or validity of the so-called " imaginary " numbers, realized the importance of such numbers. The result was that complex numbers gradually, though somewhat tentatively, took their place as an instrument in algebra, and the use of the letter i to denote $\sqrt{-1}$ was introduced by the Swiss mathematician Euler in 1748. The geometrical representation is due to Argand (1806), though earlier suggestions had also been given by Kühn in 1750 and by Wessel, a Norwegian surveyor, in 1797. It was not, however, until Gauss (1777–1855) of Brunswick and Cauchy (1789–1857) of Paris set the theory of complex numbers on a sound basis that opposition to the use of $\sqrt{-1}$ was finally broken down and a proper appreciation of the meaning and full power of numbers was made possible.

The application of complex numbers to electrical engineering problems was developed by Kennelly, Steinmetz and Heaviside during the last years of the nineteenth century.

Geometrical (or vector) representation of complex numbers

The student is already familiar with the idea of representing real numbers by points on a line, as, for example, on an ordinary scale. Points representing positive numbers are marked on one side of the origin, those representing negative numbers on the other side. We can say that the number 3 is represented in Fig. 151 by the point P or by the vector $\overrightarrow{OP}$; the number -3 is represented by the point Q or by the vector $\overrightarrow{OQ}$.

Complex numbers cannot be represented on the line $X'OX$ since every point on that line represents some real number. We therefore have to find some other way of representing complex numbers.

Since $-3 = 3j^2 = 3 \times j \times j$, the effect of multiplying a real number by j twice is to turn the vector which represents it through two right angles. It is fairly natural then to regard multiplying a real number by j as equivalent to turning the

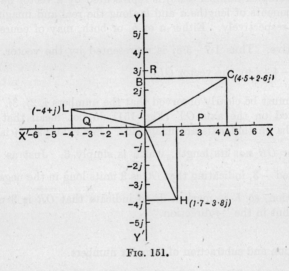

Fig. 151.

vector which represents it through one right angle in the positive (i.e. anti-clockwise) direction. We therefore represent $3j$ by a vector of length 3 units in a direction at right angles to $X'OX$, i.e. by the vector $\overrightarrow{OR}$ in Fig. 151. We sometimes prefer to say that $3j$ is represented by the point R. In the same way all purely imaginary numbers will be represented by points on YOY'. We call $X'OX$ the *real axis* and YOY' the *imaginary axis*.

We must now find a way of representing numbers like $4·5 + 2·6j$, which have a real and an imaginary part. Since $4·5$ is represented by the vector $\overrightarrow{OA}$ in Fig. 151 and $2·6j$ by the vector $\overrightarrow{OB}$, we agree to represent the sum of these two numbers, i.e. $4·5 + 2·6j$, by the sum of the vectors $\overrightarrow{OA}$ and $\overrightarrow{OB}$, that is by the resultant vector $\overrightarrow{OC}$. In the same way, any complex number $a + bj$ is represented by a vector having components of lengths a and b along the real and imaginary axes respectively. Either a or b, or both, may of course be negative. Thus $1·7 - 3·8j$ is represented by the vector $\overrightarrow{OH}$, and $-4 + j$ by the vector $\overrightarrow{OL}$.

It must be clearly observed that the numbers j, $2j$, $3j$, etc., marked on the axis OY (Fig. 151) do not mean that the lengths on that axis are imaginary. For example, $3j$ is the vector $\overrightarrow{OR}$ not its length, which is simply 3. Just as Q is marked -3, indicating that $\overrightarrow{OQ}$ is 3 units long in the negative direction, so R is marked $3j$ to indicate that $\overrightarrow{OR}$ is 3 units long but in the "j-direction."

Addition and subtraction of complex numbers

$$(5 + 7j) + (3 - 2j) = (5 + 3) + (7j - 2j) = 8 + 5j\ ;$$

$$(3 + 2j) - (2 + 5j) = (3 - 2) + (2j - 5j) = 1 - 3j\ ;$$

and, generally,

$$(a + bj) + (c + dj) = (a + c) + (b + d)j.$$

Thus to add two complex numbers we simply add their real parts and add their imaginary parts.

A complex number is often denoted by a single letter such

as z. Electrical engineers sometimes put a dot under the letter to distinguish complex symbols from real symbols; thus a complex voltage is denoted by $\dot{E}$, a complex current by $\dot{I}$.

If the vectors $\overrightarrow{OP_1}$, $\overrightarrow{OP_2}$ (Fig. 152) represent complex numbers $z_1(\equiv x_1 + jy_1)$ and $z_2(\equiv x_2 + jy_2)$, the diagonal $\overrightarrow{OQ}$ of the parallelogram has components $x_1 + x_2$ along OX and

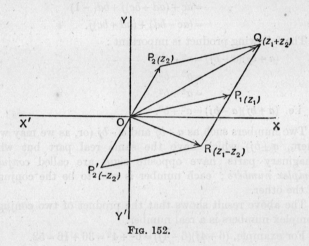

FIG. 152.

$y_1 + y_2$ along OY (see Part II, p. 277), and therefore represents the complex number $(x_1 + x_2) + j(y_1 + y_2)$, which is equal to $z_1 + z_2$. Thus complex numbers can be added by the parallelogram law for adding vectors.

To subtract z_2 from z_1 is the same as adding $(-z_2)$ to z_1. It is easily seen that $-z_2$ is represented by the vector $\overrightarrow{OP'_2}$ which is equal in length to $\overrightarrow{OP_2}$ but drawn in the opposite direction. Hence $z_1 - z_2$ is represented by the vector $\overrightarrow{OR}$.

Multiplication

$$(4 + 3j)(2 + 5j) = 8 + 20j + 6j + 15j^2$$
$$= 8 + 26j + 15(-1), \text{ since } j^2 = -1$$
$$= 8 + 26j - 15$$
$$= -7 + 26j.$$

Generally,

$$(a + bj)(c + dj) = ac + adj + bcj + bdj^2$$
$$= ac + (ad + bc)j + bd(-1)$$
$$= (ac - bd) + (ad + bc)j.$$

The following product is important :

$$(a + bj)(a - bj) = a^2 - (bj)^2$$
$$= a^2 - b^2j^2$$
$$= a^2 + b^2.$$

i.e. $(a + bj)(a - bj) = a^2 + b^2.$

Two numbers such as $a + bj$ and $a - bj$ (or, as we may write them, $a \pm bj$) which have the same real part but whose imaginary parts have opposite signs are called *conjugate complex numbers*; each number is said to be the conjugate of the other.

The above result shows that the product of two conjugate complex numbers is a real number.

For example, $(6 + 4j)(6 - 4j) = 6^2 + 4^2 = 36 + 16 = 52.$

Division

Examples.—

(1) $\dfrac{8 - 7j}{4} = \dfrac{8}{4} - \dfrac{7j}{4} = 2 - 1 \cdot 75j.$

(2) $\dfrac{2 + 3j}{3 + 4j} = \dfrac{(2 + 3j)}{(3 + 4j)} \times \dfrac{(3 - 4j)}{(3 - 4j)} = \dfrac{6 - 8j + 9j - 12j^2}{3^2 + 4^2}$

$\qquad = \dfrac{6 + j + 12}{9 + 16} = \dfrac{18 + j}{25} = \dfrac{18}{25} + \dfrac{1}{25}j$

$\qquad = 0 \cdot 72 + 0 \cdot 04j.$

In the last example the denominator was made real by multiplying both numerator and denominator by $3 - 4j$, the conjugate of $3 + 4j$. In the same way, if any complex number $a + bj$ occurs in the denominator of a fraction, we can make the denominator real by multiplying both the numerator and the denominator by the conjugate number $a - bj$.

Thus $\dfrac{1}{a + bj} = \dfrac{a - bj}{(a + bj)(a - bj)} = \dfrac{a - bj}{a^2 + b^2} = \dfrac{a}{a^2 + b^2} - j \cdot \dfrac{b}{a^2 + b^2}.$

[*Note.*—Compare Part II, page 8, where to evaluate an expression like $\dfrac{1}{5 - 3\sqrt{2}}$ containing a surd in the denominator, we first multiply numerator and denominator by the "conjugate surd" $5 + 3\sqrt{2}$, giving

$$\frac{1}{5 - 3\sqrt{2}} = \frac{5 + 3\sqrt{2}}{(5 - 3\sqrt{2})(5 + 3\sqrt{2})}$$

$$= \frac{5 + 3\sqrt{2}}{25 - 18} = \frac{5 + 3\sqrt{2}}{7} \simeq \frac{9 \cdot 242}{7} \simeq 1 \cdot 320 \ ]$$

Example.—Prove that

$$\frac{1}{\cos\theta + j\sin\theta} = \cos\theta - j\sin\theta.$$

$$\frac{1}{\cos\theta + j\sin\theta} = \frac{\cos\theta - j\sin\theta}{(\cos\theta + j\sin\theta)(\cos\theta - j\sin\theta)}$$

$$= \frac{\cos\theta - j\sin\theta}{\cos^2\theta + \sin^2\theta}$$

$$= \cos\theta - j\sin\theta, \text{ since } \cos^2\theta + \sin^2\theta = 1.$$

Example.—The total impedance Z of a circuit containing two impedances Z_1, Z_2 in parallel is given by

$$\frac{1}{Z} = \frac{1}{Z_1} + \frac{1}{Z_2}.$$

Find Z when $Z_1 = 5 \cdot 2 + 3 \cdot 4j$, $Z_2 = 8 + 4 \cdot 1j$.

[For the meaning of " impedance " see pages 298, 301.]

$$\frac{1}{Z} = \frac{1}{Z_1} + \frac{1}{Z_2} = \frac{1}{5 \cdot 2 + 3 \cdot 4j} + \frac{1}{8 + 4 \cdot 1j}$$

$$= \frac{(8 + 4 \cdot 1j) + (5 \cdot 2 + 3 \cdot 4j)}{(5 \cdot 2 + 3 \cdot 4j)(8 + 4 \cdot 1j)}$$

$$= \frac{13 \cdot 2 + 7 \cdot 5j}{27 \cdot 66 + 48 \cdot 52j}$$

$$\therefore Z = \frac{27 \cdot 66 + 48 \cdot 52j}{13 \cdot 2 + 7 \cdot 5j}$$

$$= \frac{(27 \cdot 66 + 48 \cdot 52j)(13 \cdot 2 - 7 \cdot 5j)}{(13 \cdot 2 + 7 \cdot 5j)(13 \cdot 2 - 7 \cdot 5j)}$$

$$= \frac{729 \cdot 012 + 433 \cdot 014j}{230 \cdot 49}$$

$$\eqsim 3 \cdot 16 + 1 \cdot 88j.$$

Roots of a quadratic equation

The roots of the quadratic equation $ax^2 + bx + c = 0$ are

$$x = \frac{-b \pm \sqrt{b^2 - 4ac}}{2a},$$

i.e.
$$x = -\frac{b}{2a} \pm \frac{\sqrt{b^2 - 4ac}}{2a}.$$

If a, b, c are real numbers, as they always are in the equations occurring in practical problems, $-\dfrac{b}{2a}$ is real but $\dfrac{\sqrt{b^2 - 4ac}}{2a}$ is real or imaginary according as $b^2 - 4ac$ is positive or negative. Hence if $b^2 - 4ac$ is negative, the roots are complex numbers.

If $b^2 - 4ac$ is zero, the roots are real and equal, being equal to $-\dfrac{b}{2a}$.

We can sum up as follows :

$b^2 - 4ac$	Nature of Roots
Positive	Real, unequal
Zero	Real, equal
Negative	Complex

It is evident, moreover, that if the roots are complex they are conjugate complex numbers.

Exercise XXIX

Evaluate :

1. $(8 - 3j) + (12 + j)$.

2. $(2 \cdot 5 + 6 \cdot 3j) - (4 + 8 \cdot 2j)$.

3. $(7 + 4j)(2 + 3j)$

4. $(-4 + j)(1 - 5j)$.

5. $(1 \cdot 6 - 9 \cdot 4j)(14 \cdot 3 + 2j)$.

6. $(3 + 2j)(1 + j)(5 - 4j)$.

7. $(3 + 8j)^2$.

8. $(-1 + j)^4$.

9. $(5 + 2j)(5 - 2j)$.

10. $(\cos \alpha + j \sin \alpha)(\cos \beta + j \sin \beta)$.

11. Indicate on a diagram the vectors representing the following numbers : (i) $2 + 6j$, (ii) $3 + 1 \cdot 5j$, (iii) $4 - 3j$, (iv) $-1 - j$, (v) $-2 \cdot 5 + 4 \cdot 8j$.

12. Mark on the same diagram the numbers $2 \cdot 1 - 3 \cdot 4j$, $4 \cdot 6 + 7 \cdot 3j$ and their sum.

13. Show that $j^3 = -j$, $j^4 = 1$, $j^5 = j$, $j^6 = -1$, $j^7 = -j$, and that every integral power of j is equal to either ± 1 or $\pm j$.

14. Show that $\dfrac{1}{j} = -j$ and that $\dfrac{1}{j^3} = j$.

Evaluate :

15. $\dfrac{5 - 6j}{4 + 2j}$.

16. $\dfrac{3 + 7j}{3 - 7j}$.

17. $\dfrac{1}{8 + 3j} + \dfrac{1}{8 - 3j}$.

18. $\dfrac{1}{8 + 3j} - \dfrac{1}{8 - 3j}$.

19. $\dfrac{(3 - 5j)(1 + j)}{4 + 2j}$.

20. $\dfrac{3 + 2j}{(2 + 4j)(1 - 7j)}$.

21. Find the value of $\dfrac{E_m}{R + jX}$ when $E_m = 230$, $R = 50$, $X = 5$.

10

22. Find the value of z if $\dfrac{1}{z} = \dfrac{1}{6 + 2 \cdot 5j} + \dfrac{1}{3 \cdot 2 + 4 \cdot 6j}$.

23. Solve the equation $x^2 + 2x + 17 = 0$.

24. Find the roots of the equation $x^3 = 1$. [Hint. Write the equation as $x^3 - 1 = 0$ and factorize the left-hand side.]

25. When a condenser of capacity C farads discharges through a resistance R ohms and an inductance L henrys in series, the discharge is direct or oscillatory according as the roots of the equation $Lp^2 + Rp + \dfrac{1}{C} = 0$ are real or complex. What is the nature of the discharge if $R = 200$, $L = 0 \cdot 008$, $C = 0 \cdot 5 \times 10^{-6}$?

Polar form

A vector can be specified by its length and the angle it makes with some standard direction. We shall take OX (the

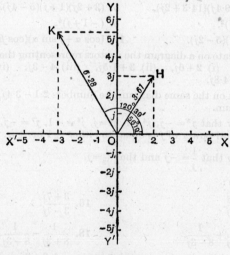

Fig. 153.

positive direction of the real axis) as our standard direction. If the vector is of length r and makes an angle θ with OX

we denote it by r_θ or by $r \angle \theta$ (cf. Part II, Chapter XII). We can therefore write any complex number in this form. For example, in Fig. 153, the vector $\overrightarrow{OH}$ represents the number $2 + 3j$ or $3 \cdot 61 \angle 56° \ 19'$, $\overrightarrow{OK}$ represents the number $-3 \cdot 2 + 5 \cdot 4j$ or $6 \cdot 28 \angle 120° \ 39'$.

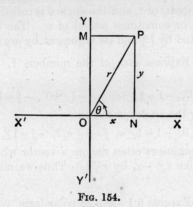

FIG. 154.

Generally, we see from Fig. 154 that

$$x + jy = r \angle \theta$$

where $r \cos \theta = x, \ r \sin \theta = y.$

Squaring and adding, we have

$$r^2 = x^2 + y^2$$

$$\therefore r = \sqrt{x^2 + y^2},$$

the positive square root being taken since r is the length of OP. Dividing, we have

$$\tan \theta = \frac{y}{x}$$

$$\therefore \theta = \tan^{-1} \frac{y}{x}.$$

The particular value of $\tan^{-1}\dfrac{y}{x}$ to be taken has to be decided by the signs of x and y which determine the quadrant in which θ lies. In a numerical case it is best to draw a rough diagram.

If $z = r \angle \theta$, the length r is called the *modulus* (or *absolute value* or *magnitude*) of z, and the angle θ is called the *argument* (or *amplitude* or sometimes *phase*) of z. The modulus of z is often denoted by $|z|$ and its argument by $arg\ z$.

Example.—Express each of the numbers 1, -1, j, $-j$ in polar form.

$$1 = 1 \angle 0°, \quad -1 = 1 \angle 180°, \quad j = 1 \angle 90°, \quad -j = 1 \angle -90° ;$$

or, expressing the angles in radians,

$$1 = 1 \angle 0, \quad -1 = 1 \angle \pi, \quad j = 1 \angle \pi/2, \quad -j = 1 \angle -\pi/2.$$

Electrical engineers often denote a vector whose argument is negative, like $r \angle -\alpha$, by $r \diagdown \alpha$. Thus we might write $-j$ as $1 \diagdown 90°$.

Example.—Express $6 \cdot 1 - 4 \cdot 5j$ in polar form.

The vector is OP in Fig. 155.

$$r = \sqrt{6 \cdot 1^2 + 4 \cdot 5^2} = \sqrt{57 \cdot 46} = 7 \cdot 58.$$

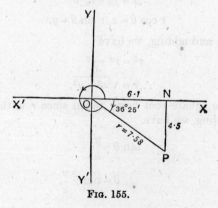

FIG. 155.

The angle θ is in the fourth quadrant.

$$\tan \widehat{NOP} = \frac{4 \cdot 5}{6 \cdot 1} = 0 \cdot 7377.$$

$$\therefore \widehat{NOP} = 36° \ 25'$$

$$\therefore \theta = -36° \ 25'$$

$$\therefore 6 \cdot 1 - 4 \cdot 5j = 7 \cdot 58 \underline{/} -36° \ 25', \text{ or } 7 \cdot 58 \diagdown 36° \ 25'.$$

It is evident that adding any multiple of 360° to the argument leaves the complex number unaltered. We could for instance write $-j = 1 \underline{/} 270°$ or $6 \cdot 1 - 4 \cdot 5j = 7 \cdot 58 \underline{/} 323° \ 35'$, but it is usual to take the numerically smallest value for the angle, that is the angle between $-180°$ and $180°$.

Note.—From Fig. 154 it is clear that

$$r \underline{/} \theta \equiv r \cos \theta + j \, r \sin \theta = r (\cos \theta + j \sin \theta).$$

Multiplication of two numbers when expressed in polar form

$$r_1 \underline{/} \theta_1 \times r_2 \underline{/} \theta_2 = r_1 (\cos \theta_1 + j \sin \theta_1) \times r_2 (\cos \theta_2 + j \sin \theta_2)$$

$$= r_1 r_2 \{ (\cos \theta_1 \cos \theta_2 - \sin \theta_1 \sin \theta_2)$$
$$+ j (\sin \theta_1 \cos \theta_2 + \cos \theta_1 \sin \theta_2) \}$$

$$= r_1 r_2 \{ \cos (\theta_1 + \theta_2) + j \sin (\theta_1 + \theta_2) \}$$

$$= r_1 r_2 \underline{/} \theta_1 + \theta_2.$$

Hence, *to multiply two complex numbers we multiply their moduli and add their arguments.*

As a particular case $(r \underline{/} \theta)^2 = r^2 \underline{/} 2\theta$; that is, to square a complex number we square its modulus and double its argument.

Also, since $j = 1 \underline{/} \frac{1}{2}\pi$,

$$j \times r \underline{/} \theta = 1 \underline{/} \tfrac{1}{2}\pi \times r \underline{/} \theta = r \underline{/} \theta + \tfrac{1}{2}\pi.$$

Thus *the effect of multiplying any complex number by j is to turn its vector through a right angle in the positive (anti-clockwise) direction, without altering its modulus.*

Division in polar form

$$\frac{r_1 \angle \theta_1}{r_2 \angle \theta_2} = \frac{r_1 (\cos \theta_1 + j \sin \theta_1)}{r_2 (\cos \theta_2 + j \sin \theta_2)}$$

$$= \frac{r_1}{r_2}(\cos \theta_1 + j \sin \theta_1)(\cos \theta_2 - j \sin \theta_2)$$

(see example on page 287)

$$= \frac{r_1}{r_2}\{(\cos \theta_1 \cos \theta_2 + \sin \theta_1 \sin \theta_2) + j(\sin \theta_1 \cos \theta_2 - \cos \theta_1 \sin \theta_2)\}$$

$$= \frac{r_1}{r_2}\{\cos (\theta_1 - \theta_2) + j \sin (\theta_1 - \theta_2)\}$$

$$= \left(\frac{r_1}{r_2}\right) \angle \theta_1 - \theta_2.$$

Hence, *to divide two complex numbers we divide their moduli and subtract their arguments.*

As a particular case,

$$\frac{1}{r \angle \theta} = \frac{1 \angle 0}{r \angle \theta} = \left(\frac{1}{r}\right) \angle - \theta$$

Square root

The rule for squaring a complex number suggests that to find the square root we should take the square root of its modulus and halve its argument. This is easily verified; for $(\sqrt{r} \angle \frac{1}{2}\theta)^2 = r \angle \theta$, so that $\sqrt{r} \angle \frac{1}{2}\theta$ is one square root of $r \angle \theta$. The other square root is the negative of this. Thus the two square roots of $r \angle \theta$ are $\pm \sqrt{r} \angle \frac{1}{2}\theta$.

[*Note.*—Since $-1 = 1 \angle \pi$, the second square root can be expressed in the form $1 \angle \pi \times \sqrt{r} \angle \frac{1}{2}\theta$ which is equal to $\sqrt{r} \angle \frac{1}{2}\theta + \pi$. We can verify this also by squaring; for

$$\{\sqrt{r} \angle \frac{1}{2}\theta + \pi\}^2 = r \angle \theta + 2\pi = r \angle \theta.]$$

Example.—Find the values of $\sqrt{2+3j}$.

In Fig. 156

$$r = \sqrt{2^2 + 3^2} = \sqrt{13} = 3 \cdot 606$$

$$\theta = \tan^{-1} \tfrac{3}{2} = \tan^{-1} 1 \cdot 5 = 56° \ 19'$$

$$\therefore \ 2 + 3j = 3 \cdot 606 \angle 56° \ 19'$$

$$\therefore \ \sqrt{2+3j} = \pm \sqrt{3 \cdot 606} \angle 28° \ 9\tfrac{1}{2}'$$

$$= \pm 1 \cdot 899 \ \angle 28° \ 9\tfrac{1}{2}'.$$

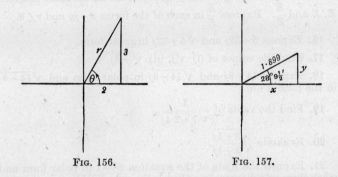

Fig. 156.   Fig. 157.

To express this in the $x + jy$ form we draw Fig. 157, from which we see that

$$1 \cdot 899 \ \angle 28° \ 9\tfrac{1}{2}' = x + jy$$

where $x = 1 \cdot 899 \cos 28° \ 9\tfrac{1}{2}' = 1 \cdot 674$ (by logs),

$$y = 1 \cdot 899 \sin 28° \ 9\tfrac{1}{2}' = 0 \cdot 8962 \text{ (by logs)}.$$

$$\therefore \ \sqrt{2+3j} = \pm (1 \cdot 674 + 0 \cdot 896j).$$

Exercise XXX

Represent the following complex numbers on a diagram and express each of them in the form $r \angle \theta$:

1. $5 + 4j$.   2. $1 \cdot 3 + 6 \cdot 5j$.   3. $12 - 5j$.

4. $-8 + 15j$.   5. $-0 \cdot 26 - 0 \cdot 09j$.   6. $-73 + 40j$.

Express each of the following complex numbers in the form $a + bj$:

7. $5 \cdot 2 \angle 36°$.   **8.** $0 \cdot 8 \angle 120°$.   **9.** $10 \triangledown 74°$.

10. If $a + jb = r \angle \theta$ show from a figure that $a - jb = r \triangledown \theta$; also express $-a + jb$ and $-a - jb$ in polar form.

Evaluate in the form $r \angle \theta$:

11. $3 \angle 50° \times 1 \cdot 5 \angle 18°$.   **12.** $0 \cdot 25 \angle 34° \times 6 \angle -70°$.

13. $\dfrac{8 \angle 45°}{5 \angle 20°}$.   **14.** $\dfrac{0 \cdot 3 \angle 76°}{4 \cdot 8 \angle -34°}$

15. If $Z = 1 \cdot 2 + 1 \cdot 6j$ and $E = 10$, represent on the same diagram Z, E and $\dfrac{E}{Z}$. Express $\dfrac{E}{Z}$ in each of the forms $x + jy$ and $r \angle \theta$.

16. Express $5 + 32j$ and $\sqrt{5 + 32j}$ in polar form.

17. Find the values of (i) $\sqrt{j}$, (ii) $\sqrt{-4j}$.

18. Express $14 - 8j$ and $\sqrt{14 - 8j}$ in polar form and $\sqrt{14 - 8j}$ in the form $a + bj$.

19. Find the value of $\dfrac{1}{\sqrt{7 + 2 \cdot 4j}}$.

20. Evaluate $\sqrt{\dfrac{3 + 4j}{3 - 4j}}$.

21. Express the roots of the equation $x^3 = 1$ in polar form and mark them on a diagram (see Hint in Exercise XXIX, Question 24). Verify that each of the complex roots is the square of the other.

22. Draw a sketch to show the vectors representing $a + bj$ and $j(a + bj)$, that is $-b + aj$, and prove from congruent triangles the statement about the effect of multiplying by j given on page 293.

Application to the theory of alternating currents

Rotating vectors

The simplest form of alternating current is one of the form $i = I_m \sin \omega t$, where I_m is a constant, namely the maximum value of the current, and $\omega = 2\pi f$ where f is the frequency (Part II, p. 239).

If we consider a vector OP of length I_m rotating about O with constant angular velocity ω radians per sec., starting from OX when $t = 0$, the instantaneous value i of the current at time t is the length of the projection on OY of the vector OP at that instant. The rotating vector OP is called the *current vector* and is usually denoted by I, the dot being placed below the symbol to remind us that it is a vector.

If we regard the vector as representing a complex number I, which varies with t,

$$I = I_m \angle \omega t = I_m (\cos \omega t + j \sin \omega t)$$
$$= I_m \cos \omega t + j I_m \sin \omega t,$$

and the current i is the coefficient of j in the imaginary part of I. For brevity we usually speak of it as simply "the imaginary part of I"—and generally we call b the imaginary part of $a + jb$—though it must always be remembered that this so-called "imaginary part" is actually real.*

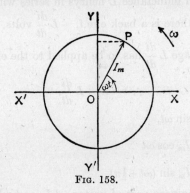

FIG. 158.

If the phase constant is not zero but α, say, so that $i = I_m \sin (\omega t + \alpha)$, the current vector leads that in Fig. 158 by an angle α, and in this case $I = I_m \angle \omega t + \alpha$.

In the same way we can regard the instantaneous value v of an alternating voltage as the imaginary part of a rotating vector (or variable complex number) V, called the *voltage vector*.

* To avoid ambiguity engineers sometimes use the term "quadrature component" for what we here call the imaginary part.

10*

Current through a non-inductive resistance

If v is the voltage necessary to maintain an alternating current i amp. through a resistance R ohms,

$$v = Ri = R \times \text{imaginary part of vector } \dot{I}$$

$$= \text{imaginary part of } R\dot{I}, \text{ since } R \text{ is real.}$$

Hence we can write $\qquad \dot{V} = R\dot{I}.$

The vector $\dot{V}$ is merely a multiple of $\dot{I}$; the two vectors are in phase.

Circuit containing a non-inductive resistance and a pure inductance in series

If there is an inductance L henrys in series with the resistance R ohms, there is a back e.m.f. $-L\dfrac{di}{dt}$ volts, and thus an additional voltage $L\dfrac{di}{dt}$ has to be applied to the circuit.

$$\therefore v = Ri + L\frac{di}{dt}.$$

If $\qquad i = I_m \sin \omega t,$

$$L\frac{di}{dt} = \omega L I_m \cos \omega t$$

$$= \omega L I_m \sin (\omega t + \tfrac{1}{2}\pi)$$

$$= \text{imaginary part of vector } \omega L I_m \underline{/\omega t + \tfrac{1}{2}\pi}$$

$$= \quad ,, \qquad ,, \qquad ,, \quad j\omega L I_m \underline{/\omega t}$$

$$= \quad ,, \qquad ,, \qquad ,, \quad j\omega L \dot{I}.$$

$$\therefore v = \text{imaginary part of } R\dot{I} + \text{imaginary part of } j\omega L \dot{I}$$

$$= \quad ,, \qquad ,, \qquad (R + j\omega L)\dot{I}.$$

Hence we can write $\dot{V} = (R + j\omega L)\dot{I}.$

$R + j\omega L$ is a constant complex number or vector, called the *impedance vector* of the circuit. We denote it by Z. Its real part R is the *resistance*, its imaginary part ωL is called the *inductive reactance* of the circuit.

Thus $\qquad \underset{\cdot}{V} = \underset{\cdot}{Z}\underset{\cdot}{I}$ where $\underset{\cdot}{Z} = R + j\omega L$.

It should be remembered that Z is not a rotating vector since it does not vary with the time.

Converting to polar form (see Fig. 159),

$$Z = Z \angle \phi$$

where $\qquad Z = \sqrt{R^2 + \omega^2 L^2},$

$$\phi = \tan^{-1} \frac{\omega L}{R}.$$

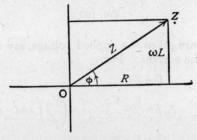

Fig. 159.

The modulus Z is called the *impedance* (or " apparent resistance ") of the circuit.

Thus $\qquad \underset{\cdot}{V} = Z \angle \phi \times I_m \angle \omega t$

$$= Z I_m \angle \omega t + \phi,$$

and v, which is the imaginary part of $\underset{\cdot}{V}$, is given by

$$v = Z I_m \sin (\omega t + \phi)$$

$$= \sqrt{R^2 + \omega^2 L^2}\, I_m \sin (\omega t + \phi), \text{ where } \phi = \tan^{-1} \frac{\omega L}{R}.$$

The vectors I, RI, $j\omega LI$ and V are shown in Fig. 160.   The voltage leads the current by an angle $\phi = \tan^{-1} \dfrac{\omega L}{R}$.

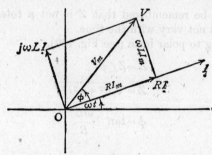

FIG. 160.

Also if we are given the applied voltage, say $v = V_m \sin \omega t$, we can find the current.   For

$$V = ZI.$$

$$\therefore I = \frac{V}{Z} = \frac{V_m \angle \omega t}{Z \angle \phi} = \left(\frac{V_m}{Z}\right) \angle \underline{\omega t - \phi},$$

and

$$i = \frac{V_m}{Z} \sin (\omega t - \phi)$$

$$= \frac{V_m}{\sqrt{R^2 + \omega^2 L^2}} \sin (\omega t - \phi).$$

Hence the current lags behind the applied voltage by an angle ϕ.

Current across a condenser

If q coulombs is the charge on the positive plate of the condenser at time t and its capacity is C farads, the potential difference v across the plates is $\dfrac{q}{C}$ volts, so that $q = Cv$.

But the current flowing from the negative plate to the positive plate of the condenser is $\dfrac{dq}{dt}$ ampères.

$$\therefore i = \frac{dq}{dt} = C\frac{dv}{dt}.$$

If
$$v = V_m \sin \omega t$$
$$i = C V_m \omega \cos \omega t$$
$$= \omega C V_m \sin (\omega t + \tfrac{1}{2}\pi)$$
$$= \text{imaginary part of } \omega C V_m \underline{/\omega t + \tfrac{1}{2}\pi}$$
$$= \quad ,, \quad\quad ,, \quad j\omega C V_m \underline{/\omega t}$$
$$= \quad ,, \quad\quad ,, \quad j\omega C \underset{\cdot}{V}.$$

Hence we can write $\quad \underset{\cdot}{I} = j\omega C \underset{\cdot}{V}.$

The current leads the voltage by an angle $\dfrac{\pi}{2}$, i.e. by a quarter of a period.

Also
$$\underset{\cdot}{V} = \frac{1}{j\omega C}\underset{\cdot}{I} = -\frac{j}{\omega C}\underset{\cdot}{I}.$$

Circuit containing resistance, inductance and capacity in series

The total voltage in this case is the sum of the voltages for the separate elements, and hence

$$\underset{\cdot}{V} = \left(R + j\omega L - \frac{j}{\omega C}\right)\underset{\cdot}{I}$$
$$= \left\{R + j\left(\omega L - \frac{1}{\omega C}\right)\right\}\underset{\cdot}{I}$$
$$= \underset{\cdot}{Z}\underset{\cdot}{I},$$

where the *impedance vector* $\underset{\cdot}{Z}$ is now given by

$$\underset{\cdot}{Z} = R + j\left(\omega L - \frac{1}{\omega C}\right).$$

This is usually written as

$$\underset{\cdot}{Z} = R + jX \quad \text{where} \quad X = \omega L - \frac{1}{\omega C}.$$

X is called the *reactance* of the circuit; ωL is the inductive reactance, $\dfrac{1}{\omega C}$ the *capacity reactance*.

In polar form, $\dot{Z} = Z \angle \phi$ where

the *impedance* $Z = \sqrt{R^2 + X^2} = \sqrt{R^2 + \left(\omega L - \dfrac{1}{\omega C}\right)^2}$,

$$\text{and } \phi = \tan^{-1} \frac{X}{R} = \tan^{-1}\left(\frac{\omega L - \dfrac{1}{\omega C}}{R}\right).$$

If $\quad i = I_m \sin \omega t$,

$$\dot{V} = \dot{Z}\dot{I} = Z\angle\phi \times I_m\angle\omega t = ZI_m \angle \omega t + \phi.$$

$$\therefore \; v = ZI_m \sin (\omega t + \phi)$$
$$= \sqrt{R^2 + X^2} \; I_m \sin (\omega t + \phi)$$
$$= \sqrt{R^2 + \left(\omega L - \frac{1}{\omega C}\right)^2} I_m \sin (\omega t + \phi).$$

Since ϕ is positive or negative according as $\omega L >$ or $< \dfrac{1}{\omega C}$, v leads or lags behind i according as $\omega L >$ or $< \dfrac{1}{\omega C}$; they are in phase if $\omega L = \dfrac{1}{\omega C}$.

If we are given the applied e.m.f., $v = V_m \sin \omega t$, and wish to find the current, we have

$$\dot{I} = \frac{\dot{V}}{\dot{Z}} = \frac{V_m \angle \omega t}{Z \angle \phi} = \left(\frac{V_m}{Z}\right) \angle \omega t - \phi,$$

whence $\quad i = \dfrac{V_m}{Z} \sin (\omega t - \phi) = \dfrac{V_m}{\sqrt{R^2 + X^2}} \sin (\omega t - \phi)$

$$= \frac{V_m}{\sqrt{R^2 + \left(\omega L - \dfrac{1}{\omega C}\right)^2}} \sin (\omega t - \phi).$$

Joint impedance of series or parallel circuits

The reciprocal of the impedance vector is called the *admittance vector* and is denoted by $\underset{.}{Y}$; its modulus Y is the *admittance*. If $\underset{.}{Y} = G + jB$, the real part G is called the *conductance* and the imaginary part B the *susceptance*.

$$\underset{.}{Y} = \frac{1}{\underset{.}{Z}} = \frac{1}{R+jX} = \frac{R-jX}{R^2+X^2}$$

$$\therefore G = \frac{R}{R^2+X^2}, \quad B = -\frac{X}{R^2+X^2}.$$

The student can immediately verify for himself that impedance vectors can be combined in exactly the same way as ordinary resistances; that is, for series circuits we add impedance vectors, for parallel circuits we add admittance vectors.

Also, we have seen above that—

(i) an inductance L is equivalent to an impedance $j\omega L$,

(ii) a capacity C is equivalent to an impedance $-\dfrac{j}{\omega C}$.

[*Note.*—For brevity we often speak rather loosely of an impedance when we mean impedance vector, or of an admittance when we mean admittance vector, but the context will always prevent any misunderstanding. For example, if we speak of adding impedances in series we obviously mean adding the impedance vectors.]

Example.—A circuit consists of two branches connected in parallel, the first branch containing a coil of inductance

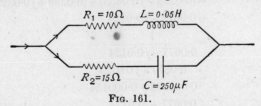

$R_1 = 10\,\Omega \quad L = 0\cdot05\,H$

$R_2 = 15\,\Omega$

$C = 250\,\mu F$

Fig. 161.

0·05 henry and resistance 10 ohms, the second branch containing a resistance of 15 ohms and a condenser of capacity

250 microfarads. Find the total impedance of the circuit for an e.m.f. of frequency 50 cycles.

Denote the impedance of the two branches by Z_1, Z_2 respectively and their admittances by Y_1, Y_2, and their joint impedance and admittance by Z and Y.

$$\omega = 2\pi \times \text{frequency} = 100\pi = 314 \cdot 16$$

$$Z_1 = R_1 + j\omega L$$
$$= 10 + j \times 314 \cdot 16 \times 0 \cdot 05$$
$$= 10 + j15 \cdot 708$$

$$Z_2 = R_2 - \frac{j}{\omega C}$$
$$= 15 - \frac{j}{314 \cdot 16 \times 250 \times 10^{-6}}$$
$$= 15 - \frac{j}{0 \cdot 07854}$$
$$= 15 - j12 \cdot 732$$

$$Y = Y_1 + Y_2$$
$$= \frac{1}{10 + j15 \cdot 708} + \frac{1}{15 - j12 \cdot 732}$$
$$= \frac{10 - j15 \cdot 708}{100 + 246 \cdot 74} + \frac{15 + j12 \cdot 732}{225 + 162 \cdot 09}$$
$$= \frac{10 - j15 \cdot 708}{346 \cdot 74} + \frac{15 + j12 \cdot 732}{387 \cdot 09}$$
$$= (0 \cdot 0288 - j0 \cdot 0453) + (0 \cdot 0389 + j0 \cdot 0329)$$
$$= 0 \cdot 0677 - j0 \cdot 0124$$

$$\therefore Z = \frac{1}{0 \cdot 0677 - j0 \cdot 0124}$$
$$= \frac{0 \cdot 0677 + j0 \cdot 0124}{0 \cdot 004583 + 0 \cdot 000154}$$
$$= \frac{0 \cdot 0677 + j0 \cdot 0124}{0 \cdot 004737}$$
$$= 14 \cdot 29 + j2 \cdot 62 \text{ ohms.}$$

Example.—If Z_1, Z_2, Z_3, Z_4 are the impedances of the arms AB, BC, CD, DA of a Wheatstone bridge, the condition for balance—i.e. that there shall be no current through the telephone T—is that $Z_1 Z_3 = Z_2 Z_4$. Show how, by means of

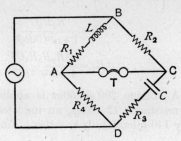

Fig. 162.

the bridge in Fig. 162 (Hay's capacity bridge), R_1 and L can be found in terms of R_2, R_3, R_4 and C.

$$Z_1 = R_1 + j\omega L, \quad Z_2 = R_2, \quad Z_3 = R_3 - \frac{j}{\omega C}, \quad Z_4 = R_4.$$

When the bridge is balanced

$$(R_1 + j\omega L)\left(R_3 - \frac{j}{\omega C}\right) = R_2 R_4$$

$$\therefore \left(R_1 R_3 + \frac{L}{C}\right) + j\left(\omega L R_3 - \frac{R_1}{\omega C}\right) = R_2 R_4.$$

If two complex numbers are equal, their real parts must obviously be equal and their imaginary parts must be equal. Hence, equating real parts and imaginary parts in the above,

$$R_1 R_3 + \frac{L}{C} = R_2 R_4 \quad . \quad . \quad . \quad . \quad (1)$$

and

$$\omega L R_3 - \frac{R_1}{\omega C} = 0 \quad . \quad . \quad . \quad . \quad (2)$$

We can solve these two equations for R_1 and L. From (2)

$$R_1 = \omega^2 CLR_3$$

Substituting in (1),

$$L\left(\omega^2 CR_3{}^2 + \frac{1}{C}\right) = R_2 R_4$$

$$\therefore L = \frac{R_2 R_4 C}{1 + \omega^2 C^2 R_3{}^2}.$$

and

$$R_1 = \frac{\omega^2 R_2 R_3 R_4 C^2}{1 + \omega^2 C^2 R_3{}^2}.$$

Example.—A voltage $200 \sin 50\pi t$ is applied to a circuit containing a resistance 12 ohms, an inductance 0·25 henry and a capacity 140 microfarads in series. Find the current.

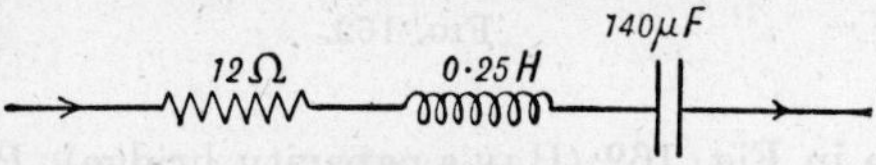

FIG. 163.

$$\omega = 50\pi = 157 \cdot 08$$

$$\dot{Z} = 12 + j\omega \times 0 \cdot 25 - \frac{j}{\omega \times 140 \times 10^{-6}}$$

$$= 12 + j39 \cdot 27 - \frac{j}{0 \cdot 02199}$$

$$= 12 + j39 \cdot 27 - j45 \cdot 475$$

$$= 12 - j6 \cdot 205$$

$$= 13 \cdot 51 \diagdown 27° \ 21' \ \text{ or } \ 13 \cdot 51 \diagup -27° \ 21'.$$

$$\dot{V} = 200 \diagup 50\pi t$$

$$\therefore \dot{I} = \frac{\dot{V}}{\dot{Z}} = \frac{200 \diagup 50\pi t}{13 \cdot 51 \diagup -27° \ 21'}$$

$$= \left(\frac{200}{13 \cdot 51}\right) \diagup 50\pi t + 27° \ 21'$$

$$= 14 \cdot 8 \diagup 50\pi t + 27° \ 21'.$$

$$\therefore i = 14 \cdot 8 \sin (50\pi t + 27° \ 21') \ \text{amp.}$$

Addition of rotating vectors

If two rotating vectors have the same angular velocity, the angle between them—i.e. their phase-difference—will remain constant for all values of t. Moreover their resultant (or vector sum) will also rotate with the same angular velocity. The same is true for any number of vectors. Thus adding the vectors $a\angle\omega t$, $b\angle\omega t+\alpha$, $c\angle\omega t+\beta$ is the same as adding the vectors $a\angle 0, b\angle\alpha, c\angle\beta$ and then turning the resultant through an angle ωt.

We therefore usually specify a rotating vector, such as a voltage vector or current vector, by its value when $t=0$ and its frequency.

For example by a voltage $3+5j$ volts, frequency 40, we mean that when $t=0$ the voltage vector is $3+5j$, i.e. $5\cdot831\angle30°\ 58'$. In t secs. this vector rotates through ωt, i.e. $2\pi ft$, i.e. $80\pi t$ radians. Hence $V=5\cdot831\angle 80\pi t+30°\ 58'$, and $v=5\cdot831 \sin(80\pi t+30°\ 58')$.

Further, since the current has the same frequency as the applied voltage, in calculating the current we need only find the current vector when $t=0$ and then turn it through an angle ωt.

[*Note.*—As previously indicated, when angles are expressed without units, the units are understood to be radians. Thus $\sin(80\pi t+30°\ 58')$ means $\sin(80\pi t^c+30°\ 58')$.]

Example.—Two e.m.f.'s of 40 volts and $20+j15$ volts, each of frequency 50, are connected in series with a resistance of 50 ohms and inductance 0·06 henry. Find the current in the circuit.

$$\text{Total e.m.f.} = 40+(20+j15) = 60+j15 \text{ volts.}$$

$$\text{Impedance} = 5+j\omega \times 0\cdot06 = 5+j18\cdot85 \text{ ohms.}$$

$$\therefore \text{ current} = \frac{60+j15}{5+j18\cdot85}$$

$$= \frac{(60+j15)(5-j18\cdot85)}{25+355\cdot29}$$

$$= \frac{582 \cdot 75 - j1056 \cdot 0}{380 \cdot 29}$$

$$= 1 \cdot 532 - j \, 2 \cdot 777 \text{ amp.}$$

This is the value of the current (or rather the current vector) when $t = 0$. Expressing in polar form, it is $3 \cdot 153 \diagdown 61° \, 7'$; hence the maximum value of the current is $3 \cdot 153$ amp., and the current lags behind the voltage by $61° \, 7'$.

At time t, $\quad \dot{I} = 3 \cdot 153 \diagup 2\pi f t - 61° \, 7' = 3 \cdot 153 \diagup 100\pi t - 61° \, 7'$,

and $\qquad i = 3 \cdot 153 \sin (100\pi t - 61° \, 7')$.

Note.—Electrical engineers usually use virtual values, i.e. R.M.S. values, of voltages and currents instead of maximum values. Since the R.M.S. value of a sine function is $\dfrac{1}{\sqrt{2}} \times$ max. value, we have only to multiply by $\sqrt{2}$ to convert to maximum values.

Exercise XXXI

Find the impedance $R + jX$ of the following circuits :

1. Resistance r, inductance L in parallel.

2. Resistance r, capacity C in parallel.

3. Inductance L, capacity C in parallel.

4. In Question 3, show that no current flows if $\omega L = \dfrac{1}{\omega C}$.

5. Find the impedance of the circuit in Fig. 164 for a frequency of 25 cycles.

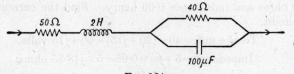

FIG. 164.

6. Find the e.m.f. necessary to maintain a current $6 \sin 100\pi t$ ampères through a resistance of 8 ohms and a capacity of 250 microfarads in series.

7. Find the current through an inductance 0·5 henry and a capacity 200 microfarads in series when a voltage $120 \sin 50\pi t$ is applied across the circuit.

8. Fig. 165 shows a Maxwell's capacity bridge. Find k_1 and C in terms of R_2, R_3, R_4 and L when the bridge is balanced.

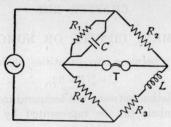

Fig. 165.

9. The currents I_1, I_2 in the primary and secondary coils of a transformer are given by the equations

$$V = (R_1 + j\omega L_1)I_1 + j\omega M I_2$$
$$0 = (R_2 + j\omega L_2)I_2 + j\omega M I_1$$

Prove that $\quad I_1 = \dfrac{V}{Z'}$

where $\quad Z' = R_1 + j\omega L_1 + \dfrac{\omega^2 M^2}{R_2 + j\omega L_2}.$

10. Express the following e.m.f.'s as complex numbers :

$e_1 = 200 \sin 100\pi t,$ $\qquad\qquad e_2 = 120 \cos 100\pi t,$

$e_3 = 150 \sin (100\pi t - \tfrac{1}{3}\pi),$ $\qquad e_4 = 50 \sin (100\pi t - \tfrac{1}{4}\pi).$

If $e = e_1 - e_2 - e_3 + e_4$, express e as a complex number and also in trigonometric form. [Cf. Exercise XI, Question 19.]

11. A voltage $10 + j6$ volts maintains a current $3 - j4$ amp. in a circuit. Find the resistance and reactance of the circuit.

12. An e.m.f., frequency 50 cycles, maximum 200 volts, is applied to a resistance 12 ohms and an inductance 0·08 henry in series. Find the current.

CHAPTER XIII

ALIGNMENT CHARTS, OR NOMOGRAMS

A relationship between two quantities, such as

$$C = \tfrac{5}{9}(F - 32),$$

which is the relation between the temperatures $C°$ Centigrade and $F°$ Fahrenheit can be represented by a graph as in Fig. 166.

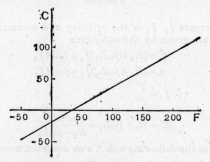

FIG. 166.

Another way of showing this relationship is seen on some thermometers which have Centigrade and Fahrenheit scales on opposite sides as in Fig. 167. These scales are made by placing any two pairs of corresponding values opposite each other, say the boiling-points of water 100° C., 212° F., and the freezing points 0° C., 32° F., and then dividing the distance between these points into 100 equal parts on the Centigrade scale and 212 − 32, which is 180, equal parts on the Fahrenheit scale.

That numbers opposite each other do satisfy the relation

$C = \frac{5}{9}(F - 32)$ is seen as follows. Let the point P be at $C°$ on the Centigrade scale and $F°$ on the Fahrenheit scale. Then $\frac{AP}{PB}$ must have the same value using either scale.

$$\therefore \frac{C}{100} = \frac{F - 32}{212 - 32} = \frac{F - 32}{180}$$

$$\therefore C = \frac{5}{9}(F - 32).$$

The above example shows that, if two uniformly graduated scales are placed on the same line, corresponding numbers on

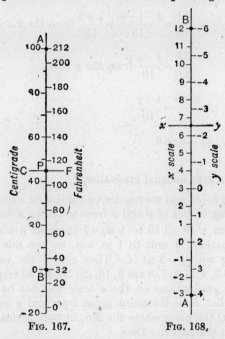

FIG. 167.   FIG. 168.

the scales satisfy a linear law. Conversely such scales can be drawn so that corresponding numbers are related by any given linear law.

Example.—Construct two scales on a line for values of x from -3 to 12 so that corresponding values of x and y satisfy the equation $2x + 3y = 6$.

When $x = -3, y = 4$ and when $x = 12, y = -6$. Draw a line AB, say 6 in. long (Fig. 168). Make a uniform scale for x from -3 at A to 12 at B; this means that 15 units must be represented by 6 in., i.e. 1 unit to 0·4 in. Make a scale for y on the other side of the line starting from 4 at A to -6 at B, using a scale of 10 units to 6 in., i.e 1 unit to 0·6 in. Then, if P is the point given by x and y on the two scales,

$$\frac{AP}{AB} = \frac{x - (-3)}{15} = \frac{x + 3}{15} \text{ from the } x \text{ scale}$$

and

$$\frac{AP}{AB} = \frac{4 - y}{10} \text{ from the } y \text{ scale.}$$

$$\therefore \frac{x + 3}{15} = \frac{4 - y}{10}$$

$$\therefore 2x + 3y = 6.$$

Use of scales with unequal graduations

Suppose $y = \sqrt{x}$ and we require two scales on a line to show corresponding values of y and x from $x = 10$ to $x = 60$. Since y varies from $\sqrt{10} = 3 \cdot 16$ to $\sqrt{60} = 7 \cdot 75$, make a y scale with equal graduations, 1 unit to 1 in. say, on one side of a line AB starting with $y = 3$ at A. Then clearly the values of x opposite $y = 3, 4, 5, 6, 7, 8$ are 9, 16, 25, 36, 49, 64 respectively, so that the graduations on the x scale will not be at equal intervals. Let P be the point given by x and y on the two scales, and O the point where the zero of both scales would be if it were on the paper. Then

$$OP = y \text{ in.} = \sqrt{x} \text{ in. and } OA = 3 \text{ in}$$

$$\therefore AP = (\sqrt{x} - 3) \text{ in.}$$

The calculation of the positions of P corresponding to $x = 10$, 20, 30, etc., is set out in the table below.

x	10	15	20	25	30	35	40	45	50	55	60
$AP = \sqrt{x} - 3$	0·162	0·873	1·472	2	2·477	2·916	3·324	3·708	4·071	4·416	4·746

Fig. 169 shows the x and y scales constructed in this way. It will be noticed that although the graduations of the x scale

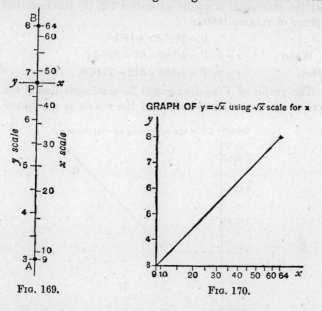

Fig. 169.

GRAPH OF $y = \sqrt{x}$ using $\sqrt{x}$ scale for x

Fig. 170.

are not uniform the distance from 45 to 50 is little different from the distance from 40 to 45, so that over a short interval such as 40 to 45 there will be little error in taking the graduation to be uniform; e.g. we find from the figure that $\sqrt{43} \simeq 6.55$, the correct value being 6·56.

The relation $y = \sqrt{x}$ may also be shown by a straight line graph   If the scales used above for x and y are used on perpendicular axes Ox, Oy (Fig. 170), taking the point O at $x = 9$, $y = 3$, the graph of y against x will be a straight line because the graph of y against x using this non-uniform graduation on Ox is the same as the graph of y against $\sqrt{x}$ using uniform graduation on Ox. The point $x = 9$, $y = 3$ is on the graph and another point is found by taking $x = 64$, $y = 8$.

Example.—Draw a straight line graph to show the volume V of a sphere of radius r from $r = 4$ to 8. From it read off (*a*) the volume of a sphere of radius $7 \cdot 2$, (*b*) the radius of a sphere of volume 1000.

$$V = \tfrac{4}{3}\pi r^3 \fallingdotseq 4 \cdot 189 r^3.$$

When $\quad r = 4, \ V = 4 \cdot 189 \times 64 = 268 \cdot 1$;

when $\quad r = 8, \ V = 4 \cdot 189 \times 512 = 2144 \cdot 8$.

The graph of V against r will be a straight line if the V axis is graduated uniformly and the r axis is graduated so

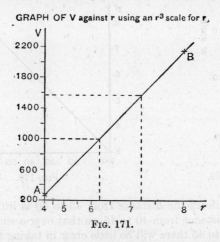

GRAPH OF V against r using an r³ scale for r,

Fig. 171.

that lengths from $r = 0$ are proportional to r^3 instead of r. Hence we make a uniform V scale from 200 to 2200 on the vertical axis using a scale of 100 units to $0 \cdot 4$ in. say. On the r axis r^3 has to go from 64 to 512 so that a suitable scale is 80 units of r^3 to 1 in.

To make the scale on the r axis, the length from 4 to r has to be $\frac{1}{80}(r^3 - 4^3) = (\frac{1}{80}r^3 - 0\cdot8)$ in. The calculation of the position of the graduations is set out below.

r	..	..	4	4·5	5·0	5·5	6·0	6·5	7·0	7·5	8·0
r^3	..	..	64	91·13	125	166·4	216	274·6	343	421·9	512
$\dfrac{r^3}{80}$	..	..	0·8	1·14	1·56	2·08	2·70	3·43	4·29	5·27	6·40
$\dfrac{r^3}{80}-0\cdot8$	..		0	0·34	0·76	1·28	1·90	2·63	3·49	4·47	5·60

The last line of this table gives the number of inches from 4 to r on the r scale. To draw the required graph we plot the points $r = 4$, $V = 268\cdot1$; $r = 8$, $V = 2144\cdot8$; and also $r = 6$, $V = 904\cdot8$ as a check, and then draw the straight line through

GRAPH OF V against r using log scales on both axes

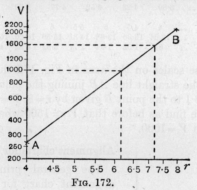

FIG. 172.

these points (Fig. 171). From this line we find that when $r = 7\cdot2$, $V \backsimeq 1560$ and when $V = 1000$, $r \backsimeq 6\cdot25$.

The student should check these results by direct calculation.

An alternative method in this example is to take logs. This gives

$$\log V = \log 4\cdot189 + 3 \log r.$$

Hence the graph of V against r is a straight line if the lengths representing V and r are actually $\log V$ and $\log r$. Since $\log 200 = 2\cdot3010$ and $\log 2200 = 3\cdot3424$ a suitable scale on the V axis is 0·2 unit of log V to 1 in. This means that the distance from 200 to V is $\dfrac{\log V - \log 200}{0·2}$ in., which is 5 log V − 11·505 in. Also, since log 4 = 0·6021 and log 8 = 0·9031, a suitable scale on the r axis is 0·05 unit of log r to 1 in. Hence the distance from 4 to r is $\dfrac{\log r - \log 4}{0·05}$ in. which is 20 log r − 12·042 in. The calculation of these lengths is set out below.

V	200	250	300	400	600	800	1000
5 log V	11·50	11·99	12·39	13·01	13·89	14·52	15·00
5 log V−11·50 ..	0	0·49	0·89	1·51	2·39	3·01	3·50

V	1200	1400	1600	1800	2000	2200
5 log V	15·40	15·73	16·02	16·28	16·50	16·71
5 log V−11·50 ..	3·89	4·23	4·52	4·77	5·00	5·21

r	4	4·5	5	5·5	6	6·5	7	7·5	8
20 log r	12·04	13·06	13·98	14·81	15·56	16·26	16·90	17·50	18·06
20 log r−12·04 ..	0	1·02	1·94	2·77	3·52	4·22	4·86	5·46	6·02

Using these scales on the axes in Fig. 172 the graph of V against r is the straight line AB joining the point A given by $r = 4$, $V = 268·1$ to the point B given by $r = 8$, $V = 2145$. From this graph we find as before that $V \fallingdotseq 1560$ when $r = 7·2$ and $r \fallingdotseq 6·2$ when $V = 1000$.

Alignment charts for two variables

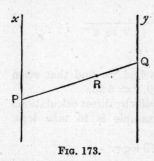

FIG. 173.

The general principle of an alignment chart for two related variables x and y is that values of x and y are shown by scales on two parallel lines and corresponding values of x and y lie on a straight line through a fixed point R. Thus to find the value of y for any given x, all that is necessary is to lay a ruler so that its edge passes through the given value of x at P and through the fixed point R and to read off the value of y

at the point Q where the edge of the ruler cuts the y scale.
The fact that these points P, Q, R are aligned gives the name
" alignment chart " to this type of chart ; it is also called a
" nomogram."

Example.—Draw an alignment chart for the relation
$2x + 3y = 6$ from $x = -3$ to $x = 12$.

Make an x scale on AB from -3 at A to 12 at B using a
scale of 1 unit to 0·4 in., and, since $y = 4$ at $x = -3$ and

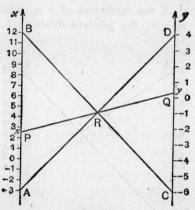

Fig. 174.

$y = -6$ at $x = 12$, make a uniform y scale on CD going from
-6 at C to 4 at D, using a scale of 1 unit to 0·6 in.

Join AD and BC and let them meet in R. Then we shall
show that R is the fixed point mentioned above. Draw any
line through R to cut the scales in P and Q, and let P be at
x on the x scale and Q be at y on the y scale. Then by
similar triangles

$$\frac{AP}{AR} = \frac{DQ}{DR} \text{ and } \frac{AB}{AR} = \frac{DC}{DR},$$

so that, on dividing,

$$\frac{AP}{AB} = \frac{DQ}{DC}.$$

Hence
$$\frac{x+3}{15} = \frac{4-y}{10}.$$

$$\therefore \ 2x + 3y = 6.$$

This shows that the values of x and y are related by the given law.

In the same way an alignment chart can be made for any linear law, i.e. any law of the form $ax + by = c$. For the above example the positive directions for both x and y scales are the same; but, if the coefficient of y is negative as in the equation $2x - 3y = 10$, the positive direction for the y scale

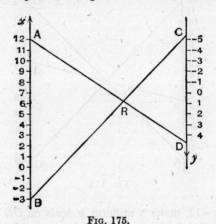

FIG. 175.

must be in the opposite direction to the positive direction for the x scale because $(-y)$ has replaced y in the equation.*
Fig. 175 shows an alignment chart for the equation $2x - 3y = 10$ from $x = -3$ to 12.

An alignment chart can also be used for any law that becomes linear when non-uniform scales are used. For

* By taking the fixed point not between the axes it is still possible to have the positive directions of the axes the same, but it is generally inconvenient to have the fixed point in this position.

instance, the logarithmic scales used on the axes in Fig. 172
for r and V are drawn on parallel lines AB and CD in
Fig. 176 the positive direction for the r scale being downwards, because the sign of $\log r$ is negative when the
equation $\log V = 4\cdot189 + 3 \log r$ (page 315) is written as
$\log V - 3 \log r = 4\cdot189$.   Two pairs of corresponding points

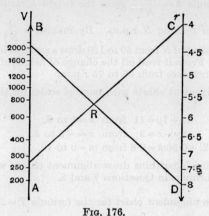

FIG. 176.

are joined to find the fixed point R.   The figure then forms
an alignment chart for V and r.

Exercise XXXII

1. If the pressure due to h in. of mercury at 0° C. is p lb./in.²,
$p = 0\cdot490\ h$.   Construct uniform scales along the same line to
convert h to p for values of h from 25 to 40.

2. Make a chart with uniform adjacent scales to convert
degrees Fahrenheit to Centigrade over a range $-50°$ F. to $50°$ F.

3. From Fig. 169 read off $\sqrt{23}$, $\sqrt{57}$ and 5^2.

4. From Fig. 171 read off the volume of a sphere of 7·6 in.
radius and the radius of a sphere with a volume of 800 cu. in.

5. Make a chart with adjacent scales (one uniform the other
non-uniform) from which to read the reciprocals of numbers
from 10 to 30.   From it read off the reciprocal of 18·7.

6. Make a chart with adjacent scales to give the sines of angles from 30° to 90°.

7. By making an r^2 scale on the r axis draw a straight line graph of the formula $A = \pi r^2$ for the area of a circle of radius r from $r = 10$ to $r = 20$. From it read off the values of r when $A = 400$ and when $A = 850$.

8. The formula $h = \dfrac{35,230}{N^2}$ gives the height h in. of a simple Watt governor making N r.p.m. By making a $\dfrac{1}{N^2}$ scale along one axis for values of N from 50 to 120 draw a straight line graph of h against N. From it read off the change of height of a governor as the speed increases from 55 to 75 r.p.m.

9. Draw alignment charts with parallel scales for the following equations :

(a) $\qquad\qquad 4x + 7y = 11$ from $x = 1$ to 8.
(b) $\qquad\qquad 2y - x = 9$ from $x = -5$ to 5.
(c) $\qquad 0 \cdot 32l + 0 \cdot 56m = 0 \cdot 8$ from $m = 0$ to 10.

10. By taking logarithms draw alignment charts with parallel axes for the formulæ in Questions 7 and 8.

11. Draw an alignment chart for the formula $T = 2\pi\sqrt{\dfrac{l}{g}}$ which gives the time of oscillation T sec. of a pendulum of length l ft. Take $g = 32 \cdot 19$, $\pi = 3 \cdot 142$ and draw the chart for values of l from 0 to 5.

The slide rule

The principle of a slide-rule is the same as that of the adjacent scales described on pages 311, 312 When the slide is put in one position the scales on the slide and the rule form a pair of adjacent logarithmic scales.

On a slide-rule there are four main scales, A and D on the rule and B and C on the slide. If the slide is pushed in so that the 1's on the four scales are in line as in Fig. 177 it will be seen that scale B is the same as scale A, and scale C the same as scale D. Scales A and B are scales in which the lengths from the 1's on the scales are proportional to the logarithms of the numbers, e.g. in a 25-cm. rule the distance

from 1 to 100 on the A and B scales is 25 cm. and hence
log 100, which is 2, is represented by 25 cm.; these are
scales, therefore, of 1 unit of log x to 12·5 cm. The distance
from 1 to a number x on these scales is log x times this unit;
we may call it log x on the assumption that the unit is 12·5 cm.

The C and D scales are similar but in them 1 unit of log x
is represented by the whole length of the scale, so that the

FIG. 177.

distance from 1 to x on this scale is 2 log x times the unit of
12·5 cm. Since 2 log $x = $ log x^2, the number x^2 on the A and
B scales is opposite x on the C and D scales. It follows that
numbers on the A and B scales are the squares of the numbers
immediately below them on the C and D scales, and numbers
on the C and D scales are the square roots of the numbers
immediately above them on the A and B scales.

Use of scales A and B for multiplication and division

If 1 on B (slide) is placed against x on A (rule) and y on B
is then opposite z on A,

$$\log z = \log x + \log y \text{ (Fig. 178)}$$
$$\therefore z = xy.$$

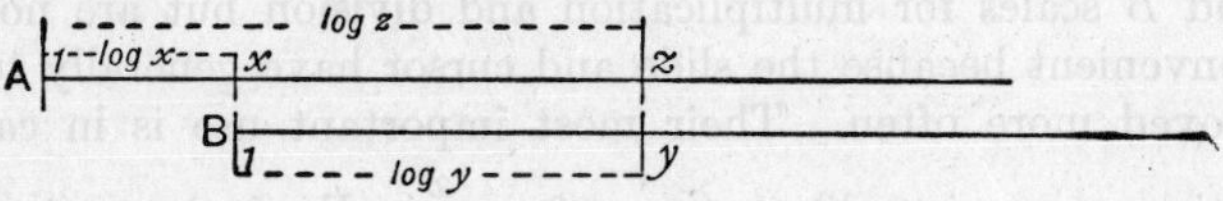

A ┌────── $\log z$ ──────┐
  ┌── $\log x$ ──┐x z
B └─────── $\log y$ ──────┘y

FIG. 178.

Conversely with the slide in the same position

$$x = \frac{z}{y}.$$

11

To save moving the slide an unnecessary number of times it is advisable to do multiplications and divisions alternately. In all calculations involving multiplications and divisions only, the decimal point is ignored, its position being afterwards found by a rough check. Because of this it is immaterial whether we use 2 or 20 on the A or B scales.

Example.—Find $\dfrac{2 \cdot 73 \times 0 \cdot 0915 \times 679}{0 \cdot 0473 \times 51 \cdot 2 \times 1024}$.

Set $473B$, meaning 473 on the B scale, against $273A$, then $1B$ is against $\dfrac{273}{473}A$. Hence $915B$ is against $\dfrac{273}{473} \times 915A$. This part of the calculation has been done with one setting of the slide. Now put the cursor at $915B$ and bring $512B$ under the cursor line. Then $1B$ is opposite $\dfrac{273 \times 915}{473 \times 512}A$, and hence $679B$ is opposite $\dfrac{273 \times 915 \times 679}{473 \times 512}A$.

Finally place the cursor over $679B$, bring $1024B$ under the cursor line and read off the answer 684 on A opposite $1B$. The approximate value of the expression is

$$\frac{3 \times 10^{-1} \times 7 \times 10^2}{5 \times 10^{-2} \times 5 \times 10 \times 10^3} = \frac{21}{250} \backsimeq 0 \cdot 08.$$

Hence   expression $= 0 \cdot 0684$.

Use of the C and D scales

The C and D scales can be used in the same way as the A and B scales for multiplication and division but are not so convenient because the slide and cursor have generally to be moved more often. Their most important use is in calculating expressions like $\sqrt{x}y$, xy^2 or $\dfrac{x}{y^2}$. For instance, to find out how to calculate $\sqrt{x}y$ we let $z = \sqrt{x}y$, then

$$z^2 = xy^2$$
$$\therefore \log z^2 = \log x + \log y^2.$$

Hence we set $1C$ opposite xA and read off the answer zD opposite yC, as shown in Fig. 179.

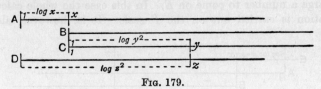

Fig. 179.

Example.—What length of a cylindrical rod of 2·17 in. radius must be cut off to give a volume of 3·75 cu. in. ?

If h is the length, $3·75 = \pi \times 2·17^2 \times h.$

$$\therefore h = \frac{3·75}{\pi \times 2·17^2}.$$

Set π on B scale against $1A$, move the cursor line to $375B$, move slide so that $217C$ comes under the cursor line and read off the answer hA opposite $1C$. The reason for this setting is left as an example for the student. It is found that $h = 0·253$.

The log log scales

At the top and bottom of the rule will be found two scales which we will call E and F (see Fig. 177, page 321). On the E scale the distance from $1D$ to xE is $(\log_{10} \log_{10} x + a \text{ con-}$ stant k) times the unit 25 cm. of the C and D scales.* On the F scale the distance from $1D$ to xF is $(\log_{10} \log_{10} x + k - 1)$ times the unit of the C and D scales. We shall see that the value of k is generally immaterial.† These scales are used in conjunction with the scale C to calculate x^y.

If $z = x^y,\ \log z = y \log x$

$$\therefore \log \log z = \log y + \log \log x$$

$$\therefore \log \log z + k = \log y + (\log \log x + k).$$

---

* Note that the unit of length in Figs. 180, 181 is 25 cm., whereas the unit in Figs. 178, 179 is 12·5 cm.

† Actually $k = 1 - \log_{10} \log_{10} e$.

Hence to find z we set $1C$ against xE and read off the answer z on E opposite yC. It is clear that x may be too large a number to come on E. In this case the whole calculation is carried out on the F scale. It is, however, also

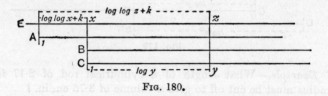

FIG. 180.

possible for x to come on scale E but yC to come outside the rule. In this case we can write the above equation.

$$\log \log z + k - 1 = (\log \log x + k) - (1 - \log y).$$

This shows that if we set $10C$ against xE the answer z is on F opposite yC as shown by Fig. 181.

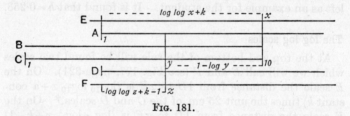

FIG. 181.

Example.—Find the value of $1 \cdot 83^{3 \cdot 67}$.

Set $10C$ against $1 \cdot 83E$ and read off the answer on F against $3 \cdot 67C$.

Exercise XXXIII

Find the values of the following by using a slide rule :

1. $39 \cdot 5^2$.   **2.** $\sqrt{195 \cdot 6}$.   **3.** $\sqrt{0 \cdot 1956}$.   **4.** $0 \cdot 769^2$.

5. $4 \cdot 96 \times 0 \cdot 0717^2$.   **6.** $\dfrac{2 \cdot 39 \times 0 \cdot 397 \times 56 \cdot 1}{43 \cdot 9 \times 193}$.   **7.** $0 \cdot 908 \times \sqrt{73 \cdot 2}$.

Explain how you would use a slide rule to calculate:

8. xy^2.   **9.** $\dfrac{x}{\sqrt{y}}$.   **10.** x^2y^2.

By using the log log scales find the values of:

11. $2 \cdot 19^{6 \cdot 95}$.   **12.** $6 \cdot 93^{1 \cdot 41}$.   **13.** $1 \cdot 14^{26 \cdot 3}$.

14. Show that if the slide is put in the opposite way round so that $10D$ comes opposite $1C$ then $\dfrac{1}{x}D$ is opposite xC so that the numbers on the D scale are the reciprocals of the numbers on the C scale.

15. Assuming that the distance from $1D$ to xE is

$$\log_{10} \log_{10} x + 1 - \log_{10} \log_{10} e$$

show that $e^{0 \cdot 1}E$ is opposite $1D$ and eE is opposite $10D$. Show also that yD is opposite $e^{0 \cdot 1y}E$.

16. Show that yD is opposite $e^y F$. Find the value of $e^{3 \cdot 7}$.

17. Make a slide rule 6 in. long in which the distances from the zeros on the rule and the slide to the point x are $\frac{1}{6}x^2$ in. Use the rule to find the hypotenuse of a right-angled triangle with sides $4 \cdot 7$ and $3 \cdot 9$ units, and to find the third side of a right-angled triangle which has a hypotenuse $7 \cdot 1$ units and one other side $5 \cdot 8$ units.

18. If a slide rule is made so that the distance from the left-hand end of the rule and the slide to the point marked x is $\dfrac{10}{x}$ in. (so that the left-hand end is marked ∞), show that the slide rule can be used to find z from x and y when $\dfrac{1}{z} = \dfrac{1}{x} + \dfrac{1}{y}$. Make such a rule and use it to find the equivalent resistance of two resistances of $6 \cdot 3$ and $2 \cdot 8$ ohms placed in parallel.

Alignment charts for relations between three variables

On page 317 an alignment chart was drawn for the equation $2x + 3y = 6$. Clearly this is a chart for the equation $2x + 3y = z$ when $z = 6$. This suggests that, if a z axis is drawn through R parallel to AB with a suitable scale, a straight line will cut the three axes of x, y and z in values of x, y and z which satisfy the equation $2x + 3y = z$.

To construct an alignment chart for $ax + by = z$

Draw x and y axes AB and CD at any convenient distance apart and let the scales on these axes be k units to 1 in. and l units to 1 in. respectively, these scales being chosen according to the range of values of x and y that have to be represented.

Suppose a z axis EF is drawn parallel to AB through a point E on AC which divides AC in the ratio $\alpha : \beta$. Let the scale on the z axis be m units to 1 in.

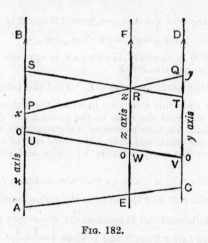

Fig. 182.

Since $z = 0$ when $x = 0$ and $y = 0$ the zero points U, V, W, of the three scales must lie on a straight line. Because the lines AB, CD and EF are parallel

$$\frac{UW}{WV} = \frac{AE}{EC} = \frac{\alpha}{\beta}.$$

Let any line cut AB, CD and EF in three points P, Q, R given by x, y and z respectively on the three scales, and let a line SRT parallel to UVW cut AB and CD in S and T.

Now, since U is the zero of the x scale and P is at x,

$$UP = \frac{x}{k} \text{ in.}$$

Similarly $$VQ = \frac{y}{l} \text{ in., } WR = \frac{z}{m} \text{ in.}$$

$$PS = US - UP$$
$$= WR - UP$$
$$= \left(\frac{z}{m} - \frac{x}{k} \right) \text{ in.}$$

and $$TQ = VQ - VT$$
$$= VQ - WR$$
$$= \left(\frac{y}{l} - \frac{z}{m} \right) \text{ in.}$$

But the triangles SRP and TRQ are similar.

$$\therefore \frac{PS}{TQ} = \frac{SR}{RT} = \frac{UW}{WV} = \frac{\alpha}{\beta}$$

$$\therefore \frac{\dfrac{z}{m} - \dfrac{x}{k}}{\dfrac{y}{l} - \dfrac{z}{m}} = \frac{\alpha}{\beta}$$

$$\therefore \beta \left(\frac{z}{m} - \frac{x}{k} \right) = \alpha \left(\frac{y}{l} - \frac{z}{m} \right)$$

$$\therefore \frac{\beta x}{k} - \frac{\beta z}{m} = \frac{\alpha z}{m} - \frac{\alpha y}{l}$$

$$\therefore \frac{\beta x}{k} + \frac{\alpha y}{l} = \frac{(\alpha + \beta)z}{m}.$$

Clearly this becomes

$$ax + by = z$$

if we make

$$\beta = ka, \ \alpha = lb \text{ and } m = \alpha + \beta = ka + lb.$$

Hence we have the following rules for the construction of the chart :

1. Draw x and y axes AB, CD at a convenient distance apart and choose the scales on them, k units to 1 in. and l units to 1 in. respectively, so that AB and CD show the required range of values of x and y. AC need not be perpendicular to AB and CD.

2. Draw a z axis EF parallel to AB and CD through a point E dividing AC in the ratio lb/ka.

3. Find the zero on the z axis by joining the zeros on the x and y axes, or, if the zeros of the x and y axes do not come on the paper, find the value of z at E from the equation $ax + by = z$.

4. Make a scale on the z axis $(ka + lb)$ units to 1 in., starting at the zero W, or at E, if W does not come on the paper. If a and b are positive, z increases with x and y, so the positive direction for z is upwards. If the sign of either x or y or z is changed, the positive direction for the corresponding axis must be downwards.

Example.—If the wheels a and b in Fig. 183 have 60 and 24 teeth respectively and N_a, N_b, N_c are the number of revolutions per minute of the wheels a and b and of the arm c,

FIG. 183.

$$N_b = 3 \cdot 5 N_c - 2 \cdot 5 N_a.$$

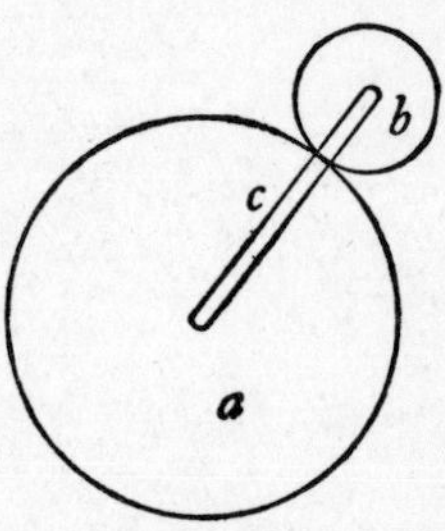

Draw an alignment chart to give the value of N_b from $N_c = 0$ to 50 and $N_a = 0$ to 100. From it read off the value of N_b when $N_c = 25$ and $N_a = 86$.

Make scales for N_c of 10 units per inch and N_a 20 units per inch on AB and CD two parallel lines 5 in. apart, the scale on CD starting from the top D because the term $2 \cdot 5 N_a$ has a negative sign prefixed to it in the equation. Then

$k = 10$, $l = 20$ and comparing the equation with $z = ax - by$, $a = 3·5$ and $b = 2·5$. Choose E on AC so that

$$\frac{AE}{EC} = \frac{lb}{ka} = \frac{20 \times 2·5}{10 \times 3·5} = \frac{50}{35}.$$

$$\therefore \frac{AE}{AC} = \frac{50}{85} = \frac{10}{17} \quad \text{and} \quad AE = \frac{10}{17} \times 5 \text{ in.} \backsimeq 2·94 \text{ in.}$$

Draw an axis EF parallel to AB on which to make the scale for N_b. Join the zeros of N_c and N_a and let the joining line cut EF in W. Then, since $N_b = 0$ when $N_c = 0$ and $N_a = 0$,

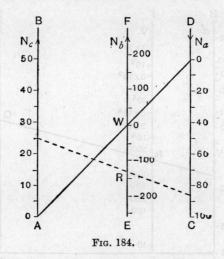

Fig. 184.

W is the zero of the N_b scale. The scale for N_b has to be $(ka + lb)$ units per inch, which is 85 units per inch. To make this scale it is useful to make the table below.

Units		50	100	150	200	250
Inches on scale		0·588	1·176	1·765	2·353	2·941

This table enables us to mark the graduations on EF from -250 to 200.

11*

Fig. 184 shows the completed nomogram. The dotted line is the line which gives the value of N_b when $N_c = 25$ and $N_a = 86$. The value of N_b at R is nearly -128. (The calculated value is $-127\cdot5$.)

Scales with unequal graduations can be used on all three axes in the same way as for two variables.

Example.—The formula $V = 3\cdot9 d^{\frac{5}{2}} h^{\frac{1}{2}}$ gives the rate of discharge of air V cu. ft. per min. through a pipe of diameter d in. when the pressure drops h in. of water per 100 ft. length

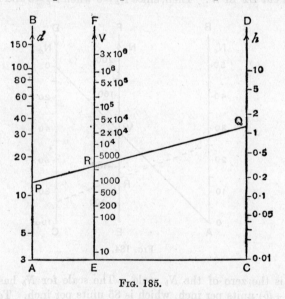

FIG. 185.

of pipe. Draw a line chart for this equation for values of d from 3 to 150 and values of h from 0·01 to 10.

Taking logs

$$\log V = \log 3\cdot9 + \tfrac{5}{2} \log d + \tfrac{1}{2} \log h$$
$$\therefore \ \log V - \log 3\cdot9 = \tfrac{5}{2} \log d + \tfrac{1}{2} \log h.$$

Comparing this with $z = ax + by$ we see that x, y and z are replaced by $\log d$, $\log h$ and $\log V - \log 3 \cdot 9$ and also $a = \frac{5}{2}$, $b = \frac{1}{2}$.

Let AB, CD and EF be the three axes for d, h and V with the points A, E and C lying on a straight line, and let P, Q and R be the points on the axes corresponding to d, h and V. Since d goes from 3 to 150, $\log d$ goes from $0 \cdot 477$ to $2 \cdot 176$, so a suitable scale on AB is $\frac{1}{4}$ unit of $\log d$ to 1 in. Because A is at 3 and P is at d the length of AP is

$$4(\log d - \log 3) = 4(\log d - 0 \cdot 477) \text{ in.}$$

In the same way, since h goes from $0 \cdot 01$ to 10, $\log h$ goes from -2 to 1, so a suitable scale for $\log h$ is 2 units to 1 in. and therefore $CQ = 2 (\log h - \log 0 \cdot 01) = 2 (\log h + 2)$ in.

To find the position of E on AC

$$\frac{AE}{EC} = \frac{lb}{ka} = \frac{\frac{1}{2} \times \frac{1}{2}}{\frac{1}{4} \times \frac{5}{2}} = \frac{2}{5}.$$

$$\therefore \frac{AE}{AC} = \frac{2}{7}.$$

This ratio makes it convenient for AC to be 7 in. so that AE is 2 in. The scale of the V axis is

$$ka + lb = \frac{5}{8} + \frac{1}{4} = \frac{7}{8} \text{ unit of } \log V \text{ to 1 in.,}$$

or   1 unit of $\log V = \frac{8}{7}$ in.

Since $d = 3$ at A and $h = 0 \cdot 01$ at C, at the point E

$$\log V = \log 3 \cdot 9 + \tfrac{5}{2} \log 3 + \tfrac{1}{2} \log 0 \cdot 01$$

$$= 0 \cdot 591 + 1 \cdot 193 - 1 = 0 \cdot 784$$

$$\therefore V = 6 \cdot 08 \text{ at } E.$$

Also the length of ER is $\frac{8}{7} (\log V - 0 \cdot 784)$ in.

Since $d = 150$ when $h = 10$, the corresponding point on EF is given by

$$\log V = \log 3 \cdot 9 + \tfrac{5}{2} \log 150 + \tfrac{1}{2} \log 10$$

$$= 0 \cdot 591 + 5 \cdot 440 + 0 \cdot 5 = 6 \cdot 531$$

$$\therefore V = 3 \cdot 40 \times 10^{6}.$$

Thus the V scale runs from roughly 6 to 3.4×10^6.

The following tables show the calculation of AP, CQ and ER for a series of values of d, h and V :

d	3	5	10	20	30	40	50
$\log d - 0.477$	0	0.222	0.523	0.824	1	1.125	1.222
$AP = 4 (\log d - 0.477)$	0	0.888	2.092	3.296	4	4.5	4.888

d	60	70	80	90	100	150
$\log d - 0.477$	1.301	1.368	1.426	1.477	1.523	1.699
$AP = 4 (\log d - 0.477)$	5.204	5.472	5.704	5.908	6.092	6.796

h	0.01	0.02	0.03	0.04	0.05	0.1	0.2	0.5	1	2	5	10
$\log h + 2$	0	0.301	0.477	0.602	0.699	1	1.301	1.699	2	2.301	2.699	3
$CQ = 2 (\log h + 2)$	0	0.602	0.954	1.204	1.398	2	2.602	3.398	4	4.602	5.398	6

V	10	100	200	500	1000	2000	5000	10^4
$\log V - 0.784$	0.216	1.216	1.517	1.915	2.216	2.517	2.915	3.216
$ER = \frac{8}{7} (\log V - 0.784)$	0.25	1.39	1.73	2.19	2.53	2.88	3.33	3.68

V	2×10^4	5×10^4	10^5	2×10^5	5×10^5	10^6	3×10^6
$\log V - 0.784$	3.517	3.915	4.216	4.517	4.915	5.216	5.693
$ER = \frac{8}{7} (\log V - 0.784)$	4.02	4.47	4.82	5.16	5.62	5.96	6.51

The points given by the tables are shown in Fig. 185.

Families of curves

Consider the equation $w = uv$. If v is given a special value, say 2, the equation becomes $w = 2u$ which is a relation between two variables only and so its graph can be drawn. By giving v a series of special values and drawing the graphs of the corresponding equations between w and u we obtain a diagram from which the value of w can be read off when u has any value and v has one of the chosen values. Fig. 186 shows the graphs of $w = uv$ for values of u from 0 to 10 and values of v at intervals of 0.25 from 0 to 2. Each value of v is written on the right-hand side against the corresponding graph.

Although the graphs are drawn only for special values of v the diagram can be used to approximate to values of w for values of v between these special values. For instance, when $u = 8.22$, $v = 0.31$ the point P which gives w is roughly in the position shown in the figure.   To find the value of w we note that $\dfrac{AP}{AB} = \dfrac{(0\cdot31 - 0\cdot25)}{(0\cdot5 - 0\cdot25)} = \dfrac{0\cdot06}{0\cdot25} \approx \dfrac{1}{4}$ and hence

$$w \approx 2 + \tfrac{1}{4}(4\cdot2 - 2) = 2\cdot55,$$

where 2 and $4\cdot2$ are the values of w at A and B.

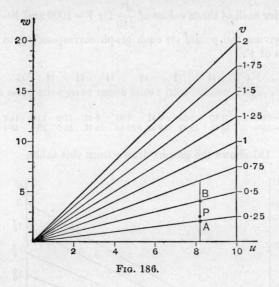

Fig. 186.

Example.—The horse-power H transmitted by cotton driving ropes is given by

$$H = \frac{d^2 V}{240}.$$

when V ft./min. is the speed and d in. is the diameter of the rope in inches.   Draw a chart to show the graphs of H against V from $V = 1000$ to $V = 3000$ for values of d at intervals of $\frac{1}{8}$ from 1 to 2.

When d has a fixed value the graph of H against V is a straight line, e.g. when $d = 1$ it is the graph of $H = \dfrac{V}{240}$. Each of these straight lines can be drawn by finding the co-ordinates of two points. In the following table the values of $\dfrac{d^2}{240}$ are calculated for each value of d and the values of H are calculated for each of these values of $\dfrac{d^2}{240}$ for $V = 1000$ and $V = 3000$, thus giving the points on each graph corresponding to these values of V.

d	..	1	$1\frac{1}{8}$	$1\frac{1}{4}$	$1\frac{3}{8}$	$1\frac{1}{2}$	$1\frac{5}{8}$	$1\frac{3}{4}$	$1\frac{7}{8}$	2
$\frac{d^2}{240}$	..	0·00417	0·00527	0·00651	0·00788	0·00937	0·0110	0·0128	0·0146	0·0167
H at $V=1000$	..	4·17	5·27	6·51	7·88	9·37	11·0	12·8	14·6	16·7
H at $V=3000$	..	12·51	15·81	19·53	23·64	28·11	33·0	38·4	43·8	50·1

Fig. 187 shows the graphs drawn from this table.

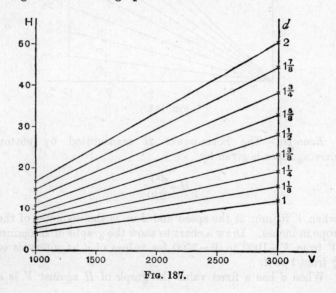

Fig. 187.

Exercise XXXIV

1. Draw alignment charts to give the value of z in the following cases :

    (a) $z = x + y$; $x = 0$ to 5, $y = 4$ to 10.

    (b) $z = x - y$; $x = 0$ to 5, $y = -2$ to 4.

    (c) $z = x - y + 3$; $x = 0$ to 5, $y = -2$ to 4.

    (d) $z = 2 \cdot 4x + 1 \cdot 3y$; $x = -2$ to 4, $y = -3$ to 9.

2. If a resistance R ohms is equivalent to resistances R_1 ohms and R_2 ohms in series, $R = R_1 + R_2$; draw an alignment chart to give R for values of R_1 from 0 to 2 and values of R_2 from 0 to 1.

3. If the pressures at two points in a pipe containing fresh water are p_1, p_2 lb. wt./in.^{2} respectively the height h ft. of one point above the other is given by $h = 0 \cdot 276(p_1 - p_2)$. Draw an alignment chart to give the values of h from $p_1 = 40$ to 100 and $p_2 = 0$ to 60.

4. If an alloy of copper, tin and zinc contains $c\%$ copper, $t\%$ tin its density d is given by

$$d = 443 + 1 \cdot 121c - 0 \cdot 13t.$$

Draw a line chart to give the value of d from $c = 80$ to 90 and $t = 6$ to 12. From it read off the value of d when $c = 82 \cdot 5$ and $t = 7 \cdot 5$.

5. From the alignment chart in Fig. 185 read (1) the value of V when $d = 55$, $h = 0 \cdot 75$, (2) the value of h necessary to make $V = 50,000$ when $d = 95$.

6. The volume V of a rectangular box of length h and with a square base of side x is given by $V = hx^2$. By taking logarithms, draw a line chart of this equation for values of x from 1 to 6 and values of h from 1 to 4.

7. The area of a sector of a circle of radius r is given by $A = \dfrac{\pi r^2 \theta}{360}$, where $\theta°$ is the angle between the bounding radii. Draw an alignment chart to give the value of A for values of r from 0 to 5 and of θ from 30 to 180. Find from it the area of a sector of a circle of radius $2 \cdot 6$ in. which contains an angle of $108°$.

8. The formula $B = \dfrac{2\pi NT}{33,000}$ gives the brake horse-power in terms of the engine speed N r.p.m. and the torque T lb. wt./ft. Draw an alignment chart to give B from $N = 200$ to 5000 and $T = 15$ to 300. From it read off the value of B when $N = 1086$ and $T = 216$.

9. If h kilometres is the difference in height between two stations and p_1, p_2 mm. of mercury are the readings of the barometer at the two stations, $p_2 = p_1 e^{-\frac{h}{8}}$ nearly.

By taking logarithms this becomes $h \backsimeq 18.42\ (\log p_1 - \log p_2)$. Using this equation make a nomogram to show the values of h for values of p_1 between 600 and 760 and values of p_2 between 400 and 760. From it read off the value of h when $p_1 = 635$ and $p_2 = 520$.

10. If the resistivity of a wire is ρ microhms per cm.[3] and its diameter is d mm., its resistance R ohms per metre is given by $R = \dfrac{\rho}{25\pi d^2}$. Draw graphs of R against ρ from $\rho = 1$ to 100 for wires of S.W.G. 10, 11, . . 20 whose diameters are given by :

S.W.G.	10	11	12	13	14	15	16	17	18	19	20
d	0·128	0·116	0·104	0·092	0·080	0·072	0·064	0·056	0·048	0·040	0·036

11. For a certain gas the relation between the pressure p lb./in.[2], the volume v in.[3] and the temperature $T°$ C. is

$$pv = 1.5(T + 273).$$

Draw the graphs of p against v for the following values of T : 20, 40, 60, 80, 100. These curves are called iso-thermal curves, i.e. equal temperature curves. From your figure, find approximately the value of p when $v = 2.4$; $T = 75$.

12. If water flows through a pipe of inside diameter d in. at v in./sec., the weight of water w lb. wt. that flows per hour is given by $w = 100d^2 v$ nearly. Draw the graphs of w against v from $v = 4$ to 120 for values of d at intervals of $\frac{1}{2}$ from $\frac{1}{2}$ to 6.

13. The empirical equation $d = \dfrac{p}{0.753(t + 460)}$ gives the density of dry air d lb./ft.[3] in terms of its pressure p in. of mercury and its temperature $t°$ F. Draw the iso-thermal lines from this equation for $t = -60,\ -40,\ -20,\ 0,\ 20,\ 40,\ 60$.

APPENDIX

Archimedes' method of finding areas as the limit of a sum

Let the area under the curve $y = x^2$ from $x = 0$ to a be divided into n strips by ordinates at equal intervals $\dfrac{a}{n}$. The lengths of these ordinates are $\dfrac{a^2}{n^2}, \dfrac{2^2 a^2}{n^2}, \dfrac{3^2 a^2}{n^2}, \ldots \dfrac{(n-1)^2 a^2}{n^2}$. The sum of the areas of the rectangles shaded in Fig. 188 is therefore

$$\left\{ \frac{a^2}{n^2} + \frac{2^2 a^2}{n^2} + \ldots + \frac{(n-1)^2 a^2}{n^2} \right\} \frac{a}{n}$$

$$= \frac{a^3}{n^3} \{ 1^2 + 2^2 + \ldots + (n-1)^2 \}.$$

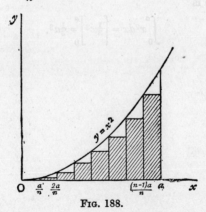

FIG. 188.

But $\qquad 1^2 + 2^2 + 3^2 + \ldots + n^2 = \tfrac{1}{6} n(n+1)(2n+1)$

(See Exercise VI, Question 12.)

Hence, writing $n - 1$ instead of n,

$$1^2 + 2^2 + \ldots + (n-1)^2 = \tfrac{1}{6}(n-1)n(2n-1) = \tfrac{1}{6}(2n^3 - 3n^2 + n)$$

Therefore the sum of the areas of the rectangles is

$$\frac{a^3}{6n^3}(2n^3 - 3n^2 + n) = \frac{a^3}{3} - \frac{a^3}{2n} + \frac{a^3}{6n^2}.$$

Now this sum approaches the area under the curve from $x = 0$ to a as the number of strips approaches infinity.

$$\therefore \text{ Area under curve} = \lim_{n \to \infty} \left(\frac{a^3}{3} - \frac{a^3}{2n} + \frac{a^3}{6n^2} \right)$$
$$= \tfrac{1}{3}a^3,$$

because $\dfrac{1}{n}$ and $\dfrac{1}{n^2}$ approach 0 as n approaches ∞.

Until the time of Newton areas and volumes were calculated by this method. The invention of the calculus made it possible to find areas and volumes by the much shorter method of definite integration. Thus, by using calculus, the area found above is

$$\int_0^a x^2 dx = \left[\tfrac{1}{3}x^3 \right]_0^a = \tfrac{1}{3}a^3.$$

$\ldots$

COLLECTED FORMULAE

Indices and logarithms

$$a^{p/q} = \sqrt[q]{a^p}, \quad a^{-m} = \frac{1}{a^m}, \quad a^\circ = 1.$$

$$\left.\begin{array}{l} a^m \times a^n = a^{m+n} \\ a^m / a^n = a^{m-n} \\ (a^n)^r = a^{nr} \end{array}\right\} \text{ for all values of } m, n, r, \text{ positive or negative.}$$

$$\log a + \log b = \log ab$$

$$\log a - \log b = \log \frac{a}{b}$$

$$\log a^n = n \log a$$

$$\log_a y = \frac{\log_{10} y}{\log_{10} a}$$

$$\log_e y = 2 \cdot 3026 \log_{10} y.$$

Products and factors

$$(a \pm b)^2 = a^2 \pm 2ab + b^2$$

$$(a \pm b)^3 = a^3 \pm 3a^2 b + 3ab^2 \pm b^3$$

$$a^2 - b^2 = (a+b)(a-b)$$

$$a^3 + b^3 = (a+b)(a^2 - ab + b^2)$$

$$a^3 - b^3 = (a-b)(a^2 + ab + b^2)$$

Quadratic equations

If $ax^2 + bx + c = 0$, $\quad x = \dfrac{-b \pm \sqrt{b^2 - 4ac}}{2a}.$

If $b^2 > 4ac$, the roots are real and unequal.

$b^2 = 4ac$,   ,,   ,,   ,,   equal.

$b^2 < 4ac$,   ,,   ,,   complex.

Sum of roots $= -b/a$;   product of roots $= c/a.$

Series

Arithmetical progression, $a + (a+d) + (a+2d) + \ldots$

$\quad$ nth term $\qquad l = a + (n-1)d$.

$\quad$ Sum of n terms $= \frac{1}{2}n(a+l) = \frac{1}{2}n\{2a + (n-1)d\}$.

Geometrical progression, $a + ar + ar^2 + \ldots$

$\quad$ nth term $\qquad = ar^{n-1}$.

$\quad$ Sum of n terms $= \dfrac{a(1 - r^n)}{1 - r}$.

$\quad$ Sum to infinity $= \dfrac{a}{1 - r}$, if r is numerically less than 1.

Binomial series

$$(1 + x)^n = 1 + nx + \frac{n(n-1)}{1.2}x^2 + \frac{n(n-1)(n-2)}{1.2.3}x^3 + \ldots;$$

the series ends with x^n if n is a positive integer; for all other values of n it is an infinite series and x must be numerically less than 1.

Exponential series

$$e^x = 1 + x + \frac{x^2}{2!} + \frac{x^3}{3!} + \ldots \text{ for all values of } x.$$

Equations of curves

$\quad y = mx + c$; straight line of gradient m through $(0, c)$.

$\quad y = ax^2 + bx + c$; parabola with axis parallel to y axis.

$\quad x^2 + y^2 = a^2$; circle, centre at the origin and radius a.

$\quad \dfrac{x^2}{a^2} + \dfrac{y^2}{b^2} = 1$; ellipse with semi-axes a and b.

$\quad \dfrac{x^2}{a^2} - \dfrac{y^2}{b^2} = 1$; hyperbola with semi-axis a.

$y = a \sin (px + \alpha)$; sine wave of amplitude a and period $\frac{2\pi}{p}$, one wave starting at $x = -\frac{a}{p}$, $y = 0$.

$y = ae^{-kx} \sin (px + a)$; wave of period $\frac{2\pi}{p}$, but with decreasing amplitude (if $k > 0$).

Trigonometry

$\sin (A \pm B) = \sin A \cos B \pm \cos A \sin B$.

$\cos (A \pm B) = \cos A \cos B \mp \sin A \sin B$.

$\tan (A \pm B) = \dfrac{\tan A \pm \tan B}{1 \mp \tan A \tan B}$.

$\sin 2A = 2 \sin A \cos A$

$\cos 2A = \cos^2 A - \sin^2 A = 2 \cos^2 A - 1 = 1 - 2 \sin^2 A$.

$\tan 2A = \dfrac{2 \tan A}{1 - \tan^2 A}$.

$\cos^2 A = \frac{1}{2}(1 + \cos 2A)$, $\sin^2 A = \frac{1}{2}(1 - \cos 2A)$.

If $\tan \dfrac{\theta}{2} = t$, $\sin \theta = \dfrac{2t}{1 + t^2}$, $\cos \theta = \dfrac{1 - t^2}{1 + t^2}$.

$\sin A \cos B = \frac{1}{2}\{\sin (A + B) + \sin (A - B)\}$

$\cos A \sin B = \frac{1}{2}\{\sin (A + B) - \sin (A - B)\}$

$\cos A \cos B = \frac{1}{2}\{\cos (A + B) + \cos (A - B)\}$

$\sin A \sin B = \frac{1}{2}\{\cos (A - B) - \cos (A + B)\}$.

$\sin A + \sin B = 2 \sin \dfrac{A + B}{2} \cos \dfrac{A - B}{2}$

$\sin A - \sin B = 2 \cos \dfrac{A + B}{2} \sin \dfrac{A - B}{2}$

$\cos A + \cos B = 2 \cos \dfrac{A + B}{2} \cos \dfrac{A - B}{2}$

$\cos A - \cos B = 2 \sin \dfrac{A + B}{2} \sin \dfrac{B - A}{2}$.

$$a \sin \theta + b \cos \theta = \sqrt{a^2 + b^2} \sin \left(\theta + \tan^{-1} \frac{b}{a} \right).$$

If θ is small, $\sin \theta^c \simeq \theta$, $\cos \theta^c \simeq 1 - \dfrac{\theta^2}{2}$.

Triangle formulæ :

$$\frac{a}{\sin A} = \frac{b}{\sin B} = \frac{c}{\sin C}.$$
$$a^2 = b^2 + c^2 - 2bc \cos A.$$

Areas

Triangle. $\frac{1}{2}bc \sin A$

$$\sqrt{s(s-a)(s-b)(s-c)}.$$

Quadrilateral. $\frac{1}{2}$ product of diagonals × sine of angle between them.

Sector of circle. $\frac{1}{2}r^2\theta$.

Ellipse. πab.

Surface of zone of sphere. $2\pi r$ × distance between plane ends.

Curved surface of cone. πrl.

Curved surface of cylinder. $2\pi rh$.

Surface of sphere. $4\pi r^2$.

Curved surface of frustum of cone. $\pi(r_1 + r_2)l$.

Simpson's rule for irregular areas.
Using an even number of strips each of width h :
Area $\simeq \frac{1}{3}h$ (sum of first and last ordinates + twice the sum of the other odd ordinates + four times the sum of the even ordinates).

Volumes

Prism. Area of base × perpendicular distance between parallel ends.

Pyramid. $\frac{1}{3}$ area of base × perpendicular height.

Cone. $\frac{1}{3}\pi r^2 h$.

Sphere. $\frac{4}{3}\pi r^3$.

Cylinder. $\pi r^2 h$.

Frustum of pyramid. $\frac{1}{3}h(A_1 + \sqrt{A_1 A_2} + A_2)$.

Frustum of cone. $\frac{1}{3}\pi h(r_1^2 + r_1 r_2 + r_2^2)$.

Segment (or cap) of sphere. $\frac{1}{3}\pi h^2(3r - h)$.

$$\frac{1}{6}\pi h(3R^2 + h^2).$$

Sector of sphere. $\frac{2}{3}\pi r^2 h$.

Differential calculus

$$\frac{d(x^n)}{dx} = nx^{n-1}, \text{ for all values of } n.$$

$$\frac{d(e^x)}{dx} = e^x, \qquad\qquad \frac{d \log_e x}{dx} = \frac{1}{x}.$$

$$\frac{d \sin x}{dx} = \cos x, \qquad\qquad \frac{d \cos x}{dx} = -\sin x.$$

$$\frac{d \tan x}{dx} = \sec^2 x, \qquad\qquad \frac{d \cot x}{dx} = -\operatorname{cosec}^2 x.$$

$$\frac{d \sec x}{dx} = \sec x \tan x, \qquad \frac{d \operatorname{cosec} x}{dx} = -\operatorname{cosec} x \cot x.$$

$$\frac{d \sin^{-1} x}{dx} = \frac{1}{\sqrt{1 - x^2}}, \qquad \frac{d \cos^{-1} x}{dx} = -\frac{1}{\sqrt{1 - x^2}}.$$

$$\frac{d \tan^{-1} x}{dx} = \frac{1}{1 + x^2}.$$

Maxima and minima

At a max. $\dfrac{dy}{dx}$ changes sign from $+$ to $-$.

„   min.   „   „   „ $-$ to $+$.

Alternative test :

If $\dfrac{dy}{dx} = 0$ and $\dfrac{d^2y}{dx^2}$ is negative, y is a max.

If $\dfrac{dy}{dx} = 0$ and $\dfrac{d^2y}{dx^2}$ is positive, y is a min.

Rules for differentiation

$$\frac{dy}{dx} = \frac{dy}{du} \times \frac{du}{dx}, \qquad\qquad \frac{dx}{dy} = \frac{1}{\dfrac{dy}{dx}},$$

$$\frac{d(uv)}{dx} = u\frac{dv}{dx} + v\frac{du}{dx}, \qquad \frac{d}{dx}\left(\frac{u}{v}\right) = \frac{v\dfrac{du}{dx} - u\dfrac{dv}{dx}}{v^2}.$$

Integral calculus

If $\dfrac{dz}{dx} = y, \quad z = \displaystyle\int y\,dx + C.$

$$\int x^n dx = \frac{x^{n+1}}{n+1} + C, \text{ if } n \text{ is not } -1.$$

$$\int \frac{1}{x}dx = \log_e x + C.$$

$$\int e^x dx = e^x + C.$$

$$\int \sin x\,dx = -\cos x + C, \quad \int \cos x\,dx = \sin x + C.$$

If $\dfrac{dy}{dx} = ky$, then $y = Ce^{kx}$ where C is an arbitrary constant.

Complex numbers

If $x + jy = r \angle \theta$, then

$$x = r \cos \theta, \qquad\qquad y = r \sin \theta ;$$

$$r = \sqrt{x^2 + y^2}, \qquad\qquad \theta = \tan^{-1} \frac{y}{x}.$$

Multiplication and division :

$$r_1 \angle \theta_1 \times r_2 \angle \theta_2 = r_1 r_2 \angle (\theta_1 + \theta_2),$$

$$\frac{r_1 \angle \theta_1}{r_2 \angle \theta_2} = \left(\frac{r_1}{r_2}\right) \angle (\theta_1 - \theta_2).$$

SPECIMEN EXAMINATION PAPERS

UNION OF LANCASHIRE AND CHESHIRE INSTITUTES, 1940

MATHEMATICS

SENIOR MECHANCIAL ENGINEERING, ELECTRICAL ENGINEERING AND NAVAL ARCHITECTURE COURSES (THIRD YEAR).

(Time 3 hrs.)

SIX *questions only are to be answered.*
Mathematical tables are supplied.   A slide rule may be used.
All questions are of equal value.

1. (a) Evaluate $(R^{\frac{2}{3}}+r^{\frac{2}{3}})^{\frac{3}{2}}$ when $R=8\cdot12$ and $r=4\cdot76$.

(b) Using the binomial theorem, show that, if x is small, the values of $(1-x)^{\frac{1}{2}}$ and $\left(1+\dfrac{x}{2}\right)^{-1}$ are approximately equal.

Write down the approximate values of $\sqrt{0\cdot994}$ and $\dfrac{1}{1\cdot003}$.

2. (a) A hollow metal sphere of external diameter 4 in. weighs 4·02 lb. Find the internal diameter of the sphere, given that 1 cu. in. of the metal weighs 0·32 lb.

(b) In a triangle ABC, $AB=2$ in., $BC=3$ in., and angle $ABC=90°$. An axis PQ outside the triangle is parallel to AB and at distance 1 in. from AB. Find the volume of the ring generated when the triangle makes one complete revolution about PQ.

3. Solve the following equations :

    (i) $5(2-x)^2=7x-8$;

    (ii) $1\cdot39^{2x}=6\cdot31$;

    (iii) $\log_e(x^2+0\cdot5)=0\cdot27$.

4. In Fig. 1, OX and OY are two straight grooves inclined at 100° to each other, and AB is a link, 20 in. long, whose ends A and B move along OX and OY respectively. Find, by calculation, the lengths OA and OB at the instant when angle OAB is 42°.

If A now moves 3·6 in. towards O, find how far B moves.

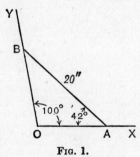

FIG. 1.

346

5. Tabulate the values of the functions $\sin(2x+10°)$ and $2\cos(x+60°)$ for the values $x=0°$, $5°$, $10°$, . . . up to $30°$. Using the same axes of reference, draw the graphs of these two functions over the range $x=0°$ to $x=30°$, and read off from your diagram a value of x (to the nearest degree) which satisfies the equation

$$\sin(2x+10°)-2\cos(x+60°)=0.$$

6. (a) In time t sec. a body is displaced s ft. in a straight path such that $s=25t+16t^2$.

Deduce from first principles, expressions for the velocity and acceleration of the body at time t sec.

(b) If $y=x^3+\dfrac{2}{x}$, find the value of $\dfrac{d^2y}{dx^2}$ when $x=2$.

(c) If $r=\theta\cos\theta$, find the value of $\dfrac{dr}{d\theta}$.

7. State the conditions which must be satisfied if a function $y=f(x)$ has a minimum value when $x=a$.

The total heat H units generated in a certain electrical circuit is given by $H=3x^2+4\cdot5(10-x)^2$, where x is a variable. Determine the value of x for which H has its least value, and deduce this least value of H.

8. Evaluate

(i) $\displaystyle\int_1^9 \frac{\sqrt{x}}{4}\,dx$; (ii) $\displaystyle\int\left(x^4+\frac{1}{x^4}\right)dx$; (iii) $\displaystyle\int_0^\pi \sin\tfrac{1}{2}\theta\,d\theta$.

A curve passes through the point $(x=0,\ y=6)$, and the gradient $\dfrac{dy}{dx}$ at any point (x, y) on the curve is given by $\dfrac{dy}{dx}=5e^x$. Determine the equation of the curve.

9. A plane figure is bounded by the curve $y=\dfrac{x}{10}(20-x^2)$, the axis of x, and the ordinates at $x=0$ and $x=4$, the unit of length along each axis of reference being 1 in. Make a rough sketch of the figure, and find its area by integration. Deduce the mean height of the figure above the axis of x.

10. AB is a thin straight rod of length l ft. and of mass m lb. per ft., and AX is an axis through A and perpendicular to AB. Find by integration the moment of inertia of the whole rod about AX.

Use your result to determine the moment of inertia of the rod about an axis through O, the mid-point of AB, and perpendicular to AB.

UNION OF EDUCATIONAL INSTITUTIONS, 1940

PRACTICAL MATHEMATICS (S 3)

(*Time* 3 *hrs.*)

Answer SEVEN *questions only.*

The figures after each question denote the number of marks obtainable.

1. (*a*) Show how to express $a \sin \theta + b \cos \theta$ in the form $A \sin (\theta + a)$ giving the values of A and a in terms of a and b.

(*b*) The voltage in an electrical circuit after time t is given by

$$E = A \sin pt + B \cos pt.$$

If $A = 75$, $B = 75\pi$ and $p = 100\pi$, calculate the smallest positive value of t for E to have a maximum value.   [15]

2. (*a*) If a, b, c are the lengths of the sides of a triangle prove that the area of the triangle is $\sqrt{s(s-a)(s-b)(s-c)}$ where s is the semi-perimeter.

(*b*) A bar of steel is 6 ft. long and its uniform section perpendicular to its length is a triangle with sides $3\frac{1}{2}$ in., $4\frac{1}{8}$ in. and $5\frac{3}{8}$ in. Calculate the volume of the bar.   [14]

3. Two quantities A and V satisfy the equation $A = a + bV + cV^2$ where a, b and c are constants. Find the values of these constants using the following table :

A	60	26	14
V	40	60	80

Calculate the two values of V corresponding to the value $A = 20$.   [15]

4. The following table of values gives the current i amps required to fuse a wire of diameter d thousandths of an inch. It is thought that there is a law of the form $i = kd^n$. Test if this is true and if so find the values of the constants k and n.

d	22	36	64	104	160	232
i	2·1	4·3	10·2	21·2	40·5	71

[14]

5. (*a*) Write down the first four terms in the expansion of $(x+a)^n$ and expand $(1-2x)^{\frac{1}{2}}$ as far as the term involving x^4.

(*b*) The formula $P = 10^{-11}wd^5n^3$ gives the loss of horse-power P of a wheel d ft. in diameter making n revolutions per minute in a medium whose density is w lb. per cu. ft. Find the percentage increase in P if d and n both increase by 1 per cent.   [14]

6. Oil flows through a pipe at the rate of 2 pints per min. The pipe is conical in shape and is 6 in. in diameter at a distance of 5 in. from

the vertex of the cone. What is the speed of the oil at a section 3 in. from the vertex ? [14]

7. (a) Show that $\dfrac{d}{dx}\left(\dfrac{x}{x+1}\right)=\dfrac{1}{(x+1)^2}$.

(b) Without assuming the result in (a) evaluate $\displaystyle\int\dfrac{1}{(x+1)^2}dx$.

(c) Using the same axes and scales draw the graphs of the functions $\dfrac{-1}{x+1}$ and $\dfrac{x}{x+1}$ for values of x from 0 to 6 and account for the difference in results (a) and (b). [14]

8. A piece of wire 12 in. long is divided into two portions; the first is bent to form a square and the second to form an equilateral triangle. Find the lengths of the sides of the square and triangle in order that the sum of the areas they enclose shall be a minimum. [14]

9. (a) Find $\dfrac{dy}{dx}$ if $x^2+y^2=4$.

(b) Given that $i=5\sin(2\pi ft+0\cdot 1)$ find $\dfrac{di}{dt}$ if $f=50$ and $t=0\cdot 01$.

(c) Evaluate $\displaystyle\int_{4}^{5}pdv$ where $pv=500$. [14]

10. Find the area enclosed between the parabola $y=x^2-3x$, the axis of x and the ordinates at $x=1$ and $x=3$. Also calculate the distance of the centroid of this area from the x axis. [14]

11. (a) Prove that the moment of inertia of a rectangular area of length a and breadth b about the side of length a is $ab^3/3$.

(b) Find the moment of inertia of the plane section shown in the figure about the axis AB. [14]

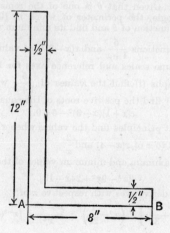

NORTHERN COUNTIES TECHNICAL EXAMINATIONS COUNCIL, 1939.

PRACTICAL MATHEMATICS (S 3)

ORDINARY NATIONAL CERTIFICATES IN MECHANICAL AND ELECTRICAL ENGINEERING AND SHIPBUILDING, AND MECHANICAL AND ELECTRICAL ENGINEERING AND SHIPBUILDING COURSES (THIRD YEAR)

(Time 3 hrs.)

NOT MORE THAN SIX *questions may be answered.*

Mathematical tables and slide-rules may be used.

The number of marks assigned to each question is given in brackets. The maximum number of marks obtainable is 100.

Marks will be deducted for slovenly work, especially for the omission of essential brackets.

1. The pulls, T_1 and T_2, at the ends of a taut rope which passes round a circular post are related by the formula $T_2 = T_1 e^{\mu\theta}$, where $e = 2.718$, $\mu = 0.22$, and θ radians is the angle through which the rope turns. Find (i) θ, given that $T_2 = 3T_1$; (ii) T_1 and T_2, given that $\theta = 3.1$ and $T_2 - T_1 = 745$ lb. wt. [16]

2. When x has the values $-2, 0, +1, +2$, the values of the function $ax^3 + bx^2 + cx + k$, where a, b, c, k are constants, are $-14, +4, -2$, and -2 respectively. For what other values of x is the value of the function equal to $+4$? [16]

3. (i) For what value of θ, between $0°$ and $180°$, is $\tan\theta + 3\sin\theta = 0$?

(ii) By expressing $\sin\theta + \cos\theta$ in the form $r\sin(\theta + a)$, find its maximum value. Given that θ is one of the remaining angles of a right-angled triangle, the perimeter of which is 10 in., express the hypotenuse as a function of θ and find its minimum value. [16]

4. Graph the functions $\dfrac{5}{1+x}$ and $x(x-3)^2$ for values of x from 0 to $+4$, using the same scales and reference axes for both graphs. By means of the graphs (i) find the values of $\dfrac{5}{1+x}$ when the value of $x(x-3)^2$ is 2.5, (ii) find the positive roots of the equation
$$x(x+1)(x-3)^2 - 5 = 0. \qquad [18]$$

5. (i) From first principles find the values when $x = 4$ of the derivatives with respect to x of $x(x-4)$ and $\dfrac{2}{x}$.

(ii) Find the maximum and minimum values of the function
$$[x^3 - 9x^2 + 24x - 13]. \qquad [16]$$

6. (i) Give the derivatives with respect to x of
$$\left[\sqrt{(x^{-3})} + \frac{4}{3x^2}\right] ; \quad \left(x^2 - \frac{1}{2x}\right)^2 ; \quad \frac{x^8 - x^2}{x^4} ; \quad [x^{-3}(x^4 - 2^4)].$$

(ii) Find the values, when $t = \dfrac{1}{\sqrt{2}}$, of the first and second derivatives with respect to t of

$$\left[(\sqrt{2})t^4 - t^3 - \left(\frac{3\sqrt{2}}{2} \right)t^2 + 5t + 1 \right].$$ [18]

7. Integrate with respect to x (after simplifying where necessary) the following functions :

$$\left[\frac{1 - 3x^3 - x^5}{x^2} \right] ; \quad \left[\frac{1}{2\sqrt[3]{x}} + \sqrt{(x^3)} \right] ; \quad [x^4(1 - \tfrac{1}{2}x^{-2})^2].$$

Evaluate

$$\int_{\frac{1}{8}}^{8} x^{-\frac{4}{3}} dx ; \quad \int_{-1}^{4} (1 + x)(4 - x) dx.$$ [16]

8. The shape of a vessel is such that the volume of water which will fill it to any depth, x in., is $(2x + \tfrac{1}{2}x^{\frac{3}{2}})$ cu. in. Obtain as a function of x the area of its horizontal cross-section at height x in. above its base.

If the vessel is filled with water to a depth of 16 in., find the height above the base of the centre of gravity of the water. [16]

9. (i) A particle is moving along a straight line in such a manner that its distance from a fixed point, O, on the line, at any instant, t sec. after zero, is x ft., where $x = \tfrac{1}{4}t^3 + 3t + 2$. Find the position, the speed, and the acceleration of the particle when $t = 2$.

(ii) Given that $\dfrac{d^2x}{dt^2} = \tfrac{1}{4}t^{\frac{1}{2}}$ and that $\dfrac{dx}{dt} = 3$ and $x = 9$ when $t = 4$, express x as a function of t. [16]

10. N is the foot of the perpendicular from the vertex, A, of a triangle ABC on the horizontal plane through BC to which the plane of ABC is inclined at $40°$. Calculate the angle BAC, given that

$$\angle NBC = 70° \ 30' \text{ and } \angle NCB = 56° \ 30'.$$ [16]

(ii) Find the values, when $t = \frac{1}{\sqrt{2}}$ of the first and second derivatives with respect to t of

$$\left[\sqrt{(2)}\,t^{-\frac{1}{t}} - \left(\frac{t\sqrt{2}}{2}\right)t^{\frac{1}{t}} + 3t + 1\right]. \qquad [18]$$

7. Integrate with respect to x (after simplifying where necessary) the following functions:

$$\left[1 - \frac{t^{-\frac{1}{2}}}{x^2}\right]^{\frac{1}{2}}; \quad \left[\frac{x^{-\ldots}}{2\sqrt{x} + \sqrt{(x)}}\right]^{2}; \quad (4 + x - \ldots)^{\frac{1}{2}}.$$

Evaluate:

$$\int_2^3 \frac{x\,dx}{x^2 + \ldots} \qquad \int_0^1 (1 + x)(4 - x)\,dx \qquad [16]$$

8. The shape of a vessel is such that the volume of water which will fill it to any depth, x in, is $(7x + \frac{1}{4}x^3)$ cu.in. Obtain as a function of x the area of its horizontal cross-section at height x in. above its base. If the vessel is filled with water to a depth of 16 in., find the height above the base of the centre of gravity of the water. [16]

9. (i) A particle is moving along a straight line in such a manner that its distance from a fixed point, O, on the line, at any instant, t sec. after start, is x ft., where $x = t^2 - 3t + 2$. Find the position, the speed, and the acceleration of the particle when $t = \chi$.

(ii) Given that $\frac{d^2x}{dt^2} = 4t$ and that $\frac{dx}{dt} = 3$ and $x = 9$ when $t = 1$, express x as a function of t. [18]

10. N is the foot of the perpendicular from the vertex, A, of a triangle ABC on the horizontal plane through BC to which the plane of ABC is inclined at 40°. Calculate the angle BAC, given that $\angle NBC = 70°\ 30'$ and $\angle ACB = 60°\ 30'$. [18]

ANSWERS

EXERCISE I (Page 4)

2. 0·015 mm.

3. $5m-n$, $(5m-n)^2(3m-2n)(2m+7n)$.

4. $2x+1$, $y^2(2x+1)(5x-7)(3y+2)$.

5. $3p-2$, $2(p-2)(3p-2)(3p+2)(9p^2+6p+4)$.

6. $b^2-5bc+25c^2$, $a(b+5c)(b^2-5bc+25c^2)$.

7. $-2, 1, 3$ amp. **8.** $-5, 0, 2$.

9. $\frac{1}{2}(b+c-a)$, $\frac{1}{2}(c+a-b)$, $\frac{1}{2}(a+b-c)$.

10. $x=-\frac{1}{3}$, $y=-1$, $z=\frac{1}{2}$. **11.** $\dfrac{R_1R_2i}{R_2R_3+R_3R_1+R_1R_2}$.

12. $\dfrac{e_1r_2+e_2r_1}{Rr_1+Rr_2+r_1r_2}$, 0·73 amp.

13. $15\cdot2$, $1\cdot56\times10^{-5}$, $14\cdot6$ tons/sq. in., $337°$ F.

14. $3, 2, -1$. **15.** $3\cdot11$, $1\cdot06\times10^{-2}$, $-2\cdot67\times10^{-6}$.

16. 0·99. **17.** $1\frac{1}{2}$. **18.** 11. **19.** 2, 8.

20. 0, 5. **21.** 3·56 **22.** ±1, ±2. **23.** 50.

24. $-1\cdot08$, $-10\cdot8$. **25.** 100 ohms.

26. $\frac{1}{2}(a+\sqrt{a^2+4ar})$. **27.** 7·5 ohms.

28. $\dfrac{1}{2e}(eR-Er-er+\sqrt{(eR-Er-er)^2+4e^2Rr})$, 21·4 ohms.

29. $b-\sqrt{(n-1)a^2-(n-2)b^2}$, 0·304 in.

30. $\dfrac{7\pm\sqrt{109}}{6}$. **32.** $4, \frac{1}{2}$. **33.** $1\cdot386$, $-2\cdot886$.

EXERCISE II (Page 8)

1. 24·6, 21·3. **2.** 5030 lb./sq. in. **3.** 0·874.

4. 115° 12′, 34° 12′, 30° 36′. **5.** 1·03.

6. $B=58°$ 53′, $C=47°$ 47′. **7.** 2·18 ft./sec.

8. 0·111. **9.** $x=0\cdot334$, $y=0\cdot250$.

10. $p=35\cdot7$, $v=15\cdot1$. **11.** 9.

12. 5%. **13.** 1·03. **14.** 0·0702 sec.

15. 1·5, 70 amp. **16.** 1·33. **17.** £28.

EXERCISE III (Page 13)

1. Max. -3, min. 5.   2. $x=4\cdot36$, $y=2\cdot27$ or $x=0\cdot31$, $y=-0\cdot77$.
3. $2\cdot78$.   4. $3\cdot46$, $3\cdot46$, $1\cdot73$ ft. ; $2\cdot37$ ft. or $4\cdot45$ ft.
5. $0\cdot43$, $-0\cdot43$.   6. $1\cdot65$.   7. $0\cdot02$ sec.
8. $0\cdot52$.   9. $0\cdot42$ l.   10. $0\cdot85$, $2\cdot60$, $5\cdot03$.
11. $1\cdot20$ to $5\cdot66$.   12. $137°$.
13. $30°+n.360°$, $150°+n.360°$, $194\frac{1}{2}°+n.360°$, $345\frac{1}{2}°+n.360°$.
14. (i) $0\cdot57$, $2\cdot04$; (ii) $0\cdot92$, $1\cdot68$; 6.
15. $2\cdot31$, $0\cdot81$ in.   16. $1\cdot91$.

EXERCISE IV. (Page 19)

1. $4\cdot5$ cm. ; $1\cdot8$ cm.   2. $7\cdot295$ sq. in., $116\cdot7$ sq. in.
3. $5\cdot58$ sq. ft.   4. 50 sq. ft.   5. 300 sq. in.
6. 182 sq. ft., $5\cdot86$ ft.   7. 12,440 sq. ml.
8. $2\cdot34$.   9. $112:13$.   10. $1\cdot31$ in.
11. $8\pi/3$ cu. ft.   12. $8\frac{5}{27}$ cu. ft.
14. $2\pi h\left(\dfrac{1}{\sqrt{b^2+h^2}}-\dfrac{1}{\sqrt{a^2+h^2}}\right)$.
16. 597.   17. 2000.   18. $6\cdot76$.
19. $79\cdot2$ lb. wt./sq. in.   20. 201 in. lb. wt.

EXERCISE V (Page 24)

1. $\sin\theta=\sqrt{1-\cos^2\theta}$, $\tan\theta=\dfrac{\sqrt{1-\cos^2\theta}}{\cos\theta}$, $\sec\theta=\dfrac{1}{\cos\theta}$,
   $\text{cosec }\theta=\dfrac{1}{\sqrt{1-\sin^2\theta}}$, $\cot\theta=\dfrac{\cos\theta}{\sqrt{1-\cos^2\theta}}$.

2. $\sin\theta=\dfrac{\tan\theta}{\sqrt{1+\tan^2\theta}}$, $\cos\theta=\dfrac{1}{\sqrt{1+\tan^2\theta}}$, $\text{cosec }\theta=\dfrac{\sqrt{1+\tan^2\theta}}{\tan\theta}$,
   $\sec\theta=\sqrt{1+\tan^2\theta}$, $\cot\theta=\dfrac{1}{\tan\theta}$.

5. $46°24'+n.360°$.   12. $\dfrac{24}{25}$, $-\dfrac{119}{169}$, $\dfrac{63}{65}$, $-\dfrac{63}{16}$.

13. $\pm\dfrac{1}{3}$, $\pm\dfrac{2\sqrt{2}}{3}$, $\pm\dfrac{\sqrt{2}}{4}$.

14. (i) $7\frac{1}{2}°$, $37\frac{1}{2}°$, $97\frac{1}{2}°$, $127\frac{1}{2}°$, $187\frac{1}{2}°$, $217\frac{1}{2}°$, $277\frac{1}{2}°$, $307\frac{1}{2}°$.
(ii) $20°$, $40°$, $80°$, $100°$, $140°$, $160°$, $200°$, $220°$, $260°$, $280°$, $320°$, $340°$.
(iii) $45°$, $105°$, $165°$, $225°$, $285°$, $345°$.
15. (i) $14°29'$, $166°31'$; (ii) $75°31'$, $284°29'$.
16. $A=48°17'$, $B=10°3'$; $A=169°57'$, $B=131°43'$.
17. $30°+n.360°$, $150°+n.360°$, $228°35'+n.360°$, $311°25'+n.360°$.
18. $36°59'$, $323°1'$.   19. $\dfrac{\pi}{12}+2n\pi$, $\dfrac{17\pi}{12}+2n\pi$; $-\dfrac{7\pi}{12}$, $\dfrac{\pi}{12}$.
20. $26°34'+n.180°$, $18°26'+n.180°$.   21. $\pi/3$, $4\pi/3$.
22. (i) 5, $126°52'$, (ii) 5, $306°52'$; $76°43'+n.360°$, $209°33'+n.360°$.

23. 0·00374.   **24.** 6·74, −6·74, 0·249.

26. 20° 18′, 7·14 lb. wt.   **27.** 56·2 ml.

28. $\cos\left(\theta+\dfrac{\pi}{3}\right)+\cos\left(\theta+\dfrac{2\pi}{3}\right)+\cos\left(\theta+\dfrac{4\pi}{3}\right)+\cos\left(\theta+\dfrac{5\pi}{3}\right)\equiv0$;

$\sin\left(\theta+\dfrac{\pi}{3}\right)+\sin\left(\theta+\dfrac{2\pi}{3}\right)+\sin\left(\theta+\dfrac{4\pi}{3}\right)+\sin\left(\theta+\dfrac{5\pi}{3}\right)\equiv0.$

29. 33° 50′.   **30.** 75° 2′.   **31.** 114 sq. ft.

32. 107 sq. in. ; 81·8 cu. in.   **33.** 214 cu. in.

35. 11·7 Kg. wt. ; 19° 25′.   **36.** 12·4 ft.

37. $B=66°$ 50′, $C=61°$ 10′, $c=13·3$ in. ; $B=113°$ 10′, $C=14°$ 50′, $c=3·90$ in.

38. 77° 15′, 57° 5′ ; 45° 40′ ; 83·8 sq. in.

39. 50° 22′, 76° 36′, 53° 2′ ; 129° 38′, 27° 49′, 22° 33′.

40. 28·0 ml.   **41.** 1·21 ml. ; 1 in 72.   **42.** 8890 sq. yd.

43. 44°   **44.** 147 ft.   **45.** 83° 54′.

46. 37° 52′.   **47.** 204 m.p.h.   **48.** 1 in 2·57.

50. 7·5′.   **51.** 0·04.   **52.** 4° 12′.

EXERCISE VI (Page 39)

1. 4950.   **2.** 67·6.   **3.** $\frac{1}{2}n(n-1)$.

4. 140.   **5.** 58 ; 590, 1790.   **6.** 50, 2500.

7. 16, 144.   **8.** −3, 162.   **9.** 78.

10. $8\frac{1}{4}$, $8\frac{1}{2}$, . . . $11\frac{1}{2}$, $11\frac{3}{4}$; 170 ft.   **11.** £350.

14. 728.   **15.** 3069.   **16.** −1023.

17. $\frac{171}{256}$.   **18.** $5\frac{125}{128}$.   **19.** 12·8.

20. $8\sqrt{2}$, 16, $16\sqrt{2}$, 32, $32\sqrt{2}$.   **21.** $e^{-0·2}$.

22. 4·689, 2·405 in.   **23.** $e^{-2\mu\pi}$, 11·5 lb. wt.   **24.** 157,300.

25. £500 $(0·95)^n$, £332.   **26.** £21·2, £85·1.

27. 1·390 ; 20, 27·8, 38·6, 53·7, 74·5, 103·6, 143·9, 200.

28. 10·368.   **29.** $\frac{3}{2}$.   **30.** $57\frac{1}{7}$.   **31.** $\frac{1}{9}$; $\frac{4}{33}$.

33. 16 ft./sec. ; $9\frac{1}{2}$ sec.   **34.** 63·822.

EXERCISE VII (Page 49)

1. $1+12x+66x^2+220x^3+495x^4$.   **2.** $1-\frac{1}{3}x-\frac{1}{9}x^2-\frac{5}{81}x^3-\frac{10}{243}x^4$.

3. $1-2x+3x^2-4x^3+5x^4$.   **4.** $1-7x+21x^2-35x^3+35x^4$.

5. $1-\frac{1}{2}x+\frac{3}{8}x^2-\frac{5}{16}x^4+\frac{35}{128}x^4$.   **6.** $1+3x+6x^2+10x^3+15x^4$.

7. $1-nx+\dfrac{n(n-1)}{1\cdot2}x^2-\dfrac{n(n-1)(n-2)}{1\cdot2\cdot3}x^3+\dfrac{n(n-1)(n-2)(n-3)}{1\cdot2\cdot3\cdot4}x^4$.

9. 1·414214.

10. (a) $1+5x+10x^2+10x^3+5x^4+x^5$.

(b) $a^6-6a^5b+15a^4b^2-20a^3b^3+15a^2b^4-6ab^5+b^6$.

11. 1, 11, 55, 165, 330, 462, 462, 330, 165, 55, 11, 1.

12. $1+14x+84x^2+280x^3$.   **13.** $1+2x+3x^2+4x^3$.

14. $2-\frac{1}{4}x-\frac{1}{64}x^2-\frac{1}{512}x^3$.   **15.** 1·0099505.

16. 1·0829.   **17.** 0·983.   **18.** (a) 0·993 ; (b) 1·068.

19. 1·5%.   **20.** 1% too large.   **21.** $4\frac{1}{2}$% nearly.

22. 1·649.   **23.** 0·9063.   **24.** 1·0986.

25. 1, 0·9385, 0·7652, 0·5118, 0·2239, −0·048 ; $J(x)=0$ at $x=2·4$.

EXERCISE VIII (Page 74)

1. $1\cdot386$, $0\cdot511$.　　**2.** $y \simeq 3\cdot44$.　　**3.** $x \simeq 0\cdot41$.
4. $2\cdot55$ ft.　　**6.** $d_0=1$, $k \simeq 0\cdot192$.　　**7.** $x \simeq 1\cdot18$.
8. $x \simeq 0\cdot70$.　　**10.** $22\cdot03$ min.　　**13.** $Q \simeq 15H^{1\cdot48}$.
14. $i \simeq 10{,}240d^{1\cdot5}$; $0\cdot013$ in.　　**15.** $p \simeq 29\cdot9e^{-0\cdot000039h}$; 8580 ft.
16. $L \simeq 0\cdot17N^2$.　　**17.** $T \simeq 185p^{0\cdot26}$.　　**18.** $i \simeq 75e^{-0\cdot86t}$.
19. $\eta \simeq 48e^{-0\cdot087\theta}$.　　**20.** $a \simeq 49$, $k \simeq 0\cdot0053$.　**21.** $k \simeq 0\cdot00088$.

EXERCISE IX (Page 81)

1. (i) $\frac{1}{2}\sin a + \frac{\sqrt{3}}{2}\cos a$, (ii) $\frac{1}{2}\cos\theta - \frac{\sqrt{3}}{2}\sin\theta$, (iii) $\frac{1}{\sqrt{2}}(\cos x - \sin x)$.

2. (i) $\sin 60°\left(=\frac{\sqrt{3}}{2}\right)$, (ii) $\cos y$, (iii) $\cos 2A$.

3. $\dfrac{\sqrt{3}+1}{2\sqrt{2}} \simeq 0\cdot966$, $\dfrac{\sqrt{3}-1}{2\sqrt{2}} \simeq 0\cdot259$.

4. $a = 210\cdot19$, $b = 64\cdot99$; $-70\cdot94$ (approx.).
5. $0\cdot6246$; $0\cdot781$.　**6.** $\frac{63}{65}$; $\frac{24}{25}$; $\frac{119}{169}$.　　**7.** $\frac{16}{65}$.
11. $\pm\frac{1}{2}$; $\pm\frac{2}{3}$; ± 1.　　　　**12.** $\cos\beta\sin(a+\beta)$.
15. $x = 60°\ 20'$.　　　　　**16.** $\theta = 1\cdot315$.
27. $x = 0\cdot421$, $1\cdot992$, $3\cdot563$ or $5\cdot134$.　　**28.** $\theta = 2\cdot237$ or $4\cdot046$.
29. $\theta =$ any integral multiple of π.　　**31.** $x = \frac{1}{2}$ or -1.
32. $x = 0\cdot317$, $-0\cdot069$ or $-0\cdot248$.

EXERCISE X (Page 89)

4. $2 - \sqrt{3} \simeq 0\cdot2679$.　　　　**5.** $\sqrt{2} - 1 \simeq 0\cdot4142$.

7. $\frac{40}{9} \simeq 4\cdot444$, $\dfrac{\sqrt{41}-5}{4} \simeq 0\cdot3508$.　　**10.** 1.

12. $\cot(A-B) = \dfrac{\cot A \cot B + 1}{\cot B - \cot A}$.　　**15.** $\tan^{-1}\frac{3}{5} \simeq 30°\ 58'$.

17. $3y + x = 12$.　　**18.** $\frac{24}{25}$, $\frac{7}{25}$, $\frac{24}{7}$.　　**19.** $\frac{1}{3}$.
24. $-143°\ 8'$, $90°$.　　**25.** $\theta = 19°\ 50'$ or $281°\ 28'$ (approx.).
26. $1\cdot0105$.

EXERCISE XI (Page 98)

1. $5\cdot39 \sin(\theta + 68°\ 12')$.　　　　**2.** $3\cdot58 \sin(\theta + 30°\ 9')$.
3. $5 \sin(\theta - 36°\ 52')$ or $5 \sin(\theta + 323°\ 8')$.
4. $133\cdot1 \sin(\theta - 55°\ 43')$ or $133\cdot1 \sin(\theta + 304°\ 17')$.
5. $2\cdot236 \sin(\theta + 116°\ 34')$.　　**6.** $17 \sin(\theta + 151°\ 56')$.
7. $A = 11\cdot66$, $a = 30°\ 58'$.　　**8.** $0\cdot1703 \sin(3\theta + 139°\ 46')$.
9. $y = 25 \sin(x + 16°\ 16')$; (i) $73°\ 44'$; (ii) $20°\ 36'$, $126°\ 52'$.
10. $167\cdot7 \sin(2\pi ft - 0\cdot4637)$.　　**11.** $2\cdot153$, $7\cdot486$.
12. $v = 120 + 9\cdot71 \sin(\omega t + 28°\ 56') + 1\cdot58 \sin(3\omega t + 124°\ 42')$ or
$v = 120 + 9\cdot71 \sin(\omega t + 28°\ 56') - 1\cdot58 \sin(3\omega t - 55°\ 18')$.

13. $Z=\sqrt{R^2+\left(\omega L-\dfrac{1}{\omega C}\right)^2}$, $\phi=\tan^{-1}\left(\dfrac{\omega L-\dfrac{1}{\omega C}}{R}\right)$; $Z=14\cdot4$, $\phi=-88^\circ\ 0'$.

14. $12\cdot81\sin(\theta-21^\circ\ 20')$ or $12\cdot81\sin(\theta+338^\circ\ 40')$.

15. $10\cdot34\sin(\theta-17^\circ\ 26')$; max. $10\cdot34$ when $\theta=107^\circ\ 26'$, min. $-10\cdot34$ when $\theta=-72^\circ\ 34'$.

16. When θ lies between $54^\circ\ 28'$ and $234^\circ\ 28'$.

17. $a=E_R{}^2+(R^2+X^2)I^2$, $b=2E_RI\sqrt{R^2+X^2}$, $a=\tan^{-1}\dfrac{R}{X}$;

$\qquad E_R\pm\sqrt{R^2+X^2}I$.

18. $i=16\cdot01\sin(\omega t-22^\circ\ 24')+7\cdot20\sin(3\omega t+37^\circ\ 40')+$
$\qquad\qquad\qquad\qquad\qquad 1\cdot97\sin(5\omega t+97^\circ\ 36')$ or
$i=16\cdot01\sin(\omega t-22^\circ\ 24')+7\cdot20\sin(3\omega t+37^\circ\ 40')-$
$\qquad\qquad\qquad\qquad\qquad 1\cdot97\sin(5\omega t-82^\circ\ 24')$ or
$i=16\cdot01\sin(\omega t-0\cdot3910)+7\cdot20\sin(3\omega t+0\cdot6574)+$
$\qquad\qquad\qquad\qquad\qquad 1\cdot97\sin(5\omega t+1\cdot7034)$.

19. $v=162\cdot4\sin(100\pi t-0\cdot1574)$.

EXERCISE XII (Page 103)

1. $\sin50^\circ+\sin14^\circ$.   **2.** $\sin120^\circ+\sin80^\circ$.

3. $\sin58^\circ-\sin28^\circ$.   **4.** $\cos82^\circ+\cos20^\circ$.

5. $\frac12(\sin90^\circ-\sin40^\circ)=\frac12(1-\sin40^\circ)$.

6. $\frac12(\cos176^\circ+\cos84^\circ)$.   **7.** $\cos78^\circ-\cos90^\circ=\cos78^\circ$.

8. $\frac12(\cos24^\circ-\cos76^\circ)$.   **9.** $\frac12(\sin88^\circ+\sin56^\circ)$.

10. $\frac12(\sin6x+\sin4x)$.   **11.** $\frac12(\cos5a+\cos a)$.

12. $\frac12\{\cos a-\cos(4\pi ft+a)\}$.

16. $\cos30^\circ-\cos60^\circ$; $\dfrac{\sqrt3-1}{2\sqrt2}=\dfrac{\sqrt6-\sqrt2}{4}\backsim0\cdot2588$.

19. Max. $\frac34$ when $\theta=40^\circ$; min. $-\frac14$ when $\theta=130^\circ$.

21. 180°.   **22.** $\frac12(\sin3x+\sin x)$.

EXERCISE XIII (Page 110)

1. $2\sin53^\circ\cos32^\circ$.   **2.** $2\cos25^\circ\sin15^\circ$.

3. $2\cos72^\circ\cos28^\circ$.   **4.** $2\sin55^\circ\sin21^\circ$.

5. $-2\sin35^\circ\sin17^\circ$.   **6.** $2\sin43\frac12^\circ\cos18\frac12^\circ$.

7. $2\sin4a\cos3a$.   **8.** $2\cos2\beta\cos\frac12\beta$.

9. $2\sin45^\circ\sin A=\sqrt2\sin A$.   **10.** $2\sin pt\cos a$.

16. $x=$any integral multiple of 60°.   **17.** $\theta=22\frac12^\circ$, 90° or $112\frac12^\circ$.

24. $i=\sin20,000\pi t+0\cdot2\cos19,000\pi t-0\cdot2\cos21,000\pi t$, or
$\quad i=\sin20,000\pi t+0\cdot2\sin(19,000\pi t+\frac12\pi)+0\cdot2\sin(21,000\pi t-\frac12\pi)$.

EXERCISE XIV (Page 122)

1. 4 ft./sec., 6·5 ft./sec.

2. -1, $-0·25$.

3. 0·33, $-0·012$.

4. -9000, -2500.

6. $\{10t . \delta t + 5 . (\delta t)^2\}$ ft., $10t$ ft./sec.

7. $\frac{1}{2}x . \delta x + \frac{1}{4}(\delta x)^2$, $-\frac{1}{2}x$.

8. $-\dfrac{3\delta x}{(x+\delta x)x}$, $-\dfrac{3}{x^2}$.

9. $8x^3 . \delta x + 12x^2 . (\delta x)^2 + 4x . (\delta x)^3 + 2(\delta x)^4$, $8x^3$.

10. $\frac{3}{100}x^2\delta x + \frac{3}{100}x . (\delta x)^2 + \frac{1}{100}(\delta x)^3$; $\frac{3}{100}x^2$.

11. $63x^6$.

12. $\frac{1}{2}x^9$.

13. $0·27x^{1·7}$.

14. $\frac{3}{2}x^{\frac{1}{2}}$.

15. $-35x^{-4·5}$.

16. $-\dfrac{210}{x^{15}}$.

17. $\dfrac{3}{x^3}$.

18. $-\dfrac{n}{ax^{n+1}}$.

19. $\frac{3}{2}h^{\frac{1}{2}}$.

20. $-120v^{-2·2}$.

21. $14m^{-\frac{5}{6}}$.

22. $-\dfrac{1}{3\lambda^2}$.

23. $-\dfrac{2}{z^{\frac{3}{2}}}$.

24. $\dfrac{n+1}{20n}\left(\dfrac{p}{20}\right)^{\frac{1}{n}}$.

25. $\dfrac{8}{x^{\frac{5}{3}}}$.

26. $\dfrac{\sqrt{5}}{2\sqrt{m}}$.

27. $-\dfrac{1}{3k^3}$.

28. $42v^{\frac{1}{6}}$.

29. $-\dfrac{0·4}{x^{11}}$.

30. $40z^{\frac{1}{4}}$.

31. $\frac{1}{4}$, -2, 16.

32. $x = \frac{1}{2}\sqrt{3}$, $y = \frac{3}{4}$.

33. $153° 26'$, $75° 58'$.

34. (a) $x = \frac{3}{4}$, $y = 2\frac{7}{8}$; (b) $x = \frac{5}{4}$, $y = 2\frac{7}{8}$.

35. At (2, 4) angle between graphs $= 30° 58'$, at $(1, -1)$ angle between graphs $= 71° 34'$.

36. $6t$ in./sec.; 12 in./sec.

37. (a) $\left(\dfrac{1}{18\pi t^2}\right)^{\frac{1}{3}}$ in./sec., 0·103 in./sec.

38. $-1·608$.

EXERCISE XV (Page 128)

1. $x^7 + 7x^6h + 21x^5h^2 + 35x^4h^3 + 35x^3h^4 + 7xh^6 + h^7$; $28x^6$.

2. 15, 0, 11, -1.

3. $3\frac{1}{3}$, $3\frac{1}{3}$, $\frac{8}{9}$, -8.

4. 3·16, 4, 1·58, 1·25.

6. $3x^2$.

7. $-0·5735$.

8. 0·43, 0·22, 0·14, 0·11, 0·087; $\dfrac{d \log_{10} x}{dx} \backsimeq \dfrac{0·43}{x}$.

9. 192.

10. $20x^9 - 45x^4$.

11. $25·2x^{5·3} - 3·5x^{1·5}$.

12. $0·18x^{0·8} + 0·27x^{-0·1}$.

13. $-\dfrac{1}{5x^2} + \dfrac{3}{x^3}$.

14. $32x^3 - 21x^2 + 4x$.

15. $\dfrac{1}{2\sqrt{x}} - \dfrac{1}{2x^{\frac{3}{2}}}$.

16. $2p + 4$.

17. $2r - 2$.

18. $1 - \dfrac{1}{z^2}$.

19. $-\dfrac{1}{4k^{\frac{3}{2}}} + \dfrac{1}{k^3}$.

20. $2\mu + \dfrac{z}{\mu^2}$.

21. $0·8x^{-0·2} - 0·2x^{-1·2}$.

ANSWERS

22. $-\dfrac{2}{x^2}-\dfrac{15}{x^4}.$ **23.** $E-2Ri.$ **24.** $2ar-\dfrac{2b}{r^3}.$

25. $Rg-\dfrac{Cx^2}{2l}.$ **26.** $1-\dfrac{x^2}{R_2{}^2}.$ **27.** $\frac{2}{5}B\sqrt{2gH}.$

28. $\dfrac{C}{v^n}.$ **29.** $a-\dfrac{b}{I^2}.$

30. $\dfrac{n-1}{n}\left\{\dfrac{1}{p_1{}^{\frac{n-1}{n}}\,p_2{}^{\frac{1}{n}}}-\dfrac{p_3{}^{\frac{n-1}{n}}}{p_2{}^{\frac{2n-1}{n}}}\right\}.$

31. $-\dfrac{2f}{u^3}+\dfrac{1}{u^2}.$ **32.** $(10-16t)$ ft./sec.

33. $0{\cdot}1161,\ 0{\cdot}3105$ lb. wt. per m.p.h.

34. $0{\cdot}0000158,\ 0{\cdot}0000248$ ft. per degree.

35. $35{\cdot}1\times10^{-7}V^{2\cdot9},\ 2{\cdot}215$ candles per volt.

36. $1{\cdot}25$ ft./sec. **37.** $2\pi r\delta r.$

38. (a) $4x^3\delta x.$ (b) $-\dfrac{1}{x^2}.\delta x.$ The negative sign in (b) means that y decreases as x increases.

39. $\sqrt{A},\ \dfrac{\delta A}{2\sqrt{A}},\ \frac{1}{120}$ in. **40.** $1{\cdot}13$ cu. in.

41. $35{\cdot}1\times10^{-7}V^{2\cdot9}\delta V,\ 1{\cdot}1.$ **42.** $\dfrac{3}{x^4}\delta x,\ \frac{1}{270}.$

EXERCISE XVI (Page 145).

1. $-3,\ y$ decreasing ; $-1,\ y$ decreasing ; $1,\ y$ increasing.

2. Increasing, decreasing.

4. y has a maximum value at $x=\frac{1}{4}.$ **5.** $\dfrac{4}{x^3}.$

6. 8. **7.** $24x^2-30x.$ **8.** $\frac{3}{4}x^{-\frac{1}{2}}.$

9. $-0{\cdot}24x^{-1\cdot6}+5{\cdot}6x^{-2\cdot4}.$

10. Clockwise, anti-clockwise, anti-clockwise.

11. (a) $3{\cdot}2$ ft./sec. (b) $-2{\cdot}4$ ft./sec.$^2.$

12. $4+\frac{1}{6}t$ radians per sec.

13. (a) $83{\cdot}8$ ft./sec. (b) $16{\cdot}8$ ft./sec. **14.** 8 ft. lb. wt.

15. $y_{max}=3\frac{1}{4}$ at $x=1\frac{1}{2}.$ **16.** $y_{min}=3$ at $x=1.$

17. $y_{max}=4$ at $x=0,\ y_{min}=0$ at $x=2.$

18. $y_{max}=0$ at $p=0,\ y_{min}=-32$ at $p=4.$

19. $y_{max}=11$ at $x=-1,\ y_{min}=-16$ at $x=2.$

20. $y_{max}=-16$ at $r=-2,\ y_{min}=16$ at $r=2.$

21. $y_{max}=-1$ at $x=-1,\ y_{min}=3$ at $x=1.$

22. $y_{max}=\frac{1}{4}$ at $u=2$ **23.** $y_{max}=4$ at $N=4.$ **24.** $y_{max}=\frac{3}{5}$ at $x=\frac{1}{4}.$

25. $y_{max}=\frac{6}{25}\sqrt{\frac{3}{5}}$ at $x=\frac{3}{5},\ y_{min}=0$ at $x=0.$

26. $y_{min.} = -12\cdot8$ at $v=32$. **27.** $\dfrac{wl^2}{8}$. **28.** $\dfrac{E}{2R}$. **29.** $\dfrac{4}{7}l$.

30. $x=2$, 12 sq. ft. **32.** $23\cdot4$, max. efficiency $=0\cdot87$.

33. (a) $1\cdot8$ in. (b) $3\cdot5$ in. ; 59 sq. in.

34. Least value $=6$ at $x=2$, greatest value $=10$ at $x=4$.

35. $0\cdot5458$.

36. 2500 sq. yd. ; smaller (area enclosed by circle $=3813$ sq. yd.).

37. $2\sqrt{\dfrac{Tg}{\rho}}$. **39.** After $1\cdot2$ hr., nearest distance $=13\cdot4$ miles.

40. $5\cdot73$, $4\cdot75$. **41.** After $2\cdot24$ sec., $12\cdot1$ ft.

EXERCISE XVII (Page 154)

1. $6t$, $3t^2$.

2. $2x\dfrac{dx}{dt}$, $24 \dfrac{\text{in.}^2}{\text{sec.}}$.

3. $4\pi r^2 \dfrac{dr}{dt}$, $12\cdot57 \dfrac{\text{ft.}^3}{\text{sec.}}$.

4. $1\cdot25 \dfrac{\text{lb. wt.}}{\text{in.}^2}$ per sec.

5. $4x^3 \dfrac{dx}{dt}$.

6 $-\dfrac{4}{x^2}\dfrac{dx}{dt}$.

7. $\dfrac{1}{2\sqrt{x}}\dfrac{dx}{dt}$.

8. $\dfrac{1}{\pi r}\dfrac{\text{in.}}{\text{sec.}}$, $0\cdot08 \dfrac{\text{in.}}{\text{sec.}}$.

9. $4(50+x)^2$, $1\cdot8$ ft.^{2}/sec.

10. $1\cdot29$ in.^{2}/sec.

11. $\frac{3}{4}$ in.^{3}/hr., $0\cdot006x^3$ in.^{3}/hr.

12. $\dfrac{1}{5h+10}\dfrac{\text{ft.}}{\text{min.}}$.

13. $\dfrac{15}{\pi x^2}\dfrac{\text{lb. wt.}}{\text{in.}^2}$ per. sec., $0\cdot075\dfrac{\text{lb. wt.}}{\text{in}^2}$ per sec.

14. $30(4+5x)^5$.

15. $\dfrac{1}{\sqrt{1+2x}}$.

16. $-24x(1-3x^2)^3$.

17. $-\dfrac{6x^2}{(1+x^3)^3}$.

18. $-n(a-x)^{n-1}$.

19. $\dfrac{a}{2\sqrt{ax+b}}$.

20. $\dfrac{v}{\sqrt{1+v^2}}$.

21. $-24(3-4l)^5$.

22. $-\dfrac{2}{(1+t)^3}$.

23. $-\dfrac{8r}{(1+4r^2)^2}$.

24. $40(2z+3)^{19}$.

25. $at(am+b)^{t-1}$.

26. $6(x+1)(x^3+2x)^2$.

27. $\dfrac{2n-1}{(1+n-n^2)^2}$.

28. $\dfrac{u}{(1-u^2)^{\frac{3}{2}}}$.

29. $\dfrac{4}{9}\dfrac{\text{ft.}}{\text{sec.}}$, $\dfrac{112\pi}{27}\dfrac{\text{ft.}^2}{\text{sec.}}$.

30. $\dfrac{2}{\sqrt{1+\dfrac{t}{273}}}\dfrac{\text{ft.}}{\text{sec.}}$ per degree.

31. $-\dfrac{x}{\sqrt{a^2-x^2}}$.

32. $\dfrac{2}{3y^2}$ or $\frac{2}{3}(2x)^{-\frac{2}{3}}$.

33. $\dfrac{32}{\sqrt{400-64x}}\dfrac{dx}{dt}$.

EXERCISE XVIII (Page 161)

1. $5x^4$, $\frac{1}{5}x^5+c$.

2. $\frac{16}{3}t^3+c$.

3. $-\frac{2}{x^3}$, $-\frac{1}{2x^2}+c$.

4. $2x^2+c$.

5. $2x^{\frac{3}{2}}+c$.

6. $-\frac{1}{5x}+c$.

7. $\frac{1}{3}x^3+x^2-3x+c$.

8. $-\frac{1}{2x^8}+c$.

9. $\frac{1}{4}x^4-\frac{1}{2x^2}+c$.

10. $\frac{1}{3\cdot6}x^{3\cdot6}+c$.

11. $-\frac{1}{1\cdot6x^{1\cdot6}}+c$.

12. $\frac{2}{7}\sqrt{10}x^{\frac{7}{2}}+c$.

13. $0\cdot4x^4-0\cdot8x^3-0\cdot3x^2+3\cdot5x+c$.

14. $\frac{1}{4}x^4+x^3+\frac{3}{2}x^2+x+c$.

15. $(0\cdot2t^3+2\cdot4)$ ft./sec., $2\cdot4$ ft./sec., $27\cdot4$ ft./sec.

16. $M=30+x-x^2$.

17. $M=\frac{1}{2}W(l^2-2lx+x^2)$, $\frac{1}{2}Wl^2$.

18. $z=x^3+\frac{5}{2}x^2-\frac{3}{2}$.

19. $(10t+2t^2+c)$ radians, $\frac{1}{4}\pi+10t+2t^2$.

EXERCISE XIX (Page 166)

1. $-\frac{1}{5x^5}+c$.

2. $\frac{2\sqrt{2}}{3}x^{\frac{3}{2}}+c$.

3. $2x^{25}+c$.

4. $-\frac{1}{2x^2}+c$.

5. $-\frac{1}{10x}+c$.

6. $-\frac{1}{2x^3}+c$.

7. $-\frac{4}{5x^{\frac{1}{2}}}+c$.

8. $5x^{0\cdot2}+c$.

9. $\frac{1}{3}x^3+x^2+c$.

10. $x-\frac{1}{x}+c$.

11. $x^2+\frac{4}{3}x^{\frac{3}{2}}+c$.

12. $\frac{1}{3}x^3-3x^2+9x+c$.

13. $0\cdot02t^2-0\cdot2t^3+c$.

14. $ar-\frac{b}{r}+c$.

15. $350v^{-0\cdot4}+c$.

16. $\frac{1}{8}s-\frac{1}{32}s^2+c$.

17. $\frac{1}{2}x^2-\frac{3}{x}+c$.

18. $4\frac{1}{2}$.

19. $4(\sqrt{2}-1)$.

20. $1\frac{1}{2}$.

21. 3.

22. $\frac{37}{864}$.

23. $0\cdot241$.

24. $\frac{1}{3\cdot5}\left(1-\frac{1}{8\sqrt{2}}\right)\simeq0\cdot260$.

25. $\frac{W^2a^3b^2}{3(a+b)^2}$.

26. $\frac{1}{8}wl^2$.

27. $2(H_1^{-\frac{1}{2}}-H_2^{-\frac{1}{2}})$.

28. $65\cdot17$.

29. $\frac{q}{R}$.

30. 1.

31. $\frac{4}{15}H^{\frac{5}{2}}$.

32. $x=t^2+3t+c$; 2, 28 ft. from O.

33. 2, 30 ft. from O.

34. $(8t^2-4)$ ft./sec.

35. $y=\frac{1}{2}x^2-x+\frac{3}{2}$.

36. $M=\frac{1}{2}wlx-\frac{1}{2}wx^2$; $\frac{1}{8}wl^2$.

37. $(3+2t-\frac{3}{16}t^2)$ ft./sec., 8 ft./sec.

12*

EXERCISE XX (Page 171)

1. $\frac{1}{2}a^2$.   **2.** 8.   **3.** $1\frac{2}{3}$, $10\frac{2}{3}$.   **4.** $\frac{1}{4}(b^4-a^4)$.

5. $2\sqrt{3}-\frac{4}{3}\sqrt{2} \backsimeq 1\cdot579$.   **6.** $4\sqrt{3}-\frac{8}{3}\sqrt{2} \backsimeq 3\cdot157$.

7. $\dfrac{1}{m-1}\left(\dfrac{1}{p^{m-1}}-\dfrac{1}{q^{m-1}}\right)$.   **8.** $\frac{3}{5}$.   **9.** $1\cdot73$.

10. $1\frac{7}{8}$.   **11.** $11\cdot0$.   **12.** $\frac{1}{6}a^3$.   **13.** $\frac{1}{4}b^4$.

14. $\dfrac{4-2\sqrt{2}}{3}a^2 \backsimeq 0\cdot391a^2$.   **15.** $1\frac{1}{3}$.

17. $(2, 4)$, $(-1, 1)$; $4\frac{1}{2}$,   **18.** $\frac{4}{3}a^3$.

EXERCISE XXI (Page 188)

1. 32 ft., $18\frac{1}{2}$ ft.   **2.** 297 yd., $15\cdot2$ m.p.h.

3. 144 ft., 24 ft./sec.   **4.** 21.   **5.** 6.   **6.** 2.

7. 75 ft. lb. wt.   **8.** 15 ft. lb. wt.   **9.** $3\frac{1}{8}$ ft. lb. **wt.**

10. $4\cdot48$ ft. lb. wt.   **11.** $\frac{5}{8}$ ft. lb. wt.

12. 32 ft. lb. wt., $7\cdot07$ ft./sec.

13. -2560 ft. lb. wt., $15\cdot9$ ft./sec., 43 lb. wt.

14. $\dfrac{500\pi}{3}$ units of volume.   **15.** $\frac{1}{3}\pi$ units of volume.

16. $\frac{4}{3}\sqrt{2}$ units of area, 2π units of volume.

17. $7\frac{1}{3}\pi$ units of volume.   **18.** $2\pi a^3$ units of volume.

20. $\dfrac{992\pi}{3} \backsimeq 1039$ in.^{3} **21.** $78\pi \backsimeq 245$ in.^{3}.

22. $\frac{1}{3}\pi(R_1{}^2+R_1R_2+R_2{}^2)$.   **23.** 8π units of volume.

24. 2π.   **25.** $\frac{4}{3}\pi ab^2$; $\frac{4}{3}\pi a^2b$.

26. $13\cdot1$ in.^{2}, $60\cdot7\pi \backsimeq 191$ in.^{3}; $4\cdot37$ in., $63\cdot6$ in.^{2}.   **27.** 6.

28. 8 ft. lb. wt., 1 lb. wt.   **29.** $\frac{2}{3}$ lb. wt.

31. 24 by Simpson's rule and by integration. (Simpson's rule is **exact** because the curve is a parabola.)

32. $0\cdot671$, $\frac{2}{3}$.   **33.** $\displaystyle\int_{v_1}^{v_2} p\,dv$, $77\cdot7$ ft. lb. wt.

34. 7000 ft. lb. wt.   **36.** $\frac{2}{3}\sqrt{2g}ab^{\frac{3}{2}}$ cu. ft.   **37.** $0\cdot45$ erg.

EXERCISE XXII (Page 198)

1. 2.   **2.** $0\cdot13\%$.   **3.** $0\cdot9391$, from tables $0\cdot9397$

4. $-\sin x$.   **5.** $0\cdot54$, $\cos 1^c = 0\cdot5402$.

6. $\omega\cos(\omega x+a)$, $\dfrac{\pi}{180}\cos x^0$.   **7.** $3\cos x+4\sin x$.

8. $8\cos 8x$.   **9.** $-\frac{1}{2}\sin 3x$.   **10.** $6\cos(2x+5)$.

11. $\sin(\frac{1}{6}\pi-x)$.   **12.** $4\cos\frac{2}{3}x$.   **13.** $2\pi n\cos 2\pi nx$.

14. $-2\sin x\cos x$.   **15.** $2\cos\frac{1}{2}x$.   **16.** $\dfrac{\cos x}{2\sqrt{\sin x}}$.

17. $\cos x-\frac{1}{2}\cos 3x$.   **18.** $-2\operatorname{cosec}2x\cot 2x$.

19. $-1\cdot6\sin 2x - 0\cdot4\sin 4x$.

20. $-5\sin(100x-5)$.

21. $-\dfrac{2\cos x}{\sin^3 x}$.

22. $-6\sin x(2+3\cos x)$.

23. $5\sin^4 x\cos x$.

24. $6\sin x\cos x$.

25. $-\dfrac{4\cos x}{(5+4\sin x)^2}$.

26. $2\sec^2 x\tan x$.

27. $\sec x\tan x - \sin x = \dfrac{\sin^3 x}{\cos^2 x}$.

28. $-10\sin 5x\cos 5x$.

29. $-1500\pi\sin 100\pi t$.

30. $a\omega\cos\omega t$.

31. $-cn\sin(nt-\beta)$.

32. $\cos 2\theta$.

33. $2\sin\phi\cos\phi$.

34. $\sec\lambda\tan\lambda$.

35. $10^{-3}(-2\sin 200t+1\cdot5\sin 600t)$.

36. $\sin(a-\phi)$.

37. $2\pi f(\cos 2\pi ft+\cos 6\pi ft)$.

38. $-2\operatorname{cosec}^2\theta\cot\theta$.

39. $-6\sin 2t$ in./sec., $-12\cos 2t$ in./sec.^{2}; 6 in./sec., 12 in./sec^2.

40. $6\sin 4\pi t$ in., $12\sin 2\pi t$ in.; $24\pi\cos 4\pi t$ in./sec., $24\cos 2\pi t$ in./sec. (a) $23\cdot3$ in./sec., $61\cdot0$ in./sec. (b) $-61\cdot0$ in./sec., $23\cdot3$ in./sec.

41. $0\cdot0377\cos 100\pi t$ volts.

42. $\dfrac{25\pi}{3}(-1\cdot04\sin\theta+1\cdot51\cos\theta)$ in./sec.;

$-\left(\dfrac{25\pi}{3}\right)^2(1\cdot04\cos\theta+1\cdot51\sin\theta)$ in./sec.^{2}.

43. Positive from $(2n-\tfrac{1}{2})\pi$ to $(2n+\tfrac{1}{2})\pi$, negative from $(2n+\tfrac{1}{2})\pi$ to $(2n+\tfrac{3}{2})\pi$.

44. 2, -2.

45. $-(3\cdot14\sin 314t+0\cdot628\sin 628t)$.

46. 5, -5.

47. $0\cdot0738$; $33\cdot5$.

50. $7\sin 300t+10\cdot5\cos 300t$, $12\cdot6$ volts, $0\cdot983$.

51. $-8\cdot333\pi\sin\dfrac{200\pi t}{3}+10\cdot44\pi\sin\dfrac{400\pi t}{3}$;

$-555\cdot6\pi^2\cos\dfrac{200\pi t}{3}+1393\pi^2\cos\dfrac{400\pi t}{3}$;

$26\cdot2$, $13{,}700$.

EXERCISE XXIII (Page 208)

1. $-\tfrac{1}{2}\cos 2x+c$.

2. $2\sin\tfrac{1}{2}x+c$.

3. $-\dfrac{1}{2\pi f}\cos(2\pi ft+a)+c$.

4. $\dfrac{1}{\omega}\sin(\omega t-\beta)+c$.

5. $-\tfrac{2}{3}\cos 3x-\tfrac{1}{4}\sin 4x+c$.

6. $\tfrac{5}{8}\sin 1\cdot6\theta+c$.

7. $2x-3\cos x+c$.

8. $at-\dfrac{b}{\omega}\cos\omega t+\dfrac{c}{\omega}\sin\omega t+k$ (k arbitrary.)

9. $\tfrac{1}{2}(\phi-\tfrac{1}{2}\sin 2\phi)+c$.

10. $\tfrac{1}{2}(\theta-\tfrac{1}{2}\sin 2\theta)+c$.

11. $\tfrac{1}{2}(x+\tfrac{1}{4}\sin 4x)+c$.

12. $\tfrac{3}{2}x-2\cos x-\tfrac{1}{4}\sin 2x+c$.

13. $\tfrac{1}{2}\left(t-\dfrac{1}{2\omega}\sin 2\omega t\right)+c$.

14. $\tfrac{1}{2}\left\{t+\dfrac{1}{2\omega}\sin 2(\omega t+a)\right\}+c$.

15. $\phi+\sin\phi+c$.

16. $\tfrac{1}{2}\cos x-\tfrac{1}{10}\cos 5x+c$.

17. $-\dfrac{1}{\omega}(\cos\omega t+\tfrac{1}{3}\cos 3\omega t)+c$.

18. $\tfrac{1}{16}(2\sin 4\theta+\sin 8\theta)+c$.

19. 2.   **20.** 6.   **21.** 2.   **22.** $\frac{1}{4}$.

23. 2.   **24.** 0·8415.   **25.** $\dfrac{a}{\omega}$.   **26.** $\frac{1}{4}\pi$.

27. $\frac{1}{4}\pi - \frac{1}{2} \backsimeq 0\cdot2854$.   **28.** 0.   **29.** 0·6.

30. $\dfrac{2}{\omega}$.   **31.** 0·9.   **32.** $\dfrac{2I_m}{\pi}, \dfrac{2\sqrt{2}}{\pi} \backsimeq 0\cdot9$.

34. 0.   **35.** $\frac{1}{2}ZI^2_m \cos \alpha$.   **36.** $(4+2\cos 2t)$ ft./sec.

37. $\dfrac{E_m}{\omega L}(1-\cos \omega t)$ **38.** $\frac{3}{4}I_m, \sqrt{\frac{2}{3}}I_m$.

39. $\dfrac{I_m}{\sqrt{2}}$.   **40.** 15,700 ft. lb. wt.

EXERCISE XXIV (Page 226)

1. $6\frac{9}{42}$ in.   **2.** $1\frac{2}{29}$ in.

2. The centroid of a face is on the axis of symmetry of the isosceles triangle at $2\frac{2}{3}$ in. from the vertex. The centre of gravity of the plate is 2 in. from the centroid in a direction perpendicular to the face.

4. (4, 0).   **5.** (15, 0).   **6.** $(\frac{3}{4}l, \frac{3}{10}l)$.   **9.** $12\frac{31}{38}$ in. from A.

10. 5·4 in. from the centre of the sphere on the axis of symmetry of the segment.

11. $\frac{2}{5}$.   **12.** $2\pi^2 a^2 b, 4\pi^2 ab$.   **13.** $\frac{1}{3}\pi r^2 h$.

14. $\dfrac{4}{3\pi} \times$ (radius) from the centre, $\dfrac{\pi}{32}(198-27\pi) \backsimeq 11\cdot1$ ft.^{3}.

15. $42\pi \backsimeq 132$ in.^{3}, $26\sqrt{10}\pi \backsimeq 258$ in.^{2}.   **16.** $18\pi^2 \backsimeq 178$ in.^{2}.

17. $\frac{1}{2}\pi^2$ units of volume, $(\frac{1}{2}\pi, \frac{1}{8}\pi)$.   **20.** 8·68 lb. wt.

21. $\pi r^3 w, \pi r^2 h w$.   **23.** $5\frac{7}{11}$ ft.

24. (i) $\frac{3}{4}h$.   (ii) $\frac{1}{2}h$, where h is the height of the triangle.

EXERCISE XXV (Page 238)

1. $\frac{2}{3}\sqrt{15}$ ft.   **2.** $\dfrac{7Wl^2}{16g}$.   **3.** $\frac{1}{2}a^2$.

5. $\sqrt{122}$ in. ; 18·6 ft. lb. wt.   **6.** $\frac{4}{3}\sqrt{3}$ ft. ; 74 ft. lb. wt.

7. $\dfrac{a}{\sqrt{2}}$, 0·39.   **9.** $1301\frac{1}{3}$ in.^{4}.   **11.** 116 in.^{4} ; 3·19 in., 2·15 in.

12. $\frac{1}{4}ah^3, \frac{1}{36}ah^3$.   **13.** $\frac{3}{2}a^3$.   **14.** 4·52 in.

EXERCISE XXVI (Page 261)

1. $3e^{3x}$.   **2.** $-0\cdot4e^{-0\cdot4x}$.   **3.** $8e^{2t}$.   **4.** $-50e^{-5}\theta$.

5. $3\cdot6e^{1\cdot2x} - 1\cdot3e^{0\cdot5x}$.   **6.** $10^x \log_e 10 \backsimeq 2\cdot303 \times 10^x$.

7. $2^s \log_e 2 \backsimeq 0\cdot693 \times 2^s$.   **8.** $5e^{5t+4}$.   **9.** $\dfrac{1}{x}$.

10. $\dfrac{1}{x}$ **11.** $\dfrac{3}{3x-2}$. **12.** $\dfrac{4}{8z+5}$.

13. $-0{\cdot}28e^{-0{\cdot}2x}+\dfrac{7}{x}$. **14.** $18{\cdot}9e^{2{\cdot}1t}+2t$. **15.** $\dfrac{2}{x}$.

16. $\dfrac{2}{r^2-1}$. **19.** $1+\log_e 2 \eqsim 1{\cdot}693$. **20.** $\log_e 2 \eqsim 0{\cdot}693$.

21. $\tfrac{1}{3}\log_e 4 \eqsim 0{\cdot}462$. **22.** $0{\cdot}311$. **23.** $64{\cdot}16$.

24. $0{\cdot}549$. **25.** $0{\cdot}347$. **26.** 1.

27. $\tfrac{1}{4}\log_e 5 \eqsim 0{\cdot}402$. **28.** $43{\cdot}83$ H.P. **30.** $y=2e^{3x}$.

31. $s=0{\cdot}742e^{-0{\cdot}5t}$. **32.** $39{\cdot}32$ r.p.m. **33.** $\dfrac{1}{k}\log\left(1+\dfrac{ku}{g}\right)$.

34. $v=\left(u+\dfrac{g}{k}\right)e^{-kt}-\dfrac{g}{k}$. **37.** $x=ab\left\{\dfrac{1-e^{k(b-a)t}}{a-be^{k(b-a)t}}\right\}$.

41. $0{\cdot}543$. **42.** $14{\cdot}51$. **43.** $0{\cdot}255$. **45.** $3{\cdot}76$. **49.** $0{\cdot}423$.

EXERCISE XXVII (Page 270)

1. $\sqrt{x}\cos x+\dfrac{\sin x}{2\sqrt{x}}$. **2.** $2\cos 2x\cos x-\sin 2x\sin x$.

3. $4x\cos 3x-6x^2\sin 3x$. **4.** $\dfrac{2+3x}{8\sqrt{1+x}}$.

5. $-a\sin ax\cos bx-b\cos ax\sin bx$ **6.** $2xe^x+x^2e^x$.

7. $\dfrac{3}{(2x+3)^2}$. **8.** $\dfrac{16}{(x+5)^2}$. **9.** $\dfrac{9-3x^2}{(x^2+3)^2}$.

10. $\dfrac{x\cos x-\sin x}{x^2}$. **11.** $\dfrac{2\cos x}{(1-\sin x)^2}$. **12.** $\dfrac{-2(x^2+x+1)}{(1+2x)^2}$.

13. $\dfrac{1-\log x}{x^2}$. **14.** $e^{2x}(2\sin x+\cos x)$. **15.** $\dfrac{\sqrt{x}}{1+x}+\dfrac{\log(1+x)}{2\sqrt{x}}$.

17. $\sin\tfrac{1}{2}x\cos\tfrac{1}{2}x$, $-\dfrac{\pi}{l}\sin\dfrac{\pi x}{l}$, $2r\pi\sec^2 2r\pi x$, $-2\operatorname{cosec} 2x\cot 2x$,

$3\sec 3x\tan 3x$, $2\operatorname{cosec}^2(1-2x)$.

18. $\cos\theta-\theta\sin\theta$. **19.** $\dfrac{1-r}{2\sqrt{r}(1+r^2)}$. **20.** $2\phi\sin 2\phi+2\phi^2\cos 2\phi$.

21. $\dfrac{4k}{(k+1)^2}$. **22.** $\dfrac{1}{(1+y^2)^{\frac{3}{2}}}$. **23.** $\dfrac{2}{(m+1)^2}$.

24. Maximum 2 at $x=-1$, minimum $\tfrac{2}{3}$ at $x=1$. **25.** $0{\cdot}685$.

EXERCISE XXVIII (Page 278)

1. $-\dfrac{1}{2y}=\mp\dfrac{1}{2\sqrt{1-x}}$. **2.** $-\dfrac{x}{y}=\mp\dfrac{x}{\sqrt{x^2-4}}$.

3. $-\dfrac{y}{x}=\mp\dfrac{100}{x^2}$. **4.** $y=e^x$.

5. $\dfrac{3x^2}{4y^3}=\dfrac{3}{4x^{\frac{1}{4}}}$. **6.** $\dfrac{2\sin x}{\sin y}=\pm\dfrac{2\sin x}{\sqrt{1-4\cos^2 x}}$.

7. 3.

8. $-\dfrac{2x}{y} = -\dfrac{2x}{\sqrt{x^2-16}}$ in./sec.

9. $3x^2 dx$.

10. $-\dfrac{dx}{x^2}$.

11. $\dfrac{dx}{x}$.

12. $2\cos 2x\, dx$.

13. $na(ax+b)^{n-1}dx$.

14. $-e^{-x}dx$.

15. $-\dfrac{dx}{(1+x)^2}$.

16. $\sec^2 x\, dx$.

17. $\dfrac{dx}{2\sqrt{x}}$.

18. $\dfrac{vdu-udv}{v^2}$.

19. $\frac{1}{5}x^5+c$.

20. $\frac{1}{2}\log x+c$.

21. $\frac{1}{4}\sin 4x+c$.

22. $\frac{1}{2}e^{2x}+c$.

23. $2\sqrt{x}+c$.

24. $-\dfrac{2}{x^2}+c$.

25. $\dfrac{(4+x^2)^{11}}{11}+c$.

26. $-\dfrac{1}{\sin x}+c$.

27. $\frac{1}{6}(1+x^3)^6+c$.

28. $\sin^6 x+c$.

29. $\frac{1}{2}e^{x^2}+c$.

30. $\dfrac{(4+x^2)^{11}}{22}+c$.

31. $-\dfrac{4}{\sin x}+c$.

32. $2\sin^5 x+c$.

33. $2(1+x^2)^{\frac{3}{2}}+c$.

34. $\frac{1}{2}\log(x^2-1)+c$.

35. $\dfrac{2}{4-x^2}+c$.

37. xe^x-e^x+c.

38. $-x\cos x+\sin x+c$.

39. $\frac{1}{2}x^2\log x-\frac{1}{4}x^2+c$.

40. $\frac{1}{2}x\sin 2x+\frac{1}{4}\cos 2x+c$.

41. $1-\dfrac{2}{e}$; centroid is $\left\{\dfrac{e-2}{e+1},\ \frac{1}{4}\left(1+\dfrac{1}{e}\right)\right\}$, which is approximately $(0\cdot418,\ 0\cdot342)$.

42. $(\frac{1}{2}\pi-1,\ \frac{1}{4}\pi)$.

43. $\dfrac{2}{\sqrt{1-4x^2}}$.

44. $\frac{1}{4}\pi$.

46. $nt=\frac{1}{2}\pi-\sin^{-1}\dfrac{x}{a}=\cos^{-1}\dfrac{x}{a}$.

EXERCISE XXIX (Page 289)

1. $20-2j$.

2. $-1\cdot5-1\cdot9j$.

3. $2+29j$.

4. $1+21j$

5. $41\cdot68-131\cdot22j$.

6. $25+21j$.

7. $-55+48j$.

8. -4.

9. 29.

10. $\cos(\alpha+\beta)+j\sin(\alpha+\beta)$.

15. $0\cdot4-1\cdot7j$.

16. $-0\cdot69+0\cdot72j$.

17. $\frac{16}{73}$.

18. $-\frac{6}{73}j$.

19. $1\cdot4-1\cdot2j$.

20. $0\cdot07+0\cdot09j$.

21. $4\cdot55-0\cdot46j$.

22. $2\cdot40+2\cdot02j$.

23. $x=1\pm4j$.

24. $1,\ -\frac{1}{2}\pm\dfrac{\sqrt{3}}{2}j$.

25. Oscillatory.

EXERCISE XXX (Page 295)

1. $6\cdot40\angle38°\ 39'$.

2. $6\cdot63\angle78°\ 41'$.

3. $13\angle-22°\ 37'$.

4. $17\angle118°\ 4'$.

5. $0\cdot275\angle-160°\ 54'$.

6. $83\cdot2\angle151°\ 17'$.

7. $4\cdot207+3\cdot057j$.

8. $-0\cdot4+0\cdot693j$.

9. $2\cdot756-9\cdot613j$.

10. $r\angle(\pi-\theta),\ r\angle(\theta+\pi)$.

11. $4\cdot5\angle68°$.

12. $1\cdot5\angle-36°$.

13. $1\cdot6\angle\,25°$.　　　**14.** $0\cdot0625\angle\,110°$.　　　**15.** $3-4j$; $5\angle-53°\,8'$.

16. $32\cdot39\angle\,81°\,7'$; $5\cdot69\angle\,40°\,33'$ and $5\cdot69\angle-139°\,27'$.

17. (i) $1\angle\,45°$ and $1\angle-135°$, i.e. $\pm\dfrac{1}{\sqrt{2}}(1+j)$;

　　(ii) $2\angle-45°$ and $2\angle\,135°$, i.e. $\pm\sqrt{2}(1-j)$.

18. $16\cdot12\angle-29°\,45'$; $4\cdot02\angle-14°\,52'$ and $4\cdot02\angle\,165°\,8'$;
$\pm(3\cdot88-1\cdot03j)$.

19. $0\cdot368\angle-9°\,28'$ and $0\cdot368\angle\,170°\,32'$; i.e. $\pm(0\cdot36-0\cdot06j)$.

20. $\pm(0\cdot6+0\cdot8j)$.　　　　　　**21.** $1\angle\,0$, $1\angle\,120°$, $1\angle-120°$.

EXERCISE XXXI (Page 308)

1. $R=\dfrac{r\omega^2L^2}{r^2+\omega^2L^2}$, $X=\dfrac{r^2\omega L}{r^2+\omega^2L^2}$.

2. $R=\dfrac{r}{1+r^2\omega^2C^2}$, $X=-\dfrac{r^2\omega C}{1+r^2\omega^2C^2}$.

3. $R=0$, $X=\dfrac{1}{\omega L-\dfrac{1}{\omega C}}$.　　　　**5.** $78\cdot68+j296\cdot2$.

6. $90\cdot2\sin(100\pi t-57°\,51')$ volts.　　**7.** $-2\cdot57\cos50\pi t$ amp.

8. $R_1=R_2R_4/R_3$; $C=\dfrac{L}{R_2R_4}$.

10. $e_1=200$, $e_2=j120$, $e_3=75-j129\cdot90$, $e_4=35\cdot36-j35\cdot36$;
$e=160\cdot36-j25\cdot46=162\cdot4\sin(100\pi t-0\cdot1574)$.

11. Resistance $0\cdot24$ ohms, reactance $2\cdot32$ ohms.

12. Maximum $7\cdot18$ amp., lagging $64°\,29'$.

EXERCISE XXXII (Page 319)

3. $4\cdot8$, $7\cdot5$　　$31\cdot4$.　　　**4.** 1840 cu. in., $5\cdot75$ in.

5. $0\cdot0535$.　　　　**7.** $11\cdot3$, $16\cdot5$.　　　　**8.** $5\cdot38$ in.

EXERCISE XXXIII (Page 324)

1. 1560.　　　**2.** $13\cdot99$.　　　**3.** $0\cdot442$　　　**4.** $0\cdot591$.

5. $0\cdot0355$.　　**6.** $0\cdot00628$.　　**7.** $7\cdot77$.

8. Set $1B$ against yD and read off answer on A opposite xB.

9. Set yB against xD and read off answer on D opposite $1C$.

10. Set $1C$ against xD and read off answer on A opposite yC.

11. 232.　　　　**12.** $15\cdot3$.　　　　**13.** $13\cdot4$.

16. $40\cdot4$.　　　　**17.** $6\cdot11$, $4\cdot10$.　　　**18.** $1\cdot94$ ohms.

EXERCISE XXXIV (Page 335)

4. 535.　　　**5.** 8×10^4, $0\cdot021$.　　　**7.** $6\cdot37$ sq. in.

8. $44\cdot7$.　　　**9.** $1\cdot6$.　　　　　**11.** 220.

SPECIMEN EXAMINATION PAPERS.

UNION OF LANCASHIRE AND CHESHIRE INSTITUTES (Page 346)

1. (a) 18·0.   (b) 0·997, 0·997.

2. (a) 3·42 in.   (b) 37·7 cu. in.

3. (i) 1·4 or 4.   (ii) 2·80.   (iii) ±0·90.

4. 12·50 in., 13·58 in. ; 2·85 in.   5. 13°.

6. (a) $25+32t$ ft./sec., 32 ft./sec.^{2}.   (b) $12\frac{1}{2}$.   (c) $\cos\theta - \theta\sin\theta$.

7. H min. $=180$ at $x=6$.

8. (i) $4\frac{1}{3}$.   (ii) $\frac{1}{5}x^5 - \frac{1}{3}x^{-3} + c$.   (iii) 2, $y=5e^x+1$.

9. 9·6 sq. in., 2·4 in.   10. $\frac{1}{3}ml^3$ lb. ft.^{2}, $\frac{1}{12}ml^3$ lb. ft.^{2}

UNION OF EDUCATIONAL INSTITUTIONS (Page 348)

1. (a) $A=\sqrt{a^2+b^2}$; a is an angle given by $\cos a = \dfrac{a}{\sqrt{a^2+b^2}}$,

    $\sin a = \dfrac{b}{\sqrt{a^2+b^2}}$.   (b) 0·00098.   2. (b) 520 cu. in.

3. $a=194$, $b=-4·45$, $c=0·0275$; 66·1 or 95·7.

4. $k=0·02$, $n=1·5$.

5. (a) $x^n + nx^{n-1}a + \dfrac{n(n-1)}{1.2}x^{n-2}a^2 + \dfrac{n(n-1)(n-2)}{1.2.3}x^{n-3}a^3$;

    $1 - x - \frac{1}{2}x^2 - \frac{1}{2}x^3 - \frac{5}{8}x^4$.   (b) 8 per cent.

6. 6·8 in. per min.   7. (b) $-\dfrac{1}{x+1}+c$.   (c) $\dfrac{x}{x+1}=1-\dfrac{1}{x+1}$.

8. Side of square $=1·31$ in., side of triangle $=2·26$ in.

9. (a) $-\dfrac{x}{y}$.   (b) -1563.   (c) 111·6.   10. $3\frac{1}{3}$, $\frac{24}{25}$.   11. $288\frac{5}{16}$ in.^{4}

NORTHERN COUNTIES TECHNICAL EXAMINATIONS COUNCIL (Page 350)

1. (i) 4·99.   (ii) $T_1=762$ lb. wt., $T_2=1507$ lb. wt.   2. -1, $2\frac{1}{2}$.

3. (i) 109° 28′.   (ii) $\sqrt{2}$; hypotenuse $=\dfrac{10}{\sin\theta + \cos\theta + 1}$ in.,

    minimum $=10(\sqrt{2}-1)$ in.

4. (i) 3·7, 1·75, 1·05.   (ii) 0·54, 2·14, 3·56.

5. (i) 4, $-\frac{1}{8}$.   (ii) maximum $=7$, minimum $=3$.

6. (i) $-\frac{3}{2}x^{-\frac{5}{2}} - \frac{8}{3}x^{-3}$, $4x^3 - 1 - \frac{1}{2}x^{-3}$, $4x^3 + 2x^{-3}$, $1 + 48x^{-4}$.

    (ii) $2\frac{1}{2}$, 0.

7. $-x^{-1} - \frac{2}{3}x^2 - \frac{1}{4}x^4 + c$, $\frac{3}{4}x^{\frac{4}{3}} + \frac{2}{5}x^{\frac{5}{2}} + c$, $\frac{1}{5}x^5 - \frac{1}{3}x^3 + \frac{1}{4}x + c$; $4\frac{1}{2}$, $20\frac{5}{6}$.

8. $2 + \frac{3}{4}x^{\frac{1}{2}}$ sq. in., $8\frac{4}{5}$ in.

9. (i) $x=10$ ft., $\dot{x}=6$ ft./sec., $\ddot{x}=3$ ft./sec.^{2}

    (ii) $x=\frac{1}{15}t^{\frac{5}{2}} + \frac{5}{3}t + \frac{1}{5}$.   10. 42° 4′.

INDEX

LOGARITHMS

	0	1	2	3	4	5	6	7	8	9	Differences								
											1	2	3	4	5	6	7	8	9
10	0000	0043	0086	0128	0170	0212	0253	0294	0334	0374	4	8	12	17	21	25	29	33	37
11	0414	0453	0492	0531	0569	0607	0645	0682	0719	0755	4	8	11	15	19	23	26	30	34
12	0792	0828	0864	0899	0934	0969	1004	1038	1072	1106	3	7	10	14	17	21	24	28	31
13	1139	1173	1206	1239	1271	1303	1335	1367	1399	1430	3	6	10	13	16	19	23	26	29
14	1461	1492	1523	1553	1584	1614	1644	1673	1703	1732	3	6	9	12	15	18	21	24	27
15	1761	1790	1818	1847	1875	1903	1931	1959	1987	2014	3	6	8	11	14	17	20	22	25
16	2041	2068	2095	2122	2148	2175	2201	2227	2253	2279	3	5	8	11	13	16	18	21	24
17	2304	2330	2355	2380	2405	2430	2455	2480	2504	2529	2	5	7	10	12	15	17	20	22
18	2553	2577	2601	2625	2648	2672	2695	2718	2742	2765	2	5	7	9	12	14	16	19	21
19	2788	2810	2833	2856	2878	2900	2923	2945	2967	2989	2	4	7	9	11	13	16	18	20
20	3010	3032	3054	3075	3096	3118	3139	3160	3181	3201	2	4	6	8	11	13	15	17	19
21	3222	3243	3263	3284	3304	3324	3345	3365	3385	3404	2	4	6	8	10	12	14	16	18
22	3424	3444	3464	3483	3502	3522	3541	3560	3579	3598	2	4	6	8	10	12	14	15	17
23	3617	3636	3655	3674	3692	3711	3729	3747	3766	3784	2	4	6	7	9	11	13	15	17
24	3802	3820	3838	3856	3874	3892	3909	3927	3945	3962	2	4	5	7	9	11	12	14	16
25	3979	3997	4014	4031	4048	4065	4082	4099	4116	4133	2	3	5	7	9	10	12	14	15
26	4150	4166	4183	4200	4216	4232	4249	4265	4281	4298	2	3	5	7	8	10	11	13	15
27	4314	4330	4346	4362	4378	4393	4409	4425	4440	4456	2	3	5	6	8	9	11	13	14
28	4472	4487	4502	4518	4533	4548	4564	4579	4594	4609	2	3	5	6	8	9	11	12	14
29	4624	4639	4654	4669	4683	4698	4713	4728	4742	4757	1	3	4	6	7	9	10	12	13
30	4771	4786	4800	4814	4829	4843	4857	4871	4886	4900	1	3	4	6	7	9	10	11	13
31	4914	4928	4942	4955	4969	4983	4997	5011	5024	5038	1	3	4	6	7	8	10	11	12
32	5051	5065	5079	5092	5105	5119	5132	5145	5159	5172	1	3	4	5	7	8	9	11	12
33	5185	5198	5211	5224	5237	5250	5263	5276	5289	5302	1	3	4	5	6	8	9	10	12
34	5315	5328	5340	5353	5366	5378	5391	5403	5416	5428	1	3	4	5	6	8	9	10	11
35	5441	5453	5465	5478	5490	5502	5514	5527	5539	5551	1	2	4	5	6	7	9	10	11
36	5563	5575	5587	5599	5611	5623	5635	5647	5658	5670	1	2	4	5	6	7	8	10	11
37	5682	5694	5705	5717	5729	5740	5752	5763	5775	5786	1	2	3	5	6	7	8	9	10
38	5798	5809	5821	5832	5843	5855	5866	5877	5888	5899	1	2	3	5	6	7	8	9	10
39	5911	5922	5933	5944	5955	5966	5977	5988	5999	6010	1	2	3	4	5	7	8	9	10
40	6021	6031	6042	6053	6064	6075	6085	6096	6107	6117	1	2	3	4	5	6	8	9	10
41	6128	6138	6149	6160	6170	6180	6191	6201	6212	6222	1	2	3	4	5	6	7	8	9
42	6232	6243	6253	6263	6274	6284	6294	6304	6314	6325	1	2	3	4	5	6	7	8	9
43	6335	6345	6355	6365	6375	6385	6395	6405	6415	6425	1	2	3	4	5	6	7	8	9
44	6435	6444	6454	6464	6474	6484	6493	6503	6513	6522	1	2	3	4	5	6	7	8	9
45	6532	6542	6551	6561	6571	6580	6590	6599	6609	6618	1	2	3	4	5	6	7	8	9
46	6628	6637	6646	6656	6665	6675	6684	6693	6702	6712	1	2	3	4	5	6	7	7	8
47	6721	6730	6739	6749	6758	6767	6776	6785	6794	6803	1	2	3	4	5	5	6	7	8
48	6812	6821	6830	6839	6848	6857	6866	6875	6884	6893	1	2	3	4	4	5	6	7	8
49	6902	6911	6920	6928	6937	6946	6955	6964	6972	6981	1	2	3	4	4	5	6	7	8
50	6990	6998	7007	7016	7024	7033	7042	7050	7059	7067	1	2	3	3	4	5	6	7	8
51	7076	7084	7093	7101	7110	7118	7126	7135	7143	7152	1	2	3	3	4	5	6	7	8
52	7160	7168	7177	7185	7193	7202	7210	7218	7226	7235	1	2	2	3	4	5	6	7	7
53	7243	7251	7259	7267	7275	7284	7292	7300	7308	7316	1	2	2	3	4	5	6	6	7
54	7324	7332	7340	7348	7356	7364	7372	7380	7388	7396	1	2	2	3	4	5	6	6	7

LOGARITHMS

	0	1	2	3	4	5	6	7	8	9	1	2	3	4	5	6	7	8	9
															Differences				
55	7404	7412	7419	7427	7435	7443	7451	7459	7466	7474	1	2	2	3	4	5	5	6	7
56	7482	7490	7497	7505	7513	7520	7528	7536	7543	7551	1	2	2	3	4	5	5	6	7
57	7559	7566	7574	7582	7589	7597	7604	7612	7619	7627	1	2	2	3	4	5	5	6	7
58	7634	7642	7649	7657	7664	7672	7679	7686	7694	7701	1	1	2	3	4	4	5	6	7
59	7709	7716	7723	7731	7738	7745	7752	7760	7767	7774	1	1	2	3	4	4	5	6	7
60	7782	7789	7796	7803	7810	7818	7825	7832	7839	7846	1	1	2	3	4	4	5	6	6
61	7853	7860	7868	7875	7882	7889	7896	7903	7910	7917	1	1	2	3	4	4	5	6	6
62	7924	7931	7938	7945	7952	7959	7966	7973	7980	7987	1	1	2	3	3	4	5	6	6
63	7993	8000	8007	8014	8021	8028	8035	8041	8048	8055	1	1	2	3	3	4	5	5	6
64	8062	8069	8075	8082	8089	8096	8102	8109	8116	8122	1	1	2	3	3	4	5	5	6
65	8129	8136	8142	8149	8156	8162	8169	8176	8182	8189	1	1	2	3	3	4	5	5	6
66	8195	8202	8209	8215	8222	8228	8235	8241	8248	8254	1	1	2	3	3	4	5	5	6
67	8261	8267	8274	8280	8287	8293	8299	8306	8312	8319	1	1	2	3	3	4	5	5	6
68	8325	8331	8338	8344	8351	8357	8363	8370	8376	8382	1	1	2	3	3	4	4	5	6
69	8388	8395	8401	8407	8414	8420	8426	8432	8439	8445	1	1	2	2	3	4	4	5	6
70	8451	8457	8463	8470	8476	8482	8488	8494	8500	8506	1	1	2	2	3	4	4	5	6
71	8513	8519	8525	8531	8537	8543	8549	8555	8561	8567	1	1	2	2	3	4	4	5	5
72	8573	8579	8585	8591	8597	8603	8609	8615	8621	8627	1	1	2	2	3	4	4	5	5
73	8633	8639	8645	8651	8657	8663	8669	8675	8681	8686	1	1	2	2	3	4	4	5	5
74	8692	8698	8704	8710	8716	8722	8727	8733	8739	8745	1	1	2	2	3	4	4	5	5
75	8751	8756	8762	8768	8774	8779	8785	8791	8797	8802	1	1	2	2	3	3	4	5	5
76	8808	8814	8820	8825	8831	8837	8842	8848	8854	8859	1	1	2	2	3	3	4	5	5
77	8865	8871	8876	8882	8887	8893	8899	8904	8910	8915	1	1	2	2	3	3	4	4	5
78	8921	8927	8932	8938	8943	8949	8954	8960	8965	8971	1	1	2	2	3	3	4	4	5
79	8976	8982	8987	8993	8998	9004	9009	9015	9020	9025	1	1	2	2	3	3	4	4	5
80	9031	9036	9042	9047	9053	9058	9063	9069	9074	9079	1	1	2	2	3	3	4	4	5
81	9085	9090	9096	9101	9106	9112	9117	9122	9128	9133	1	1	2	2	3	3	4	4	5
82	9138	9143	9149	9154	9159	9165	9170	9175	9180	9186	1	1	2	2	3	3	4	4	5
83	9191	9196	9201	9206	9212	9217	9222	9227	9232	9238	1	1	2	2	3	3	4	4	5
84	9243	9248	9253	9258	9263	9269	9274	9279	9284	9289	1	1	2	2	3	3	4	4	5
85	9294	9299	9304	9309	9315	9320	9325	9330	9335	9340	1	1	2	2	3	3	4	4	5
86	9345	9350	9355	9360	9365	9370	9375	9380	9385	9390	1	1	2	2	3	3	4	4	5
87	9395	9400	9405	9410	9415	9420	9425	9430	9435	9440	0	1	1	2	2	3	3	4	4
88	9445	9450	9455	9460	9465	9469	9474	9479	9484	9489	0	1	1	2	2	3	3	4	4
89	9494	9499	9504	9509	9513	9518	9523	9528	9533	9538	0	1	1	2	2	3	3	4	4
90	9542	9547	9552	9557	9562	9566	9571	9576	9581	9586	0	1	1	2	2	3	3	4	4
91	9590	9595	9600	9605	9609	9614	9619	9624	9628	9633	0	1	1	2	2	3	3	4	4
92	9638	9643	9647	9652	9657	9661	9666	9671	9675	9680	0	1	1	2	2	3	3	4	4
93	9685	9689	9694	9699	9703	9708	9713	9717	9722	9727	0	1	1	2	2	3	3	4	4
94	9731	9736	9741	9745	9750	9754	9759	9763	9768	9773	0	1	1	2	2	3	3	4	4
95	9777	9782	9786	9791	9795	9800	9805	9809	9814	9818	0	1	1	2	2	3	3	4	4
96	9823	9827	9832	9836	9841	9845	9850	9854	9859	9863	0	1	1	2	2	3	3	4	4
97	9868	9872	9877	9881	9886	9890	9894	9899	9903	9908	0	1	1	2	2	3	3	4	4
98	9912	9917	9921	9926	9930	9934	9939	9943	9948	9952	0	1	1	2	2	3	3	4	4
99	9956	9961	9965	9969	9974	9978	9983	9987	9991	9996	0	1	1	2	2	3	3	3	4

ANTI-LOGARITHMS

	0	1	2	3	4	5	6	7	8	9	1	2	3	4	5	6	7	8	9
														Differences					
·00	1000	1002	1005	1007	1009	1012	1014	1016	1019	1021	0	0	1	1	1	1	2	2	2
·01	1023	1026	1028	1030	1033	1035	1038	1040	1042	1045	0	0	1	1	1	1	2	2	2
·02	1047	1050	1052	1054	1057	1059	1062	1064	1067	1069	0	0	1	1	1	1	2	2	2
·03	1072	1074	1076	1079	1081	1084	1086	1089	1091	1094	0	0	1	1	1	1	2	2	2
·04	1096	1099	1102	1104	1107	1109	1112	1114	1117	1119	0	1	1	1	1	2	2	2	2
·05	1122	1125	1127	1130	1132	1135	1138	1140	1143	1146	0	1	1	1	1	2	2	2	2
·06	1148	1151	1153	1156	1159	1161	1164	1167	1169	1172	0	1	1	1	1	2	2	2	2
·07	1175	1178	1180	1183	1186	1189	1191	1194	1197	1199	0	1	1	1	1	2	2	2	2
·08	1202	1205	1208	1211	1213	1216	1219	1222	1225	1227	0	1	1	1	1	2	2	2	3
·09	1230	1233	1236	1239	1242	1245	1247	1250	1253	1256	0	1	1	1	1	2	2	2	3
·10	1259	1262	1265	1268	1271	1274	1276	1279	1282	1285	0	1	1	1	1	2	2	2	3
·11	1288	1291	1294	1297	1300	1303	1306	1309	1312	1315	0	1	1	1	2	2	2	2	3
·12	1318	1321	1324	1327	1330	1334	1337	1340	1343	1346	0	1	1	1	2	2	2	2	3
·13	1349	1352	1355	1358	1361	1365	1368	1371	1374	1377	0	1	1	1	2	2	2	3	3
·14	1380	1384	1387	1390	1393	1396	1400	1403	1406	1409	0	1	1	1	2	2	2	3	3
·15	1413	1416	1419	1422	1426	1429	1432	1435	1439	1442	0	1	1	1	2	2	2	3	3
·16	1445	1449	1452	1455	1459	1462	1466	1469	1472	1476	0	1	1	1	2	2	2	3	3
·17	1479	1483	1486	1489	1493	1496	1500	1503	1507	1510	0	1	1	1	2	2	2	3	3
·18	1514	1517	1521	1524	1528	1531	1535	1538	1542	1545	0	1	1	1	2	2	2	3	3
·19	1549	1552	1556	1560	1563	1567	1570	1574	1578	1581	0	1	1	1	2	2	3	3	3
·20	1585	1589	1592	1596	1600	1603	1607	1611	1614	1618	0	1	1	1	2	2	3	3	3
·21	1622	1626	1629	1633	1637	1641	1644	1648	1652	1656	0	1	1	2	2	2	3	3	3
·22	1660	1663	1667	1671	1675	1679	1683	1687	1690	1694	0	1	1	2	2	2	3	3	3
·23	1698	1702	1706	1710	1714	1718	1722	1726	1730	1734	0	1	1	2	2	2	3	3	4
·24	1738	1742	1746	1750	1754	1758	1762	1766	1770	1774	0	1	1	2	2	2	3	3	4
·25	1778	1782	1786	1791	1795	1799	1803	1807	1811	1816	0	1	1	2	2	2	3	3	4
·26	1820	1824	1828	1832	1837	1841	1845	1849	1854	1858	0	1	1	2	2	3	3	3	4
·27	1862	1866	1871	1875	1879	1884	1888	1892	1897	1901	0	1	1	2	2	3	3	4	4
·28	1905	1910	1914	1919	1923	1928	1932	1936	1941	1945	0	1	1	2	2	3	3	4	4
·29	1950	1954	1959	1963	1968	1972	1977	1982	1986	1991	0	1	1	2	2	3	3	4	4
·30	1995	2000	2004	2009	2014	2018	2023	2028	2032	2037	0	1	1	2	2	3	3	4	4
·31	2042	2046	2051	2056	2061	2065	2070	2075	2080	2084	0	1	1	2	2	3	3	4	4
·32	2089	2094	2099	2104	2109	2113	2118	2123	2128	2133	0	1	1	2	2	3	3	4	4
·33	2138	2143	2148	2153	2158	2163	2168	2173	2178	2183	0	1	1	2	2	3	3	4	4
·34	2188	2193	2198	2203	2208	2213	2218	2223	2228	2234	1	1	2	2	3	3	4	4	5
·35	2239	2244	2249	2254	2259	2265	2270	2275	2280	2286	1	1	2	2	3	3	4	4	5
·36	2291	2296	2301	2307	2312	2317	2323	2328	2333	2339	1	1	2	2	3	3	4	4	5
·37	2344	2350	2355	2360	2366	2371	2377	2382	2388	2393	1	1	2	2	3	3	4	4	5
·38	2399	2404	2410	2415	2421	2427	2432	2438	2443	2449	1	1	2	2	3	3	4	4	5
·39	2455	2460	2466	2472	2477	2483	2489	2495	2500	2506	1	1	2	2	3	3	4	5	5
·40	2512	2518	2523	2529	2535	2541	2547	2553	2559	2564	1	1	2	2	3	4	4	5	5
·41	2570	2576	2582	2588	2594	2600	2606	2612	2618	2624	1	1	2	2	3	4	4	5	5
·42	2630	2636	2642	2649	2655	2661	2667	2673	2679	2685	1	1	2	2	3	4	4	5	6
·43	2692	2698	2704	2710	2716	2723	2729	2735	2742	2748	1	1	2	2	3	4	4	5	6
·44	2754	2761	2767	2773	2780	2786	2793	2799	2805	2812	1	1	2	3	3	4	4	5	6
·45	2818	2825	2831	2838	2844	2851	2858	2864	2871	2877	1	1	2	3	3	4	5	5	6
·46	2884	2891	2897	2904	2911	2917	2924	2931	2938	2944	1	1	2	3	3	4	5	5	6
·47	2951	2958	2965	2972	2979	2985	2992	2999	3006	3013	1	1	2	3	3	4	5	5	6
·48	3020	3027	3034	3041	3048	3055	3062	3069	3076	3083	1	1	2	3	4	4	5	6	6
·49	3090	3097	3105	3112	3119	3126	3133	3141	3148	3155	1	1	2	3	4	4	5	6	6

ANTI-LOGARITHMS

	0	1	2	3	4	5	6	7	8	9	1	2	3	4	5	6	7	8	9
·50	3162	3170	3177	3184	3192	3199	3206	3214	3221	3228	1	1	2	3	4	4	5	6	7
·51	3236	3243	3251	3258	3266	3273	3281	3289	3296	3304	1	2	2	3	4	5	5	6	7
·52	3311	3319	3327	3334	3342	3350	3357	3365	3373	3381	1	2	2	3	4	5	5	6	7
·53	3388	3396	3404	3412	3420	3428	3436	3443	3451	3459	1	2	2	3	4	5	6	6	7
·54	3467	3475	3483	3491	3499	3508	3516	3524	3532	3540	1	2	2	3	4	5	6	6	7
·55	3548	3556	3565	3573	3581	3589	3597	3606	3614	3622	1	2	2	3	4	5	6	7	7
·56	3631	3639	3648	3656	3664	3673	3681	3690	3698	3707	1	2	3	3	4	5	6	7	8
·57	3715	3724	3733	3741	3750	3758	3767	3776	3784	3793	1	2	3	3	4	5	6	7	8
·58	3802	3811	3819	3828	3837	3846	3855	3864	3873	3882	1	2	3	4	4	5	6	7	8
·59	3890	3899	3908	3917	3926	3936	3945	3954	3963	3972	1	2	3	4	5	5	6	7	8
·60	3981	3990	3999	4009	4018	4027	4036	4046	4055	4064	1	2	3	4	5	6	6	7	8
·61	4074	4083	4093	4102	4111	4121	4130	4140	4150	4159	1	2	3	4	5	6	7	8	9
·62	4169	4178	4188	4198	4207	4217	4227	4236	4246	4256	1	2	3	4	5	6	7	8	9
·63	4266	4276	4285	4295	4305	4315	4325	4335	4345	4355	1	2	3	4	5	6	7	8	9
·64	4365	4375	4385	4395	4406	4416	4426	4436	4446	4457	1	2	3	4	5	6	7	8	9
·65	4467	4477	4487	4498	4508	4519	4529	4539	4550	4560	1	2	3	4	5	6	7	8	9
·66	4571	4581	4592	4603	4613	4624	4634	4645	4656	4667	1	2	3	4	5	6	7	9	10
·67	4677	4688	4699	4710	4721	4732	4742	4753	4764	4775	1	2	3	4	5	7	8	9	10
·68	4786	4797	4808	4819	4831	4842	4853	4864	4875	4887	1	2	3	4	6	7	8	9	10
·69	4898	4909	4920	4932	4943	4955	4966	4977	4989	5000	1	2	3	5	6	7	8	9	10
·70	5012	5023	5035	5047	5058	5070	5082	5093	5105	5117	1	2	4	5	6	7	8	9	11
·71	5129	5140	5152	5164	5176	5188	5200	5212	5224	5236	1	2	4	5	6	7	8	10	11
·72	5248	5260	5272	5284	5297	5309	5321	5333	5346	5358	1	2	4	5	6	7	9	10	11
·73	5370	5383	5395	5408	5420	5433	5445	5458	5470	5483	1	3	4	5	6	8	9	10	11
·74	5495	5508	5521	5534	5546	5559	5572	5585	5598	5610	1	3	4	5	6	8	9	10	12
·75	5623	5636	5649	5662	5675	5689	5702	5715	5728	5741	1	3	4	5	7	8	9	10	12
·76	5754	5768	5781	5794	5808	5821	5834	5848	5861	5875	1	3	4	5	7	8	9	11	12
·77	5888	5902	5916	5929	5943	5957	5970	5984	5998	6012	1	3	4	5	7	8	10	11	12
·78	6026	6039	6053	6067	6081	6095	6109	6124	6138	6152	1	3	4	6	7	8	10	11	13
·79	6166	6180	6194	6209	6223	6237	6252	6266	6281	6295	1	3	4	6	7	9	10	11	13
·80	6310	6324	6339	6353	6368	6383	6397	6412	6427	6442	1	3	4	6	7	9	10	12	13
·81	6457	6471	6486	6501	6516	6531	6546	6561	6577	6592	2	3	5	6	8	9	11	12	14
·82	6607	6622	6637	6653	6668	6683	6699	6714	6730	6745	2	3	5	6	8	9	11	12	14
·83	6761	6776	6792	6808	6823	6839	6855	6871	6887	6902	2	3	5	6	8	9	11	13	14
·84	6918	6934	6950	6966	6982	6998	7015	7031	7047	7063	2	3	5	6	8	10	11	13	15
·85	7079	7096	7112	7129	7145	7161	7178	7194	7211	7228	2	3	5	7	8	10	12	13	15
·86	7244	7261	7278	7295	7311	7328	7345	7362	7379	7396	2	3	5	7	8	10	12	13	15
·87	7413	7430	7447	7464	7482	7499	7516	7534	7551	7568	2	3	5	7	9	10	12	14	16
·88	7586	7603	7621	7638	7656	7674	7691	7709	7727	7745	2	4	5	7	9	11	12	14	16
·89	7762	7780	7798	7816	7834	7852	7870	7889	7907	7925	2	4	5	7	9	11	13	14	16
·90	7943	7962	7980	7998	8017	8035	8054	8072	8091	8110	2	4	6	7	9	11	13	15	17
·91	8128	8147	8166	8185	8204	8222	8241	8260	8279	8299	2	4	6	8	9	11	13	15	17
·92	8318	8337	8356	8375	8395	8414	8433	8453	8472	8492	2	4	6	8	10	12	14	15	17
·93	8511	8531	8551	8570	8590	8610	8630	8650	8670	8690	2	4	6	8	10	12	14	16	18
·94	8710	8730	8750	8770	8790	8810	8831	8851	8872	8892	2	4	6	8	10	12	14	16	18
·95	8913	8933	8954	8974	8995	9016	9036	9057	9078	9099	2	4	6	8	10	12	15	17	19
·96	9120	9141	9162	9183	9204	9226	9247	9268	9290	9311	2	4	6	8	11	13	15	17	19
·97	9333	9354	9376	9397	9419	9441	9462	9484	9506	9528	2	4	7	9	11	13	15	17	20
·98	9550	9572	9594	9616	9638	9661	9683	9705	9727	9750	2	4	7	9	11	13	16	18	20
·99	9772	9795	9817	9840	9863	9886	9908	9931	9954	9977	2	5	7	9	11	14	16	18	20

Differences

NATURAL SINES

	0′	6′	12′	18′	24′	30′	36′	42′	48′	54′	1′	2′	3′	4′	5′
0	·0000	0017	0035	0052	0070	0087	0105	0122	0140	0157	3	6	9	12	15
1	·0175	0192	0209	0227	0244	0262	0279	0297	0314	0332	3	6	9	12	15
2	·0349	0366	0384	0401	0419	0436	0454	0471	0488	0506	3	6	9	12	15
3	·0523	0541	0558	0576	0593	0610	0628	0645	0663	0680	3	6	9	12	15
4	·0698	0715	0732	0750	0767	0785	0802	0819	0837	0854	3	6	9	12	14
5	·0872	0889	0906	0924	0941	0958	0976	0993	1011	1028	3	6	9	12	14
6	·1045	1063	1080	1097	1115	1132	1149	1167	1184	1201	3	6	9	12	14
7	·1219	1236	1253	1271	1288	1305	1323	1340	1357	1374	3	6	9	12	14
8	·1392	1409	1426	1444	1461	1478	1495	1513	1530	1547	3	6	9	12	14
9	·1564	1582	1599	1616	1633	1650	1668	1685	1702	1719	3	6	9	12	14
10	·1736	1754	1771	1788	1805	1822	1840	1857	1874	1891	3	6	9	11	14
11	·1908	1925	1942	1959	1977	1994	2011	2028	2045	2062	3	6	9	11	14
12	·2079	2096	2113	2130	2147	2164	2181	2198	2215	2233	3	6	9	11	14
13	·2250	2267	2284	2300	2317	2334	2351	2368	2385	2402	3	6	8	11	14
14	·2419	2436	2453	2470	2487	2504	2521	2538	2554	2571	3	6	8	11	14
15	·2588	2605	2622	2639	2656	2672	2689	2706	2723	2740	3	6	8	11	14
16	·2756	2773	2790	2807	2823	2840	2857	2874	2890	2907	3	6	8	11	14
17	·2924	2940	2957	2974	2990	3007	3024	3040	3057	3074	3	6	8	11	14
18	·3090	3107	3123	3140	3156	3173	3190	3206	3223	3239	3	6	8	11	14
19	·3256	3272	3289	3305	3322	3338	3355	3371	3387	3404	3	5	8	11	14
20	·3420	3437	3453	3469	3486	3502	3518	3535	3551	3567	3	5	8	11	14
21	·3584	3600	3616	3633	3649	3665	3681	3697	3714	3730	3	5	8	11	14
22	·3746	3762	3778	3795	3811	3827	3843	3859	3875	3891	3	5	8	11	14
23	·3907	3923	3939	3955	3971	3987	4003	4019	4035	4051	3	5	8	11	14
24	·4067	4083	4099	4115	4131	4147	4163	4179	4195	4210	3	5	8	11	13
25	·4226	4242	4258	4274	4289	4305	4321	4337	4352	4368	3	5	8	11	13
26	·4384	4399	4415	4431	4446	4462	4478	4493	4509	4524	3	5	8	10	13
27	·4540	4555	4571	4586	4602	4617	4633	4648	4664	4679	3	5	8	10	13
28	·4695	4710	4726	4741	4756	4772	4787	4802	4818	4833	3	5	8	10	13
29	·4848	4863	4879	4894	4909	4924	4939	4955	4970	4985	3	5	8	10	13
30	·5000	5015	5030	5045	5060	5075	5090	5105	5120	5135	3	5	8	10	13
31	·5150	5165	5180	5195	5210	5225	5240	5255	5270	5284	2	5	7	10	12
32	·5299	5314	5329	5344	5358	5373	5388	5402	5417	5432	2	5	7	10	12
33	·5446	5461	5476	5490	5505	5519	5534	5548	5563	5577	2	5	7	10	12
34	·5592	5606	5621	5635	5650	5664	5678	5693	5707	5721	2	5	7	10	12
35	·5736	5750	5764	5779	5793	5807	5821	5835	5850	5864	2	5	7	9	12
36	·5878	5892	5906	5920	5934	5948	5962	5976	5990	6004	2	5	7	9	12
37	·6018	6032	6046	6060	6074	6088	6101	6115	6129	6143	2	5	7	9	12
38	·6157	6170	6184	6198	6211	6225	6239	6252	6266	6280	2	5	7	9	11
39	·6293	6307	6320	6334	6347	6361	6374	6388	6401	6414	2	4	7	9	11
40	·6428	6441	6455	6468	6481	6494	6508	6521	6534	6547	2	4	7	9	11
41	·6561	6574	6587	6600	6613	6626	6639	6652	6665	6678	2	4	7	9	11
42	·6691	6704	6717	6730	6743	6756	6769	6782	6794	6807	2	4	6	9	11
43	·6820	6833	6845	6858	6871	6884	6896	6909	6921	6934	2	4	6	8	11
44	·6947	6959	6972	6984	6997	7009	7022	7034	7046	7059	2	4	6	8	10

NATURAL SINES

°	0′	6′	12′	18′	24′	30′	36′	42′	48′	54′	1′	2′	3′	4′	5′
45	·7071	7083	7096	7108	7120	7133	7145	7157	7169	7181	2	4	6	8	10
46	·7193	7206	7218	7230	7242	7254	7266	7278	7290	7302	2	4	6	8	10
47	·7314	7325	7337	7349	7361	7373	7385	7396	7408	7420	2	4	6	8	10
48	·7431	7443	7455	7466	7478	7490	7501	7513	7524	7536	2	4	6	8	10
49	·7547	7559	7570	7581	7593	7604	7615	7627	7638	7649	2	4	6	8	9
50	·7660	7672	7683	7694	7705	7716	7727	7738	7749	7760	2	4	6	7	9
51	·7771	7782	7793	7804	7815	7826	7837	7848	7859	7869	2	4	5	7	9
52	·7880	7891	7902	7912	7923	7934	7944	7955	7965	7976	2	4	5	7	9
53	·7986	7997	8007	8018	8028	8039	8049	8059	8070	8080	2	3	5	7	9
54	·8090	8100	8111	8121	8131	8141	8151	8161	8171	8181	2	3	5	7	8
55	·8192	8202	8211	8221	8231	8241	8251	8261	8271	8281	2	3	5	7	8
56	·8290	8300	8310	8320	8329	8339	8348	8358	8368	8377	2	3	5	6	8
57	·8387	8396	8406	8415	8425	8434	8443	8453	8462	8471	2	3	5	6	8
58	·8480	8490	8499	8508	8517	8526	8536	8545	8554	8563	2	3	5	6	8
59	·8572	8581	8590	8599	8607	8616	8625	8634	8643	8652	1	3	4	6	7
60	·8660	8669	8678	8686	8695	8704	8712	8721	8729	8738	1	3	4	6	7
61	·8746	8755	8763	8771	8780	8788	8796	8805	8813	8821	1	3	4	6	7
62	·8829	8838	8846	8854	8862	8870	8878	8886	8894	8902	1	3	4	5	7
63	·8910	8918	8926	8934	8942	8949	8957	8965	8973	8980	1	3	4	5	6
64	·8988	8996	9003	9011	9018	9026	9033	9041	9048	9056	1	3	4	5	6
65	·9063	9070	9078	9085	9092	9100	9107	9114	9121	9128	1	2	4	5	6
66	·9135	9143	9150	9157	9164	9171	9178	9184	9191	9198	1	2	3	5	6
67	·9205	9212	9219	9225	9232	9239	9245	9252	9259	9265	1	2	3	4	6
68	·9272	9278	9285	9291	9298	9304	9311	9317	9323	9330	1	2	3	4	5
69	·9336	9342	9348	9354	9361	9367	9373	9379	9385	9391	1	2	3	4	5
70	·9397	9403	9409	9415	9421	9426	9432	9438	9444	9449	1	2	3	4	5
71	·9455	9461	9466	9472	9478	9483	9489	9494	9500	9505	1	2	3	4	5
72	·9511	9516	9521	9527	9532	9537	9542	9548	9553	9558	1	2	3	3	4
73	·9563	9568	9573	9578	9583	9588	9593	9598	9603	9608	1	2	2	3	4
74	·9613	9617	9622	9627	9632	9636	9641	9646	9650	9655	1	2	2	3	4
75	·9659	9664	9668	9673	9677	9681	9686	9690	9694	9699	1	1	2	3	4
76	·9703	9707	9711	9715	9720	9724	9728	9732	9736	9740	1	1	2	3	3
77	·9744	9748	9751	9755	9759	9763	9767	9770	9774	9778	1	1	2	3	3
78	·9781	9785	9789	9792	9796	9799	9803	9806	9810	9813	1	1	2	2	3
79	·9816	9820	9823	9826	9829	9833	9836	9839	9842	9845	1	1	2	2	3
80	·9848	9851	9854	9857	9860	9863	9866	9869	9871	9874	0	1	1	2	2
81	·9877	9880	9882	9885	9888	9890	9893	9895	9898	9900	0	1	1	2	2
82	·9903	9905	9907	9910	9912	9914	9917	9919	9921	9923	0	1	1	2	2
83	·9925	9928	9930	9932	9934	9936	9938	9940	9942	9943	0	1	1	1	2
84	·9945	9947	9949	9951	9952	9954	9956	9957	9959	9960	0	1	1	1	1
85	·9962	9963	9965	9966	9968	9969	9971	9972	9973	9974	0	0	1	1	1
86	·9976	9977	9978	9979	9980	9981	9982	9983	9984	9985	0	0	1	1	1
87	·9986	9987	9988	9989	9990	9990	9991	9992	9993	9993					
88	·9994	9995	9995	9996	9996	9997	9997	9997	9998	9998					
89	·9998	9999	9999	9999	9999	1·000	1·000	1·000	1·000	1·000					

NATURAL COSINES

°	0′	6′	12′	18′	24′	30′	36′	42′	48′	54′	Subtract Differences				
											1′	2′	3′	4′	5′
0	1·000	1·000	1·000	1·000	1·000	1·000	9̄999	9̄999	9999	9̄999					
1	·9998	9998	9998	9997	9997	9997	9996	9996	9995	9995					
2	·9994	9993	9993	9992	9991	9990	9990	9989	9988	9987					
3	·9986	9985	9984	9983	9982	9981	9980	9979	9978	9977	0	0	1	1	1
4	·9976	9974	9973	9972	9971	9969	9968	9966	9965	9963	0	0	1	1	1
5	·9962	9960	9959	9957	9956	9954	9952	9951	9949	9947	0	1	1	1	1
6	·9945	9943	9942	9940	9938	9936	9934	9932	9930	9928	0	1	1	1	2
7	·9925	9923	9921	9919	9917	9914	9912	9910	9907	9905	0	1	1	2	2
8	·9903	9900	9898	9895	9893	9890	9888	9885	9882	9880	0	1	1	2	2
9	·9877	9874	9871	9869	9866	9863	9860	9857	9854	9851	0	1	1	2	2
10	·9848	9845	9842	9839	9836	9833	9829	9826	9823	9820	1	1	2	2	3
11	·9816	9813	9810	9806	9803	9799	9796	9792	9789	9785	1	1	2	2	3
12	·9781	9778	9774	9770	9767	9763	9759	9755	9751	9748	1	1	2	3	3
13	·9744	9740	9736	9732	9728	9724	9720	9715	9711	9707	1	1	2	3	3
14	·9703	9699	9694	9690	9686	9681	9677	9673	9668	9664	1	1	2	3	4
15	·9659	9655	9650	9646	9641	9636	9632	9627	9622	9617	1	2	2	3	4
16	·9613	9608	9603	9598	9593	9588	9583	9578	9573	9568	1	2	2	3	4
17	·9563	9558	9553	9548	9542	9537	9532	9527	9521	9516	1	2	3	4	4
18	·9511	9505	9500	9494	9489	9483	9478	9472	9466	9461	1	2	3	4	5
19	·9455	9449	9444	9438	9432	9426	9421	9415	9409	9403	1	2	3	4	5
20	·9397	9391	9385	9379	9373	9367	9361	9354	9348	9342	1	2	3	4	5
21	·9336	9330	9323	9317	9311	9304	9298	9291	9285	9278	1	2	3	4	5
22	·9272	9265	9259	9252	9245	9239	9232	9225	9219	9212	1	2	3	4	6
23	·9205	9198	9191	9184	9178	9171	9164	9157	9150	9143	1	2	3	5	6
24	·9135	9128	9121	9114	9107	9100	9092	9085	9078	9070	1	2	4	5	6
25	·9063	9056	9048	9041	9033	9026	9018	9011	9003	8996	1	3	4	5	6
26	·8988	8980	8973	8965	8957	8949	8942	8934	8926	8918	1	3	4	5	6
27	·8910	8902	8894	8886	8878	8870	8862	8854	8846	8838	1	3	4	5	7
28	·8829	8821	8813	8805	8796	8788	8780	8771	8763	8755	1	3	4	6	7
29	·8746	8738	8729	8721	8712	8704	8695	8686	8678	8669	1	3	4	6	7
30	·8660	8652	8643	8634	8625	8616	8607	8599	8590	8581	1	3	4	6	7
31	·8572	8563	8554	8545	8536	8526	8517	8508	8499	8490	2	3	5	6	8
32	·8480	8471	8462	8453	8443	8434	8425	8415	8406	8396	2	3	5	6	8
33	·8387	8377	8368	8358	8348	8339	8329	8320	8310	8300	2	3	5	6	8
34	·8290	8281	8271	8261	8251	8241	8231	8221	8211	8202	2	3	5	7	8
35	·8192	8181	8171	8161	8151	8141	8131	8121	8111	8100	2	3	5	7	8
36	·8090	8080	8070	8059	8049	8039	8028	8018	8007	7997	2	3	5	7	9
37	·7986	7976	7965	7955	7944	7934	7923	7912	7902	7891	2	4	5	7	9
38	·7880	7869	7859	7848	7837	7826	7815	7804	7793	7782	2	4	6	7	9
39	·7771	7760	7749	7738	7727	7716	7705	7694	7683	7672	2	4	6	7	9
40	·7660	7649	7638	7627	7615	7604	7593	7581	7570	7559	2	4	6	8	9
41	·7547	7536	7524	7513	7501	7490	7478	7466	7455	7443	2	4	6	8	10
42	·7431	7420	7408	7396	7385	7373	7361	7349	7337	7325	2	4	6	8	10
43	·7314	7302	7290	7278	7266	7254	7242	7230	7218	7206	2	4	6	8	10
44	·7193	7181	7169	7157	7145	7133	7120	7108	7096	7083	2	4	6	8	10

NATURAL COSINES

°	0′	6′	12′	18′	24′	30′	36′	42′	48′	54′	Subtract Differences				
											1′	2′	3′	4′	5′
45	·7071	7059	7046	7034	7022	7009	6997	6984	6972	6959	2	4	6	8	10
46	·6947	6934	6921	6909	6896	6884	6871	6858	6845	6833	2	4	6	8	11
47	·6820	6807	6794	6782	6769	6756	6743	6730	6717	6704	2	4	6	9	11
48	·6691	6678	6665	6652	6639	6626	6613	6600	6587	6574	2	4	7	9	11
49	·6561	6547	6534	6521	6508	6494	6481	6468	6455	6441	2	4	7	9	11
50	·6428	6414	6401	6388	6374	6361	6347	6334	6320	6307	2	4	7	9	11
51	·6293	6280	6266	6252	6239	6225	6211	6198	6184	6170	2	5	7	9	11
52	·6157	6143	6129	6115	6101	6088	6074	6060	6046	6032	2	5	7	9	12
53	·6018	6004	5990	5976	5962	5948	5934	5920	5906	5892	2	5	7	9	12
54	·5878	5864	5850	5835	5821	5807	5793	5779	5764	5750	2	5	7	9	12
55	·5736	5721	5707	5693	5678	5664	5650	5635	5621	5606	2	5	7	10	12
56	·5592	5577	5563	5548	5534	5519	5505	5490	5476	5461	2	5	7	10	12
57	·5446	5432	5417	5402	5388	5373	5358	5344	5329	5314	2	5	7	10	12
58	·5299	5284	5270	5255	5240	5225	5210	5195	5180	5165	2	5	7	10	12
59	·5150	5135	5120	5105	5090	5075	5060	5045	5030	5015	3	5	8	10	13
60	·5000	4985	4970	4955	4939	4924	4909	4894	4879	4863	3	5	8	10	13
61	·4848	4833	4818	4802	4787	4772	4756	4741	4726	4710	3	5	8	10	13
62	·4695	4679	4664	4648	4633	4617	4602	4586	4571	4555	3	5	8	10	13
63	·4540	4524	4509	4493	4478	4462	4446	4431	4415	4399	3	5	8	10	13
64	·4384	4368	4352	4337	4321	4305	4289	4274	4258	4242	3	5	8	11	13
65	·4226	4210	4195	4179	4163	4147	4131	4115	4099	4083	3	5	8	11	13
66	·4067	4051	4035	4019	4003	3987	3971	3955	3939	3923	3	5	8	11	13
67	·3907	3891	3875	3859	3843	3827	3811	3795	3778	3762	3	5	8	11	13
68	·3746	3730	3714	3697	3681	3665	3649	3633	3616	3600	3	5	8	11	14
69	·3584	3567	3551	3535	3518	3502	3486	3469	3453	3437	3	5	8	11	14
70	·3420	3404	3387	3371	3355	3338	3322	3305	3289	3272	3	5	8	11	14
71	·3256	3239	3223	3206	3190	3173	3156	3140	3123	3107	3	6	8	11	14
72	·3090	3074	3057	3040	3024	3007	2990	2974	2957	2940	3	6	8	11	14
73	·2924	2907	2890	2874	2857	2840	2823	2807	2790	2773	3	6	8	11	14
74	·2756	2740	2723	2706	2689	2672	2656	2639	2622	2605	3	6	8	11	14
75	·2588	2571	2554	2538	2521	2504	2487	2470	2453	2436	3	6	8	11	14
76	·2419	2402	2385	2368	2351	2334	2317	2300	2284	2267	3	6	8	11	14
77	·2250	2233	2215	2198	2181	2164	2147	2130	2113	2096	3	6	9	11	14
78	·2079	2062	2045	2028	2011	1994	1977	1959	1942	1925	3	6	9	11	14
79	·1908	1891	1874	1857	1840	1822	1805	1788	1771	1754	3	6	9	11	14
80	·1736	1719	1702	1685	1668	1650	1633	1616	1599	1582	3	6	9	11	14
81	·1564	1547	1530	1513	1495	1478	1461	1444	1426	1409	3	6	9	12	14
82	·1392	1374	1357	1340	1323	1305	1288	1271	1253	1236	3	6	9	12	14
83	·1219	1201	1184	1167	1149	1132	1115	1097	1080	1063	3	6	9	12	14
84	·1045	1028	1011	0993	0976	0958	0941	0924	0906	0889	3	6	9	12	14
85	·0872	0854	0837	0819	0802	0785	0767	0750	0732	0715	3	6	9	12	14
86	·0698	0680	0663	0645	0628	0610	0593	0576	0558	0541	3	6	9	12	15
87	·0523	0506	0488	0471	0454	0436	0419	0401	0384	0366	3	6	9	12	15
88	·0349	0332	0314	0297	0279	0262	0244	0227	0209	0192	3	6	9	12	15
89	·0175	0157	0140	0122	0105	0087	0070	0052	0035	0017	3	6	9	12	15

NATURAL TANGENTS

	0'	6'	12'	18'	24'	30'	36'	42'	48'	54'	Differences				
											1'	2'	3'	4'	5'
0	·0000	0017	0035	0052	0070	0087	0105	0122	0140	0157	3	6	9	12	15
1	·0175	0192	0209	0227	0244	0262	0279	0297	0314	0332	3	6	9	12	15
2	·0349	0367	0384	0402	0419	0437	0454	0472	0489	0507	3	6	9	12	15
3	·0524	0542	0559	0577	0594	0612	0629	0647	0664	0682	3	6	9	12	15
4	·0699	0717	0734	0752	0769	0787	0805	0822	0840	0857	3	6	9	12	15
5	·0875	0892	0910	0928	0945	0963	0981	0998	1016	1033	3	6	9	12	15
6	·1051	1069	1086	1104	1122	1139	1157	1175	1192	1210	3	6	9	12	15
7	·1228	1246	1263	1281	1299	1317	1334	1352	1370	1388	3	6	9	12	15
8	·1405	1423	1441	1459	1477	1495	1512	1530	1548	1566	3	6	9	12	15
9	·1584	1602	1620	1638	1655	1673	1691	1709	1727	1745	3	6	9	12	15
10	·1763	1781	1799	1817	1835	1853	1871	1890	1908	1926	3	6	9	12	15
11	·1944	1962	1980	1998	2016	2035	2053	2071	2089	2107	3	6	9	12	15
12	·2126	2144	2162	2180	2199	2217	2235	2254	2272	2290	3	6	9	12	15
13	·2309	2327	2345	2364	2382	2401	2419	2438	2456	2475	3	6	9	12	15
14	·2493	2512	2530	2549	2568	2586	2605	2623	2642	2661	3	6	9	12	16
15	·2679	2698	2717	2736	2754	2773	2792	2811	2830	2849	3	6	9	13	16
16	·2867	2886	2905	2924	2943	2962	2981	3000	3019	3038	3	6	9	13	16
17	·3057	3076	3096	3115	3134	3153	3172	3191	3211	3230	3	6	10	13	16
18	·3249	3269	3288	3307	3327	3346	3365	3385	3404	3424	3	6	10	13	16
19	·3443	3463	3482	3502	3522	3541	3561	3581	3600	3620	3	7	10	13	16
20	·3640	3659	3679	3699	3719	3739	3759	3779	3799	3819	3	7	10	13	17
21	·3839	3859	3879	3899	3919	3939	3959	3979	4000	4020	3	7	10	13	17
22	·4040	4061	4081	4101	4122	4142	4163	4183	4204	4224	3	7	10	14	17
23	·4245	4265	4286	4307	4327	4348	4369	4390	4411	4431	3	7	10	14	17
24	·4452	4473	4494	4515	4536	4557	4578	4599	4621	4642	4	7	11	14	18
25	·4663	4684	4706	4727	4748	4770	4791	4813	4834	4856	4	7	11	14	18
26	·4877	4899	4921	4942	4964	4986	5008	5029	5051	5073	4	7	11	15	18
27	·5095	5117	5139	5161	5184	5206	5228	5250	5272	5295	4	7	11	15	18
28	·5317	5340	5362	5384	5407	5430	5452	5475	5498	5520	4	8	11	15	19
29	·5543	5566	5589	5612	5635	5658	5681	5704	5727	5750	4	8	12	15	19
30	·5774	5797	5820	5844	5867	5890	5914	5938	5961	5985	4	8	12	16	20
31	·6009	6032	6056	6080	6104	6128	6152	6176	6200	6224	4	8	12	16	20
32	·6249	6273	6297	6322	6346	6371	6395	6420	6445	6469	4	8	12	16	20
33	·6494	6519	6544	6569	6594	6619	6644	6669	6694	6720	4	8	13	17	21
34	·6745	6771	6796	6822	6847	6873	6899	6924	6950	6976	4	9	13	17	21
35	·7002	7028	7054	7080	7107	7133	7159	7186	7212	7239	4	9	13	18	22
36	·7265	7292	7319	7346	7373	7400	7427	7454	7481	7508	5	9	14	18	23
37	·7536	7563	7590	7618	7646	7673	7701	7729	7757	7785	5	9	14	18	23
38	·7813	7841	7869	7898	7926	7954	7983	8012	8040	8069	5	9	14	19	24
39	·8098	8127	8156	8185	8214	8243	8273	8302	8332	8361	5	10	15	20	24
40	·8391	8421	8451	8481	8511	8541	8571	8601	8632	8662	5	10	15	20	25
41	·8693	8724	8754	8785	8816	8847	8878	8910	8941	8972	5	10	16	21	26
42	·9004	9036	9067	9099	9131	9163	9195	9228	9260	9293	5	11	16	21	27
43	·9325	9358	9391	9424	9457	9490	9523	9556	9590	9623	6	11	17	22	28
44	·9657	9691	9725	9759	9793	9827	9861	9896	9930	9965	6	11	17	23	29

NATURAL TANGENTS

°	0'	6'	12'	18'	24'	30'	36'	42'	48'	54'	Differences				
											1'	2'	3'	4'	5'
45	1·0000	0035	0070	0105	0141	0176	0212	0247	0283	0319	6	12	18	24	30
46	1·0355	0392	0428	0464	0501	0538	0575	0612	0649	0686	6	12	18	25	31
47	1·0724	0761	0799	0837	0875	0913	0951	0990	1028	1067	6	13	19	25	32
48	1·1106	1145	1184	1224	1263	1303	1343	1383	1423	1463	7	13	20	26	33
49	1·1504	1544	1585	1626	1667	1708	1750	1792	1833	1875	7	14	21	28	34
50	1·1918	1960	2002	2045	2088	2131	2174	2218	2261	2305	7	14	22	29	36
51	1·2349	2393	2437	2482	2527	2572	2617	2662	2708	2753	8	15	23	30	38
52	1·2799	2846	2892	2938	2985	3032	3079	3127	3175	3222	8	16	24	31	39
53	1·3270	3319	3367	3416	3465	3514	3564	3613	3663	3713	8	16	25	33	41
54	1·3764	3814	3865	3916	3968	4019	4071	4124	4176	4229	9	17	26	34	43
55	1·4281	4335	4388	4442	4496	4550	4605	4659	4715	4770	9	18	27	36	45
56	1·4826	4882	4938	4994	5051	5108	5166	5224	5282	5340	10	19	29	38	48
57	1·5399	5458	5517	5577	5637	5697	5757	5818	5880	5941	10	20	30	40	50
58	1·6003	6066	6128	6191	6255	6319	6383	6447	6512	6577	11	21	32	43	53
59	1·6643	6709	6775	6842	6909	6977	7045	7113	7182	7251	11	23	34	45	56
60	1·7321	7391	7461	7532	7603	7675	7747	7820	7893	7966	12	24	36	48	60
61	1·8040	8115	8190	8265	8341	8418	8495	8572	8650	8728	13	26	38	51	64
62	1·8807	8887	8967	9047	9128	9210	9292	9375	9458	9542	14	27	41	55	68
63	1·9626	9711	9797	9883	9970	0057	0145	0233	0323	0413	15	29	44	58	73
64	2·0503	0594	0686	0778	0872	0965	1060	1155	1251	1348	16	31	47	63	78
65	2·1445	1543	1642	1742	1842	1943	2045	2148	2251	2355	17	34	51	68	85
66	2·2460	2566	2673	2781	2889	2998	3109	3220	3332	3445	18	37	55	73	91
67	2·3559	3673	3789	3906	4023	4142	4262	4383	4504	4627	20	40	60	79	99
68	2·4751	4876	5002	5129	5257	5386	5517	5649	5782	5916	22	43	65	87	108
69	2·6051	6187	6325	6464	6605	6746	6889	7034	7179	7326	24	47	71	95	119
70	2·7475	7625	7776	7929	8083	8239	8397	8556	8716	8878	26	52	78	104	131
71	2·9042	9208	9375	9544	9714	9887	0061	0237	0415	0595	29	58	87	116	145
72	3·0777	0961	1146	1334	1524	1716	1910	2106	2305	2506	32	64	96	129	161
73	3·2709	2914	3122	3332	3544	3759	3977	4197	4420	4646	36	72	108	144	180
74	3·4874	5105	5339	5576	5816	6059	6305	6554	6806	7062	41	81	122	163	204
75	3·7321	7583	7848	8118	8391	8667	8947	9232	9520	9812	46	93	139	186	232
76	4·0108	0408	0713	1022	1335	1653	1976	2303	2635	2972					
77	4·3315	3662	4015	4373	4737	5107	5483	5864	6252	6646					
78	4·7046	7453	7867	8288	8716	9152	9594	0045	0504	0970					
79	5·1446	1929	2422	2924	3435	3955	4486	5026	5578	6140					
80	5·6713	7297	7894	8502	9124	9758	0405	1066	1742	2432					
81	6·3138	3859	4596	5350	6122	6912	7720	8548	9395	0264					
82	7·1154	2066	3002	3962	4947	5958	6996	8062	9158	0285					
83	8·1443	2636	3863	5126	6427	7769	9152	0579	2052	3572					
84	9·514	9·677	9·845	10·02	10·20	10·39	10·58	10·78	10·99	11·20					
85	11·43	11·66	11·91	12·16	12·43	12·71	13·00	13·30	13·62	13·95					
86	14·30	14·67	15·06	15·46	15·89	16·35	16·83	17·34	17·89	18·46					
87	19·08	19·74	20·45	21·20	22·02	22·90	23·86	24·90	26·03	27·27					
88	28·64	30·14	31·82	33·69	35·80	38·19	40·92	44·07	47·74	52·08					
89	57·29	63·66	71·62	81·85	95·49	114·6	143·2	191·0	286·5	573·0					

LOG. SINES

°	0′	6′	12′	18′	24′	30′	36′	42′	48′	54′	1′	2′	3′	4′	5′
0	—∞	$\bar{3}$·242	$\bar{3}$·543	$\bar{3}$·719	$\bar{3}$·844	$\bar{3}$·941	$\bar{2}$·020	$\bar{2}$·087	$\bar{2}$·145	$\bar{2}$·196					
1	$\bar{2}$·2419	2832	3210	3558	3880	4179	4459	4723	4971	5206					
2	$\bar{2}$·5428	5640	5842	6035	6220	6397	6567	6731	6889	7041					
3	$\bar{2}$·7188	7330	7468	7602	7731	7857	7979	8098	8213	8326					
4	$\bar{2}$·8436	8543	8647	8749	8849	8946	9042	9135	9226	9315					
5	$\bar{2}$·9403	9489	9573	9655	9736	9816	9894	9970	$\bar{0}$046	$\bar{0}$120	13	26	39	52	66
6	$\bar{1}$·0192	0264	0334	0403	0472	0539	0605	0670	0734	0797	11	22	33	44	55
7	$\bar{1}$·0859	0920	0981	1040	1099	1157	1214	1271	1326	1381	10	19	29	38	48
8	$\bar{1}$·1436	1489	1542	1594	1646	1697	1747	1797	1847	1895	8	17	25	34	42
9	$\bar{1}$·1943	1991	2038	2085	2131	2176	2221	2266	2310	2353	8	15	23	30	38
10	$\bar{1}$·2397	2439	2482	2524	2565	2606	2647	2687	2727	2767	7	14	20	27	34
11	$\bar{1}$·2806	2845	2883	2921	2959	2997	3034	3070	3107	3143	6	12	19	25	31
12	$\bar{1}$·3179	3214	3250	3284	3319	3353	3387	3421	3455	3488	6	11	17	23	28
13	$\bar{1}$·3521	3554	3586	3618	3650	3682	3713	3745	3775	3806	5	11	16	21	26
14	$\bar{1}$·3837	3867	3897	3927	3957	3986	4015	4044	4073	4102	5	10	15	20	24
15	$\bar{1}$·4130	4158	4186	4214	4242	4269	4296	4323	4350	4377	5	9	14	18	23
16	$\bar{1}$·4403	4430	4456	4482	4508	4533	4559	4584	4609	4634	4	9	13	17	21
17	$\bar{1}$·4659	4684	4709	4733	4757	4781	4805	4829	4853	4876	4	8	12	16	20
18	$\bar{1}$·4900	4923	4946	4969	4992	5015	5037	5060	5082	5104	4	8	11	15	19
19	$\bar{1}$·5126	5148	5170	5192	5213	5235	5256	5278	5299	5320	4	7	11	14	18
20	$\bar{1}$·5341	5361	5382	5402	5423	5443	5463	5484	5504	5523	3	7	10	14	17
21	$\bar{1}$·5543	5563	5583	5602	5621	5641	5660	5679	5698	5717	3	6	10	13	16
22	$\bar{1}$·5736	5754	5773	5792	5810	5828	5847	5865	5883	5901	3	6	9	12	15
23	$\bar{1}$·5919	5937	5954	5972	5990	6007	6024	6042	6059	6076	3	6	9	12	15
24	$\bar{1}$·6093	6110	6127	6144	6161	6177	6194	6210	6227	6243	3	6	8	11	14
25	$\bar{1}$·6259	6276	6292	6308	6324	6340	6356	6371	6387	6403	3	5	8	11	13
26	$\bar{1}$·6418	6434	6449	6465	6480	6495	6510	6526	6541	6556	3	5	8	10	13
27	$\bar{1}$·6570	6585	6600	6615	6629	6644	6659	6673	6687	6702	2	5	7	10	12
28	$\bar{1}$·6716	6730	6744	6759	6773	6787	6801	6814	6828	6842	2	5	7	9	12
29	$\bar{1}$·6856	6869	6883	6896	6910	6923	6937	6950	6963	6977	2	4	7	9	11
30	$\bar{1}$·6990	7003	7016	7029	7042	7055	7068	7080	7093	7106	2	4	6	9	11
31	$\bar{1}$·7118	7131	7144	7156	7168	7181	7193	7205	7218	7230	2	4	6	8	10
32	$\bar{1}$·7242	7254	7266	7278	7290	7302	7314	7326	7338	7349	2	4	6	8	10
33	$\bar{1}$·7361	7373	7384	7396	7407	7419	7430	7442	7453	7464	2	4	6	8	10
34	$\bar{1}$·7476	7487	7498	7509	7520	7531	7542	7553	7564	7575	2	4	6	7	9
35	$\bar{1}$·7586	7597	7607	7618	7629	7640	7650	7661	7671	7682	2	4	5	7	9
36	$\bar{1}$·7692	7703	7713	7723	7734	7744	7754	7764	7774	7785	2	3	5	7	9
37	$\bar{1}$·7795	7805	7815	7825	7835	7844	7854	7864	7874	7884	2	3	5	7	8
38	$\bar{1}$·7893	7903	7913	7922	7932	7941	7951	7960	7970	7979	2	3	5	6	8
39	$\bar{1}$·7989	7998	8007	8017	8026	8035	8044	8053	8063	8072	2	3	5	6	8
40	$\bar{1}$·8081	8090	8099	8108	8117	8125	8134	8143	8152	8161	1	3	4	6	7
41	$\bar{1}$·8169	8178	8187	8195	8204	8213	8221	8230	8238	8247	1	3	4	6	7
42	$\bar{1}$·8255	8264	8272	8280	8289	8297	8305	8313	8322	8330	1	3	4	6	7
43	$\bar{1}$·8338	8346	8354	8362	8370	8378	8386	8394	8402	8410	1	3	4	5	7
44	$\bar{1}$·8418	8426	8433	8441	8449	8457	8464	8472	8480	8487	1	3	4	5	6

LOG. SINES

°	0′	6′	12′	18′	24′	30′	36′	42′	48′	54′	Differences				
											1′	2′	3′	4′	5′
45	1·8495	8502	8510	8517	8525	8532	8540	8547	8555	8562	1	2	4	5	6
46	1·8569	8577	8584	8591	8598	8606	8613	8620	8627	8634	1	2	4	5	6
47	1·8641	8648	8655	8662	8669	8676	8683	8690	8697	8704	1	2	3	5	6
48	1·8711	8718	8724	8731	8738	8745	8751	8758	8765	8771	1	2	3	4	6
49	1·8778	8784	8791	8797	8804	8810	8817	8823	8830	8836	1	2	3	4	5
50	1·8843	8849	8855	8862	8868	8874	8880	8887	8893	8899	1	2	3	4	5
51	1·8905	8911	8917	8923	8929	8935	8941	8947	8953	8959	1	2	3	4	5
52	1·8965	8971	8977	8983	8989	8995	9000	9006	9012	9018	1	2	3	4	5
53	1·9023	9029	9035	9041	9046	9052	9057	9063	9069	9074	1	2	3	4	5
54	1·9080	9085	9091	9096	9101	9107	9112	9118	9123	9128	1	2	3	4	5
55	1·9134	9139	9144	9149	9155	9160	9165	9170	9175	9181	1	2	3	3	4
56	1·9186	9191	9196	9201	9206	9211	9216	9221	9226	9231	1	2	3	3	4
57	1·9236	9241	9246	9251	9255	9260	9265	9270	9275	9279	1	2	2	3	4
58	1·9284	9289	9294	9298	9303	9308	9312	9317	9322	9326	1	2	2	3	4
59	1·9331	9335	9340	9344	9349	9353	9358	9362	9367	9371	1	1	2	3	4
60	1·9375	9380	9384	9388	9393	9397	9401	9406	9410	9414	1	1	2	3	4
61	1·9418	9422	9427	9431	9435	9439	9443	9447	9451	9455	1	1	2	3	3
62	1·9459	9463	9467	9471	9475	9479	9483	9487	9491	9495	1	1	2	3	3
63	1·9499	9503	9506	9510	9514	9518	9522	9525	9529	9533	1	1	2	3	3
64	1·9537	9540	9544	9548	9551	9555	9558	9562	9566	9569	1	1	2	2	3
65	1·9573	9576	9580	9583	9587	9590	9594	9597	9601	9604	1	1	2	2	3
66	1·9607	9611	9614	9617	9621	9624	9627	9631	9634	9637	1	1	2	2	3
67	1·9640	9643	9647	9650	9653	9656	9659	9662	9666	9669	1	1	2	2	3
68	1·9672	9675	9678	9681	9684	9687	9690	9693	9696	9699	0	1	1	2	2
69	1·9702	9704	9707	9710	9713	9716	9719	9722	9724	9727	0	1	1	2	2
70	1·9730	9733	9735	9738	9741	9743	9746	9749	9751	9754	0	1	1	2	2
71	1·9757	9759	9762	9764	9767	9770	9772	9775	9777	9780	0	1	1	2	2
72	1·9782	9785	9787	9789	9792	9794	9797	9799	9801	9804	0	1	1	2	2
73	1·9806	9808	9811	9813	9815	9817	9820	9822	9824	9826	0	1	1	1	2
74	1·9828	9831	9833	9835	9837	9839	9841	9843	9845	9847	0	1	1	1	2
75	1·9849	9851	9853	9855	9857	9859	9861	9863	9865	9867	0	1	1	1	2
76	1·9869	9871	9873	9875	9876	9878	9880	9882	9884	9885	0	1	1	1	1
77	1·9887	9889	9891	9892	9894	9896	9897	9899	9901	9902	0	1	1	1	1
78	1·9904	9906	9907	9909	9910	9912	9913	9915	9916	9918	0	1	1	1	1
79	1·9919	9921	9922	9924	9925	9927	9928	9929	9931	9932	0	0	1	1	1
80	1·9934	9935	9936	9937	9939	9940	9941	9943	9944	9945	0	0	1	1	1
81	1·9946	9947	9949	9950	9951	9952	9953	9954	9955	9956	0	0	1	1	1
82	1·9958	9959	9960	9961	9962	9963	9964	9965	9966	9967	0	0	0	1	1
83	1·9968	9968	9969	9970	9971	9972	9973	9974	9975	9975					
84	1·9976	9977	9978	9978	9979	9980	9981	9981	9982	9983					
85	1·9983	9984	9985	9985	9986	9987	9987	9988	9988	9989					
86	1·9989	9990	9990	9991	9991	9992	9992	9993	9993	9994					
87	1·9994	9994	9995	9995	9996	9996	9996	9996	9997	9997					
88	1·9997	9998	9998	9998	9998	9999	9999	9999	9999	9999					
89	1·9999	9999	0̄000	0̄000	0̄000	0̄000	0̄000	0̄000	0̄000	0̄000					

LOG. COSINES

	0′	6′	12′	18′	24′	30′	36′	42′	48′	54′	Subtract Differences				
											1′	2′	3′	4′	5′
0	0·0000	0000	0000	0000	0000	0000	0000	0000	0000	9̄999					
1	1̄·9999	9999	9999	9999	9999	9999	9998	9998	9998	9998					
2	1̄·9997	9997	9997	9996	9996	9996	9996	9995	9995	9994					
3	1̄·9994	9994	9993	9993	9992	9992	9991	9991	9990	9990					
4	1̄·9989	9989	9988	9988	9987	9987	9986	9985	9985	9984					
5	1̄·9983	9983	9982	9981	9981	9980	9979	9978	9978	9977					
6	1̄·9976	9975	9975	9974	9973	9972	9971	9970	9969	9968					
7	1̄·9968	9967	9966	9965	9964	9963	9962	9961	9960	9959	0	0	0	1	1
8	1̄·9958	9956	9955	9954	9953	9952	9951	9950	9949	9947	0	0	1	1	1
9	1̄·9946	9945	9944	9943	9941	9940	9939	9937	9936	9935	0	0	1	1	1
10	1̄·9934	9932	9931	9929	9928	9927	9925	9924	9922	9921	0	0	1	1	1
11	1̄·9919	9918	9916	9915	9913	9912	9910	9909	9907	9906	0	1	1	1	1
12	1̄·9904	9902	9901	9899	9897	9896	9894	9892	9891	9889	0	1	1	1	1
13	1̄·9887	9885	9884	9882	9880	9878	9876	9875	9873	9871	0	1	1	1	2
14	1̄·9869	9867	9865	9863	9861	9859	9857	9855	9853	9851	0	1	1	1	2
15	1̄·9849	9847	9845	9843	9841	9839	9837	9835	9833	9831	0	1	1	1	2
16	1̄·9828	9826	9824	9822	9820	9817	9815	9813	9811	9808	0	1	1	1	2
17	1̄·9806	9804	9801	9799	9797	9794	9792	9789	9787	9785	0	1	1	2	2
18	1̄·9782	9780	9777	9775	9772	9770	9767	9764	9762	9759	0	1	1	2	2
19	1̄·9757	9754	9751	9749	9746	9743	9741	9738	9735	9733	0	1	1	2	2
20	1̄·9730	9727	9724	9722	9719	9716	9713	9710	9707	9704	0	1	1	2	2
21	1̄·9702	9699	9696	9693	9690	9687	9684	9681	9678	9675	0	1	1	2	2
22	1̄·9672	9669	9666	9662	9659	9656	9653	9650	9647	9643	1	1	2	2	3
23	1̄·9640	9637	9634	9631	9627	9624	9621	9617	9614	9611	1	1	2	2	3
24	1̄·9607	9604	9601	9597	9594	9590	9587	9583	9580	9576	1	1	2	2	3
25	1̄·9573	9569	9566	9562	9558	9555	9551	9548	9544	9540	1	1	2	2	3
26	1̄·9537	9533	9529	9525	9522	9518	9514	9510	9506	9503	1	1	2	3	3
27	1̄·9499	9495	9491	9487	9483	9479	9475	9471	9467	9463	1	1	2	3	3
28	1̄·9459	9455	9451	9447	9443	9439	9435	9431	9427	9422	1	1	2	3	3
29	1̄·9418	9414	9410	9406	9401	9397	9393	9388	9384	9380	1	1	2	3	4
30	1̄·9375	9371	9367	9362	9358	9353	9349	9344	9340	9335	1	1	2	3	4
31	1̄·9331	9326	9322	9317	9312	9308	9303	9298	9294	9289	1	2	2	3	4
32	1̄·9284	9279	9275	9270	9265	9260	9255	9251	9246	9241	1	2	2	3	4
33	1̄·9236	9231	9226	9221	9216	9211	9206	9201	9196	9191	1	2	3	3	4
34	1̄·9186	9181	9175	9170	9165	9160	9155	9149	9144	9139	1	2	3	3	4
35	1̄·9134	9128	9123	9118	9112	9107	9101	9096	9091	9085	1	2	3	4	5
36	1̄·9080	9074	9069	9063	9057	9052	9046	9041	9035	9029	1	2	3	4	5
37	1̄·9023	9018	9012	9006	9000	8995	8989	8983	8977	8971	1	2	3	4	5
38	1̄·8965	8959	8953	8947	8941	8935	8929	8923	8917	8911	1	2	3	4	5
39	1̄·8905	8899	8893	8887	8880	8874	8868	8862	8855	8849	1	2	3	4	5
40	1̄·8843	8836	8830	8823	8817	8810	8804	8797	8791	8784	1	2	3	4	5 6
41	1̄·8778	8771	8765	8758	8751	8745	8738	8731	8724	8718	1	2	3	5	5 6
42	1̄·8711	8704	8697	8690	8683	8676	8669	8662	8655	8648	1	2	3	5	6 6
43	1̄·8641	8634	8627	8620	8613	8606	8598	8591	8584	8577	1	2	4	5	6 6
44	1̄·8569	8562	8555	8547	8540	8532	8525	8517	8510	8502	1	2	4	5	6 6

LOG. TANGENTS

°	0′	6′	12′	18′	24′	30′	36′	42′	48′	54′	Differences 1′	2′	3′	4′	5′
0	−∞	3̄·242	3̄·543	3̄·719	3̄·844	3̄·941	2̄·020	2̄·087	2̄·145	2̄·196					
1	2̄·2419	2833	3211	3559	3881	4181	4461	4725	4973	5208					
2	2̄·5431	5643	5845	6038	6223	6401	6571	6736	6894	7046					
3	2̄·7194	7337	7475	7609	7739	7865	7988	8107	8223	8336					
4	2̄·8446	8554	8659	8762	8862	8960	9056	9150	9241	9331					
5	2̄·9420	9506	9591	9674	9756	9836	9915	9992	0̄068	0̄143	13	26	40	53	66
6	1̄·0216	0289	0360	0430	0499	0567	0633	0699	0764	0828	11	22	34	45	56
7	1̄·0891	0954	1015	1076	1135	1194	1252	1310	1367	1423	10	20	29	39	49
8	1̄·1478	1533	1587	1640	1693	1745	1797	1848	1898	1948	9	17	26	35	43
9	1̄·1997	2046	2094	2142	2189	2236	2282	2328	2374	2419	8	16	23	31	39
10	1̄·2463	2507	2551	2594	2637	2680	2722	2764	2805	2846	7	14	21	28	35
11	1̄·2887	2927	2967	3006	3046	3085	3123	3162	3200	3237	6	13	19	26	32
12	1̄·3275	3312	3349	3385	3422	3458	3493	3529	3564	3599	6	12	18	24	30
13	1̄·3634	3668	3702	3736	3770	3804	3837	3870	3903	3935	6	11	17	22	28
14	1̄·3968	4000	4032	4064	4095	4127	4158	4189	4220	4250	5	10	16	21	26
15	1̄·4281	4311	4341	4371	4400	4430	4459	4488	4517	4546	5	10	15	20	25
16	1̄·4575	4603	4632	4660	4688	4716	4744	4771	4799	4826	5	9	14	19	23
17	1̄·4853	4880	4907	4934	4961	4987	5014	5040	5066	5092	4	9	13	18	22
18	1̄·5118	5143	5169	5195	5220	5245	5270	5295	5320	5345	4	8	13	17	21
19	1̄·5370	5394	5419	5443	5467	5491	5516	5539	5563	5587	4	8	12	16	20
20	1̄·5611	5634	5658	5681	5704	5727	5750	5773	5796	5819	4	8	12	15	19
21	1̄·5842	5864	5887	5909	5932	5954	5976	5998	6020	6042	4	7	11	15	19
22	1̄·6064	6086	6108	6129	6151	6172	6194	6215	6236	6257	4	7	11	14	18
23	1̄·6279	6300	6321	6341	6362	6383	6404	6424	6445	6465	3	7	10	14	17
24	1̄·6486	6506	6527	6547	6567	6587	6607	6627	6647	6667	3	7	10	13	17
25	1̄·6687	6706	6726	6746	6765	6785	6804	6824	6843	6863	3	7	10	13	16
26	1̄·6882	6901	6920	6939	6958	6977	6996	7015	7034	7053	3	6	9	13	16
27	1̄·7072	7090	7109	7128	7146	7165	7183	7202	7220	7238	3	6	9	12	15
28	1̄·7257	7275	7293	7311	7330	7348	7366	7384	7402	7420	3	6	9	12	15
29	1̄·7438	7455	7473	7491	7509	7526	7544	7562	7579	7597	3	6	9	12	15
30	1̄·7614	7632	7649	7667	7684	7701	7719	7736	7753	7771	3	6	9	12	14
31	1̄·7788	7805	7822	7839	7856	7873	7890	7907	7924	7941	3	6	9	11	14
32	1̄·7958	7975	7992	8008	8025	8042	8059	8075	8092	8109	3	6	8	11	14
33	1̄·8125	8142	8158	8175	8191	8208	8224	8241	8257	8274	3	5	8	11	14
34	1̄·8290	8306	8323	8339	8355	8371	8388	8404	8420	8436	3	5	8	11	14
35	1̄·8452	8468	8484	8501	8517	8533	8549	8565	8581	8597	3	5	8	11	13
36	1̄·8613	8629	8644	8660	8676	8692	8708	8724	8740	8755	3	5	8	11	13
37	1̄·8771	8787	8803	8818	8834	8850	8865	8881	8897	8912	3	5	8	10	13
38	1̄·8928	8944	8959	8975	8990	9006	9022	9037	9053	9068	3	5	8	10	13
39	1̄·9084	9099	9115	9130	9146	9161	9176	9192	9207	9223	3	5	8	10	13
40	1̄·9238	9254	9269	9284	9300	9315	9330	9346	9361	9376	3	5	8	10	13
41	1̄·9392	9407	9422	9438	9453	9468	9483	9499	9514	9529	3	5	8	10	13
42	1̄·9544	9560	9575	9590	9605	9621	9636	9651	9666	9681	3	5	8	10	13
43	1̄·9697	9712	9727	9742	9757	9772	9788	9803	9818	9833	3	5	8	10	13
44	1̄·9848	9864	9879	9894	9909	9924	9939	9955	9970	9985	3	5	8	10	13

LOG. COSINES

	0'	6'	12'	18'	24'	30'	36'	42'	48'	54'	1'	2'	3'	4'	5'
											Subtract Differences				
45	$\bar{1}$·8495	8487	8480	8472	8464	8457	8449	8441	8433	8426	1	3	4	5	6
46	$\bar{1}$·8418	8410	8402	8394	8386	8378	8370	8362	8354	8346	1	3	4	5	7
47	$\bar{1}$·8338	8330	8322	8313	8305	8297	8289	8280	8272	8264	1	3	4	6	7
48	$\bar{1}$·8255	8247	8238	8230	8221	8213	8204	8195	8187	8178	1	3	4	6	7
49	$\bar{1}$·8169	8161	8152	8143	8134	8125	8117	8108	8099	8090	1	3	4	6	7
50	$\bar{1}$·8081	8072	8063	8053	8044	8035	8026	8017	8007	7998	2	3	5	6	8
51	$\bar{1}$·7989	7979	7970	7960	7951	7941	7932	7922	7913	7903	2	3	5	6	8
52	$\bar{1}$·7893	7884	7874	7864	7854	7844	7835	7825	7815	7805	2	3	5	7	8
53	$\bar{1}$·7795	7785	7774	7764	7754	7744	7734	7723	7713	7703	2	3	5	7	9
54	$\bar{1}$·7692	7682	7671	7661	7650	7640	7629	7618	7607	7597	2	4	5	7	9
55	$\bar{1}$·7586	7575	7564	7553	7542	7531	7520	7509	7498	7487	2	4	6	7	9
56	$\bar{1}$·7476	7464	7453	7442	7430	7419	7407	7396	7384	7373	2	4	6	8	10
57	$\bar{1}$·7361	7349	7338	7326	7314	7302	7290	7278	7266	7254	2	4	6	8	10
58	$\bar{1}$·7242	7230	7218	7205	7193	7181	7168	7156	7144	7131	2	4	6	8	10
59	$\bar{1}$·7118	7106	7093	7080	7068	7055	7042	7029	7016	7003	2	4	6	9	11
60	$\bar{1}$·6990	6977	6963	6950	6937	6923	6910	6896	6883	6869	2	4	7	9	11
61	$\bar{1}$·6856	6842	6828	6814	6801	6787	6773	6759	6744	6730	2	5	7	9	12
62	$\bar{1}$·6716	6702	6687	6673	6659	6644	6629	6615	6600	6585	2	5	7	10	12
63	$\bar{1}$·6570	6556	6541	6526	6510	6495	6480	6465	6449	6434	3	5	8	10	13
64	$\bar{1}$·6418	6403	6387	6371	6356	6340	6324	6308	6292	6276	3	5	8	11	13
65	$\bar{1}$·6259	6243	6227	6210	6194	6177	6161	6144	6127	6110	3	6	8	11	14
66	$\bar{1}$·6093	6076	6059	6042	6024	6007	5990	5972	5954	5937	3	6	9	12	15
67	$\bar{1}$·5919	5901	5883	5865	5847	5828	5810	5792	5773	5754	3	6	9	12	15
68	$\bar{1}$·5736	5717	5698	5679	5660	5641	5621	5602	5583	5563	3	6	10	13	16
69	$\bar{1}$·5543	5523	5504	5484	5463	5443	5423	5402	5382	5361	3	7	10	14	17
70	$\bar{1}$·5341	5320	5299	5278	5256	5235	5213	5192	5170	5148	4	7	11	14	18
71	$\bar{1}$·5126	5104	5082	5060	5037	5015	4992	4969	4946	4923	4	8	11	15	19
72	$\bar{1}$·4900	4876	4853	4829	4805	4781	4757	4733	4709	4684	4	8	12	16	20
73	$\bar{1}$·4659	4634	4609	4584	4559	4533	4508	4482	4456	4430	4	9	13	17	21
74	$\bar{1}$·4403	4377	4350	4323	4296	4269	4242	4214	4186	4158	5	9	14	18	23
75	$\bar{1}$·4130	4102	4073	4044	4015	3986	3957	3927	3897	3867	5	10	15	20	24
76	$\bar{1}$·3837	3806	3775	3745	3713	3682	3650	3618	3586	3554	5	11	16	21	26
77	$\bar{1}$·3521	3488	3455	3421	3387	3353	3319	3284	3250	3214	6	11	17	23	28
78	$\bar{1}$·3179	3143	3107	3070	3034	2997	2959	2921	2883	2845	6	12	19	25	31
79	$\bar{1}$·2806	2767	2727	2687	2647	2606	2565	2524	2482	2439	7	14	20	27	34
80	$\bar{1}$·2397	2353	2310	2266	2221	2176	2131	2085	2038	1991	8	15	23	30	38
81	$\bar{1}$·1943	1895	1847	1797	1747	1697	1646	1594	1542	1489	8	17	25	34	42
82	$\bar{1}$·1436	1381	1326	1271	1214	1157	1099	1040	0981	0920	10	19	29	38	48
83	$\bar{1}$·0859	0797	0734	0670	0605	0539	0472	0403	0334	0264	11	22	33	44	55
84	$\bar{1}$·0192	0120	0046	$\overline{9970}$	$\overline{9894}$	$\overline{9816}$	$\overline{9736}$	$\overline{9655}$	$\overline{9573}$	$\overline{9489}$	13	26	39	52	66
85	$\bar{2}$·9403	9315	9226	9135	9042	8946	8849	8749	8647	8543					
86	$\bar{2}$·8436	8326	8213	8098	7979	7857	7731	7602	7468	7330					
87	$\bar{2}$·7188	7041	6889	6731	6567	6397	6220	6035	5842	5640					
88	$\bar{2}$·5428	5206	4971	4723	4459	4179	3880	3558	3210	2832					
89	$\bar{3}$·242	$\bar{2}$·196	$\bar{2}$·145	$\bar{2}$·087	$\bar{2}$·020	$\bar{3}$·941	$\bar{3}$·844	$\bar{3}$·719	$\bar{3}$·543	$\bar{3}$·242					

LOG. TANGENTS

°	0'	6'	12'	18'	24'	30'	36'	42'	48'	54'	1'	2'	3'	4'	5'
45	·0000	0015	0030	0045	0061	0076	0091	0106	0121	0136	3	5	8	10	13
46	·0152	0167	0182	0197	0212	0228	0243	0258	0273	0288	3	5	8	10	13
47	·0303	0319	0334	0349	0364	0379	0395	0410	0425	0440	3	5	8	10	13
48	·0456	0471	0486	0501	0517	0532	0547	0562	0578	0593	3	5	8	10	13
49	·0608	0624	0639	0654	0670	0685	0700	0716	0731	0746	3	5	8	10	13
50	·0762	0777	0793	0808	0824	0839	0854	0870	0885	0901	3	5	8	10	13
51	·0916	0932	0947	0963	0978	0994	1010	1025	1041	1056	3	5	8	10	13
52	·1072	1088	1103	1119	1135	1150	1166	1182	1197	1213	3	5	8	10	13
53	·1229	1245	1260	1276	1292	1308	1324	1340	1356	1371	3	5	8	11	13
54	·1387	1403	1419	1435	1451	1467	1483	1499	1516	1532	3	5	8	11	13
55	·1548	1564	1580	1596	1612	1629	1645	1661	1677	1694	3	5	8	11	14
56	·1710	1726	1743	1759	1776	1792	1809	1825	1842	1858	3	5	8	11	14
57	·1875	1891	1908	1925	1941	1958	1975	1992	2008	2025	3	6	8	11	14
58	·2042	2059	2076	2093	2110	2127	2144	2161	2178	2195	3	6	9	11	14
59	·2212	2229	2247	2264	2281	2299	2316	2333	2351	2368	3	6	9	12	14
60	·2386	2403	2421	2438	2456	2474	2491	2509	2527	2545	3	6	9	12	15
61	·2562	2580	2598	2616	2634	2652	2670	2689	2707	2725	3	6	9	12	15
62	·2743	2762	2780	2798	2817	2835	2854	2872	2891	2910	3	6	9	12	15
63	·2928	2947	2966	2985	3004	3023	3042	3061	3080	3099	3	6	9	13	16
64	·3118	3137	3157	3176	3196	3215	3235	3254	3274	3294	3	7	10	13	16
65	·3313	3333	3353	3373	3393	3413	3433	3453	3473	3494	3	7	10	13	17
66	·3514	3535	3555	3576	3596	3617	3638	3659	3679	3700	3	7	10	14	17
67	·3721	3743	3764	3785	3806	3828	3849	3871	3892	3914	4	7	11	14	18
68	·3936	3958	3980	4002	4024	4046	4068	4091	4113	4136	4	7	11	15	19
69	·4158	4181	4204	4227	4250	4273	4296	4319	4342	4366	4	8	12	15	19
70	·4389	4413	4437	4461	4484	4509	4533	4557	4581	4606	4	8	12	16	20
71	·4630	4655	4680	4705	4730	4755	4780	4805	4831	4857	4	8	13	17	21
72	·4882	4908	4934	4960	4986	5013	5039	5066	5093	5120	4	9	13	18	22
73	·5147	5174	5201	5229	5256	5284	5312	5340	5368	5397	5	9	14	19	23
74	·5425	5454	5483	5512	5541	5570	5600	5629	5659	5689	5	10	15	20	25
75	·5719	5750	5780	5811	5842	5873	5905	5936	5968	6000	5	10	16	21	26
76	·6032	6065	6097	6130	6163	6196	6230	6264	6298	6332	6	11	17	22	28
77	·6366	6401	6436	6471	6507	6542	6578	6615	6651	6688	6	12	18	24	30
78	·6725	6763	6800	6838	6877	6915	6954	6994	7033	7073	6	13	19	26	32
79	·7113	7154	7195	7236	7278	7320	7363	7406	7449	7493	7	14	21	28	35
80	·7537	7581	7626	7672	7718	7764	7811	7858	7906	7954	8	16	23	31	39
81	·8003	8052	8102	8152	8203	8255	8307	8360	8413	8467	9	17	26	35	43
82	·8522	8577	8633	8690	8748	8806	8865	8924	8985	9046	10	20	29	39	49
83	·9109	9172	9236	9301	9367	9433	9501	9570	9640	9711	11	22	34	45	56
84	·9784	9857	9932	0̄008	0̄085	0̄164	0̄244	0̄326	0̄409	0̄494	13	26	40	53	66
85	1·0580	0669	0759	0850	0944	1040	1138	1238	1341	1446					
86	1·1554	1664	1777	1893	2012	2135	2261	2391	2525	2663					
87	1·2806	2954	3106	3264	3429	3599	3777	3962	4155	4357					
88	1·4569	4792	5027	5275	5539	5819	6119	6441	6789	7167					
89	1·7581	8038	8550	9130	9800	0̄591	1̄561	7̄810	4̄571	7̄581					

13*

SQUARES

	0	1	2	3	4	5	6	7	8	9	1	2	3	4	5	6	7	8	9
											\multicolumn{9}{Differences}								
10	1000	1020	1040	1061	1082	1103	1124	1145	1166	1188	2	4	6	8	11	13	15	17	19
11	1210	1232	1254	1277	1300	1323	1346	1369	1392	1416	2	5	7	9	12	14	16	18	21
12	1440	1464	1488	1513	1538	1563	1588	1613	1638	1664	3	5	8	10	13	15	18	20	23
13	1690	1716	1742	1769	1796	1823	1850	1877	1904	1932	3	5	8	11	14	16	19	22	24
14	1960	1988	2016	2045	2074	2103	2132	2161	2190	2220	3	6	9	12	15	17	20	23	26
15	2250	2280	2310	2341	2372	2403	2434	2465	2496	2528	3	6	9	12	16	19	22	25	28
16	2560	2592	2624	2657	2690	2723	2756	2789	2822	2856	3	7	10	13	17	20	23	26	30
17	2890	2924	2958	2993	3028	3063	3098	3133	3168	3204	4	7	11	14	18	21	25	28	32
18	3240	3276	3312	3349	3386	3423	3460	3497	3534	3572	4	7	11	15	19	22	26	30	33
19	3610	3648	3686	3725	3764	3803	3842	3881	3920	3960	4	8	12	16	20	23	27	31	35
20	4000	4040	4080	4121	4162	4203	4244	4285	4326	4368	4	8	12	16	21	25	29	33	37
21	4410	4452	4494	4537	4580	4623	4666	4709	4752	4796	4	9	13	17	22	26	30	34	39
22	4840	4884	4928	4973	5018	5063	5108	5153	5198	5244	5	9	14	18	23	27	32	36	41
23	5290	5336	5382	5429	5476	5523	5570	5617	5664	5712	5	9	14	19	24	28	33	38	42
24	5760	5808	5856	5905	5954	6003	6052	6101	6150	6200	5	10	15	20	25	29	34	39	44
25	6250	6300	6350	6401	6452	6503	6554	6605	6656	6708	5	10	15	20	26	31	36	41	46
26	6760	6812	6864	6917	6970	7023	7076	7129	7182	7236	5	11	16	21	27	32	37	42	48
27	7290	7344	7398	7453	7508	7563	7618	7673	7728	7784	6	11	17	22	28	33	39	44	50
28	7840	7896	7952	8009	8066	8123	8180	8237	8294	8352	6	11	17	23	29	34	40	46	51
29	8410	8468	8526	8585	8644	8703	8762	8821	8880	8940	6	12	18	24	30	35	41	47	53
30	9000	9060	9120	9181	9242	9303	9364	9425	9486	9548	6	12	18	24	31	37	43	49	55
31	9610	9672	9734	9797	9860	9923	9986				6	13	19	25	32	38	44	50	57
31								1005	1011	1018	1	1	2	3	3	4	4	5	6
32	1024	1030	1037	1043	1050	1056	1063	1069	1076	1082	1	1	2	3	3	4	4	5	6
33	1089	1096	1102	1109	1116	1122	1129	1136	1142	1149	1	1	2	3	3	4	5	5	6
34	1156	1163	1170	1176	1183	1190	1197	1204	1211	1218	1	1	2	3	3	4	5	6	6
35	1225	1232	1239	1246	1253	1260	1267	1274	1282	1289	1	1	2	3	4	4	5	6	6
36	1296	1303	1310	1318	1325	1332	1340	1347	1354	1362	1	1	2	3	4	4	5	6	7
37	1369	1376	1384	1391	1399	1406	1414	1421	1429	1436	1	2	2	3	4	5	5	6	7
38	1444	1452	1459	1467	1475	1482	1490	1498	1505	1513	1	2	2	3	4	5	5	6	7
39	1521	1529	1537	1544	1552	1560	1568	1576	1584	1592	1	2	2	3	4	5	6	6	7
40	1600	1608	1616	1624	1632	1640	1648	1656	1665	1673	1	2	2	3	4	5	6	6	7
41	1681	1689	1697	1706	1714	1722	1731	1739	1747	1756	1	2	2	3	4	5	6	7	7
42	1764	1772	1781	1789	1798	1806	1815	1823	1832	1840	1	2	3	3	4	5	6	7	8
43	1849	1858	1866	1875	1884	1892	1901	1910	1918	1927	1	2	3	4	4	5	6	7	8
44	1936	1945	1954	1962	1971	1980	1989	1998	2007	2016	1	2	3	4	5	5	6	7	8
45	2025	2034	2043	2052	2061	2070	2079	2088	2098	2107	1	2	3	4	5	5	6	7	8
46	2116	2125	2134	2144	2153	2162	2172	2181	2190	2200	1	2	3	4	5	6	7	7	8
47	2209	2218	2228	2237	2247	2256	2266	2275	2285	2294	1	2	3	4	5	6	7	8	9
48	2304	2314	2323	2333	2343	2352	2362	2372	2381	2391	1	2	3	4	5	6	7	8	9
49	2401	2411	2421	2430	2440	2450	2460	2470	2480	2490	1	2	3	4	5	6	7	8	9
50	2500	2510	2520	2530	2540	2550	2560	2570	2581	2591	1	2	3	4	5	6	7	8	9
51	2601	2611	2621	2632	2642	2652	2663	2673	2683	2694	1	2	3	4	5	6	7	8	9
52	2704	2714	2725	2735	2746	2756	2767	2777	2788	2798	1	2	3	4	5	6	7	8	9
53	2809	2820	2830	2841	2852	2862	2873	2884	2894	2905	1	2	3	4	5	6	7	9	10
54	2916	2927	2938	2948	2959	2970	2981	2992	3003	3014	1	2	3	4	6	7	8	9	10

SQUARES

	0	1	2	3	4	5	6	7	8	9	Differences								
											1	2	3	4	5	6	7	8	9
55	3025	3036	3047	3058	3069	3080	3091	3102	3114	3125	1	2	3	4	6	7	8	9	10
56	3136	3147	3158	3170	3181	3192	3204	3215	3226	3238	1	2	3	5	6	7	8	9	10
57	3249	3260	3272	3283	3295	3306	3318	3329	3341	3352	1	2	3	5	6	7	8	9	10
58	3364	3376	3387	3399	3411	3422	3434	3446	3457	3469	1	2	4	5	6	7	8	9	11
59	3481	3493	3505	3516	3528	3540	3552	3564	3576	3588	1	2	4	5	6	7	8	10	11
60	3600	3612	3624	3636	3648	3660	3672	3684	3697	3709	1	2	4	5	6	7	8	10	11
61	3721	3733	3745	3758	3770	3782	3795	3807	3819	3832	1	2	4	5	6	7	9	10	11
62	3844	3856	3869	3881	3894	3906	3919	3931	3944	3956	1	3	4	5	6	8	9	10	11
63	3969	3982	3994	4007	4020	4032	4045	4058	4070	4083	1	3	4	5	6	8	9	10	11
64	4096	4109	4122	4134	4147	4160	4173	4186	4199	4212	1	3	4	5	6	8	9	10	12
65	4225	4238	4251	4264	4277	4290	4303	4316	4330	4343	1	3	4	5	7	8	9	10	12
66	4356	4369	4382	4396	4409	4422	4436	4449	4462	4476	1	3	4	5	7	8	9	11	12
67	4489	4502	4516	4529	4543	4556	4570	4583	4597	4610	1	3	4	5	7	8	9	11	12
68	4624	4638	4651	4665	4679	4692	4706	4720	4733	4747	1	3	4	5	7	8	10	11	12
69	4761	4775	4789	4802	4816	4830	4844	4858	4872	4886	1	3	4	6	7	8	10	11	13
70	4900	4914	4928	4942	4956	4970	4984	4998	5013	5027	1	3	4	6	7	8	10	11	13
71	5041	5055	5069	5084	5098	5112	5127	5141	5155	5170	1	3	4	6	7	9	10	11	13
72	5184	5198	5213	5227	5242	5256	5271	5285	5300	5314	1	3	4	6	7	9	10	12	13
73	5329	5344	5358	5373	5388	5402	5417	5432	5446	5461	1	3	4	6	7	9	10	12	13
74	5476	5491	5506	5520	5535	5550	5565	5580	5595	5610	1	3	4	6	7	9	10	12	13
75	5625	5640	5655	5670	5685	5700	5715	5730	5746	576‧	2	3	5	6	8	9	11	12	14
76	5776	5791	5806	5822	5837	5852	5868	5883	5898	5914	2	3	5	6	8	9	11	12	14
77	5929	5944	5960	5975	5991	6006	6022	6037	6053	6068	2	3	5	6	8	9	11	12	14
78	6084	6100	6115	6131	6147	6162	6178	6194	6209	6225	2	3	5	6	8	9	11	13	14
79	6241	6257	6273	6288	6304	6320	6336	6352	6368	6384	2	3	5	6	8	10	11	13	14
80	6400	6416	6432	6448	6464	6480	6496	6512	6529	6545	2	3	5	6	8	10	11	13	14
81	6561	6577	6593	6610	6626	6642	6659	6675	6692	6708	2	3	5	7	8	10	11	13	15
82	6724	6740	6757	6773	6790	6806	6823	6839	6856	6872	2	3	5	7	8	10	12	13	15
83	6889	6906	6922	6939	6956	6972	6989	7006	7022	7039	2	3	5	7	8	10	12	13	15
84	7056	7073	7090	7106	7123	7140	7157	7174	7191	7208	2	3	5	7	8	10	12	14	15
85	7225	7242	7259	7276	7293	7310	7327	7344	7362	7379	2	3	5	7	9	10	12	14	15
86	7396	7413	7430	7448	7465	7482	7500	7517	7534	7552	2	3	5	7	9	10	12	14	16
87	7569	7586	7604	7621	7639	7656	7674	7691	7709	7726	2	4	5	7	9	11	12	14	16
88	7744	7762	7779	7797	7815	7832	7850	7868	7885	7903	2	4	5	7	9	11	12	14	16
89	7921	7939	7957	7974	7992	8010	8028	8046	8064	8082	2	4	5	7	9	11	13	14	16
90	8100	8118	8136	8154	8172	8190	8208	8226	8245	8263	2	4	5	7	9	11	13	14	16
91	8281	8299	8317	8336	8354	8372	8391	8409	8427	8446	2	4	5	7	9	11	13	15	16
92	8464	8482	8501	8519	8538	8556	8575	8593	8612	8630	2	4	6	7	9	11	13	15	17
93	8649	8668	8686	8705	8724	8742	8761	8780	8798	8817	2	4	6	7	9	11	13	15	17
94	8836	8855	8874	8892	8911	8930	8949	8968	8987	9006	2	4	6	8	9	11	13	15	17
95	9025	9044	9063	9082	9101	9120	9139	9158	9178	9197	2	4	6	8	10	11	13	15	17
96	9216	9235	9254	9274	9293	9312	9332	9351	9370	9390	2	4	6	8	10	12	13	15	17
97	9409	9428	9448	9467	9487	9506	9526	9545	9565	9584	2	4	6	8	10	12	14	16	18
98	9604	9624	9643	9663	9683	9702	9722	9742	9761	9781	2	4	6	8	10	12	14	16	18
99	9801	9821	9841	9860	9880	9900	9920	9940	9960	9980	2	4	6	8	10	12	14	16	18

RECIPROCALS

	0	1	2	3	4	5	6	7	8	9	Subtract Differences								
											1	2	3	4	5	6	7	8	9
1·0	1·0000	9901	9804	9709	9615	9524	9434	9346	9259	9174	9	18	27	36	45	55	64	73	82
1·1	·9091	9009	8929	8850	8772	8696	8621	8547	8475	8403	8	15	23	30	38	45	53	61	68
1·2	·8333	8264	8197	8130	8065	8000	7937	7874	7813	7752	6	13	19	26	32	38	45	51	58
1·3	·7692	7634	7576	7519	7463	7407	7353	7299	7246	7194	5	11	16	22	27	33	38	44	49
1·4	·7143	7092	7042	6993	6944	6897	6849	6803	6757	6711	5	10	14	19	24	29	33	38	43
1·5	·6667	6623	6579	6536	6494	6452	6410	6369	6329	6289	4	8	13	17	21	25	29	33	38
1·6	·6250	6211	6173	6135	6098	6061	6024	5988	5952	5917	4	7	11	15	18	22	26	29	33
1·7	·5882	5848	5814	5780	5747	5714	5682	5650	5618	5587	3	6	10	13	16	20	23	26	29
1·8	·5556	5525	5495	5464	5435	5405	5376	5348	5319	5291	3	6	9	12	15	18	20	23	26
1·9	·5263	5236	5208	5181	5155	5128	5102	5076	5051	5025	3	5	8	11	13	16	18	21	24
2·0	·5000	4975	4950	4926	4902	4878	4854	4831	4808	4785	2	5	7	10	12	14	17	19	21
2·1	·4762	4739	4717	4695	4673	4651	4630	4608	4587	4566	2	4	7	9	11	13	15	17	20
2·2	·4545	4525	4505	4484	4464	4444	4425	4405	4386	4367	2	4	6	8	10	12	14	16	18
2·3	·4348	4329	4310	4292	4274	4255	4237	4219	4202	4184	2	4	5	7	9	11	13	14	16
2·4	·4167	4149	4132	4115	4098	4082	4065	4049	4032	4016	2	3	5	7	8	10	12	13	15
2·5	·4000	3984	3968	3953	3937	3922	3906	3891	3876	3861	2	3	5	6	8	9	11	12	14
2·6	·3846	3831	3817	3802	3788	3774	3759	3745	3731	3717	1	3	4	6	7	9	10	11	13
2·7	·3704	3690	3676	3663	3650	3636	3623	3610	3597	3584	1	3	4	5	7	8	9	11	12
2·8	·3571	3559	3546	3534	3521	3509	3497	3484	3472	3460	1	2	4	5	6	7	9	10	11
2·9	·3448	3436	3425	3413	3401	3390	3378	3367	3356	3344	1	2	3	5	6	7	8	9	10
3·0	·3333	3322	3311	3300	3289	3279	3268	3257	3247	3236	1	2	3	4	5	6	7	9	10
3·1	·3226	3215	3205	3195	3185	3175	3165	3155	3145	3135	1	2	3	4	5	6	7	8	9
3·2	·3125	3115	3106	3096	3086	3077	3067	3058	3049	3040	1	2	3	4	5	6	7	8	9
3·3	·3030	3021	3012	3003	2994	2985	2976	2967	2959	2950	1	2	3	4	4	5	6	7	8
3·4	·2941	2933	2924	2915	2907	2899	2890	2882	2874	2865	1	2	3	3	4	5	6	7	8
3·5	·2857	2849	2841	2833	2825	2817	2809	2801	2793	2786	1	2	2	3	4	5	6	6	7
3·6	·2778	2770	2762	2755	2747	2740	2732	2725	2717	2710	1	2	2	3	4	5	5	6	7
3·7	·2703	2695	2688	2681	2674	2667	2660	2653	2646	2639	1	1	2	3	4	4	5	6	6
3·8	·2632	2625	2618	2611	2604	2597	2591	2584	2577	2571	1	1	2	3	3	4	5	5	6
3·9	·2564	2558	2551	2545	2538	2532	2525	2519	2513	2506	1	1	2	3	3	4	4	5	6
4·0	·2500	2494	2488	2481	2475	2469	2463	2457	2451	2445	1	1	2	2	3	4	4	5	5
4·1	·2439	2433	2427	2421	2415	2410	2404	2398	2392	2387	1	1	2	2	3	3	4	5	5
4·2	·2381	2375	2370	2364	2358	2353	2347	2342	2336	2331	1	1	2	2	3	3	4	4	5
4·3	·2326	2320	2315	2309	2304	2299	2294	2288	2283	2278	1	1	2	2	3	3	4	4	5
4·4	·2273	2268	2262	2257	2252	2247	2242	2237	2232	2227	1	1	2	2	3	3	4	4	5
4·5	·2222	2217	2212	2208	2203	2198	2193	2188	2183	2179	0	1	1	2	2	3	3	4	4
4·6	·2174	2169	2165	2160	2155	2151	2146	2141	2137	2132	0	1	1	2	2	3	3	4	4
4·7	·2128	2123	2119	2114	2110	2105	2101	2096	2092	2088	0	1	1	2	2	3	3	4	4
4·8	·2083	2079	2075	2070	2066	2062	2058	2053	2049	2045	0	1	1	2	2	3	3	3	4
4·9	·2041	2037	2033	2028	2024	2020	2016	2012	2008	2004	0	1	1	2	2	2	3	3	4
5·0	·2000	1996	1992	1988	1984	1980	1976	1972	1969	1965	0	1	1	2	2	2	3	3	4
5·1	·1961	1957	1953	1949	1946	1942	1938	1934	1931	1927	0	1	1	2	2	2	3	3	3
5·2	·1923	1919	1916	1912	1908	1905	1901	1898	1894	1890	0	1	1	1	2	2	3	3	3
5·3	·1887	1883	1880	1876	1873	1869	1866	1862	1859	1855	0	1	1	1	2	2	2	3	3
5·4	·1852	1848	1845	1842	1838	1835	1832	1828	1825	1821	0	1	1	1	2	2	2	3	3

RECIPROCALS

	0	1	2	3	4	5	6	7	8	9	Subtract Differences								
											1	2	3	4	5	6	7	8	9
5·5	·1818	1815	1812	1808	1805	1802	1799	1795	1792	1789	0	1	1	1	2	2	2	3	3
5·6	·1786	1783	1779	1776	1773	1770	1767	1764	1761	1757	0	1	1	1	2	2	2	3	3
5·7	·1754	1751	1748	1745	1742	1739	1736	1733	1730	1727	0	1	1	1	2	2	2	2	3
5·8	·1724	1721	1718	1715	1712	1709	1706	1704	1701	1698	0	1	1	1	1	2	2	2	3
5·9	·1695	1692	1689	1686	1684	1681	1678	1675	1672	1669	0	1	1	1	1	2	2	2	3
6·0	·1667	1664	1661	1658	1656	1653	1650	1647	1645	1642	0	1	1	1	1	2	2	2	2
6·1	·1639	1637	1634	1631	1629	1626	1623	1621	1618	1616	0	1	1	1	1	2	2	2	2
6·2	·1613	1610	1608	1605	1603	1600	1597	1595	1592	1590	0	1	1	1	1	1	2	2	2
6·3	·1587	1585	1582	1580	1577	1575	1572	1570	1567	1565	0	0	1	1	1	1	2	2	2
6·4	·1563	1560	1558	1555	1553	1550	1548	1546	1543	1541	0	0	1	1	1	1	2	2	2
6·5	·1538	1536	1534	1531	1529	1527	1524	1522	1520	1517	0	0	1	1	1	1	2	2	2
6·6	·1515	1513	1511	1508	1506	1504	1502	1499	1497	1495	0	0	1	1	1	1	2	2	2
6·7	·1493	1490	1488	1486	1484	1481	1479	1477	1475	1473	0	0	1	1	1	1	2	2	2
6·8	·1471	1468	1466	1464	1462	1460	1458	1456	1453	1451	0	0	1	1	1	1	2	2	2
6·9	·1449	1447	1445	1443	1441	1439	1437	1435	1433	1431	0	0	1	1	1	1	1	2	2
7·0	·1429	1427	1425	1422	1420	1418	1416	1414	1412	1410	0	0	1	1	1	1	1	2	2
7·1	·1408	1406	1404	1403	1401	1399	1397	1395	1393	1391	0	0	1	1	1	1	1	2	2
7·2	·1389	1387	1385	1383	1381	1379	1377	1376	1374	1372	0	0	1	1	1	1	1	2	2
7·3	·1370	1368	1366	1364	1362	1361	1359	1357	1355	1353	0	0	1	1	1	1	1	2	2
7·4	·1351	1350	1348	1346	1344	1342	1340	1339	1337	1335	0	0	1	1	1	1	1	2	2
7·5	·1333	1332	1330	1328	1326	1325	1323	1321	1319	1318	0	0	1	1	1	1	1	1	2
7·6	·1316	1314	1312	1311	1309	1307	1305	1304	1302	1300	0	0	1	1	1	1	1	1	2
7·7	·1299	1297	1295	1294	1292	1290	1289	1287	1285	1284	0	0	0	1	1	1	1	1	1
7·8	·1282	1280	1279	1277	1276	1274	1272	1271	1269	1267	0	0	0	1	1	1	1	1	1
7·9	·1266	1264	1263	1261	1259	1258	1256	1255	1253	1252	0	0	0	1	1	1	1	1	1
8·0	·1250	1248	1247	1245	1244	1242	1241	1239	1238	1236	0	0	0	1	1	1	1	1	1
8·1	·1235	1233	1232	1230	1229	1227	1225	1224	1222	1221	0	0	0	1	1	1	1	1	1
8·2	·1220	1218	1217	1215	1214	1212	1211	1209	1208	1206	0	0	0	1	1	1	1	1	1
8·3	·1205	1203	1202	1200	1199	1198	1196	1195	1193	1192	0	0	0	1	1	1	1	1	1
8·4	·1190	1189	1188	1186	1185	1183	1182	1181	1179	1178	0	0	0	1	1	1	1	1	1
8·5	·1176	1175	1174	1172	1171	1170	1168	1167	1166	1164	0	0	0	1	1	1	1	1	1
8·6	·1163	1161	1160	1159	1157	1156	1155	1153	1152	1151	0	0	0	1	1	1	1	1	1
8·7	·1149	1148	1147	1145	1144	1143	1142	1140	1139	1138	0	0	0	1	1	1	1	1	1
8·8	·1136	1135	1134	1133	1131	1130	1129	1127	1126	1125	0	0	0	1	1	1	1	1	1
8·9	·1124	1122	1121	1120	1119	1117	1116	1115	1114	1112	0	0	0	1	1	1	1	1	1
9·0	·1111	1110	1109	1107	1106	1105	1104	1103	1101	1100	0	0	0	1	1	1	1	1	1
9·1	·1099	1098	1096	1095	1094	1093	1092	1091	1089	1088	0	0	0	1	1	1	1	1	1
9·2	·1087	1086	1085	1083	1082	1081	1080	1079	1078	1076	0	0	0	0	1	1	1	1	1
9·3	·1075	1074	1073	1072	1071	1070	1068	1067	1066	1065	0	0	0	0	1	1	1	1	1
9·4	·1064	1063	1062	1060	1059	1058	1057	1056	1055	1054	0	0	0	0	1	1	1	1	1
9·5	·1053	1052	1050	1049	1048	1047	1046	1045	1044	1043	0	0	0	0	1	1	1	1	1
9·6	·1042	1041	1040	1038	1037	1036	1035	1034	1033	1032	0	0	0	0	1	1	1	1	1
9·7	·1031	1030	1029	1028	1027	1026	1025	1024	1022	1021	0	0	0	0	1	1	1	1	1
9·8	·1020	1019	1018	1017	1016	1015	1014	1013	1012	1011	0	0	0	0	1	1	1	1	1
9·9	·1010	1009	1008	1007	1006	1005	1004	1003	1002	1001	0	0	0	0	0	1	1	1	1

DEGREES TO RADIANS

| | | Differences— | 1' 3 | 2' 6 | 3' 9 | 4' 12 | 5' 15 |

	Radians	6'	12'	18'	24'	30'	36'	42'	48'	54'
0	·0000	0017	0035	0052	0070	0087	0105	0122	0140	0157
1	·0175	0192	0209	0227	0244	0262	0279	0297	0314	0332
2	·0349	0367	0384	0401	0419	0436	0454	0471	0489	0506
3	·0524	0541	0559	0576	0593	0611	0628	0646	0663	0681
4	·0698	0716	0733	0750	0768	0785	0803	0820	0838	0855
5	·0873	0890	0908	0925	0942	0960	0977	0995	1012	1030
6	·1047	1065	1082	1100	1117	1134	1152	1169	1187	1204
7	·1222	1239	1257	1274	1292	1309	1326	1344	1361	1379
8	·1396	1414	1431	1449	1466	1484	1501	1518	1536	1553
9	·1571	1588	1606	1623	1641	1658	1676	1693	1710	1728
10	·1745	1763	1780	1798	1815	1833	1850	1868	1885	1902
11	·1920	1937	1955	1972	1990	2007	2025	2042	2059	2077
12	·2094	2112	2129	2147	2164	2182	2199	2217	2234	2251
13	·2269	2286	2304	2321	2339	2356	2374	2391	2409	2426
14	·2443	2461	2478	2496	2513	2531	2548	2566	2583	2601
15	·2618	2635	2653	2670	2688	2705	2723	2740	2758	2775
16	·2793	2810	2827	2845	2862	2880	2897	2915	2932	2950
17	·2967	2985	3002	3019	3037	3054	3072	3089	3107	3124
18	·3142	3159	3176	3194	3211	3229	3246	3264	3281	3299
19	·3316	3334	3351	3368	3386	3403	3421	3438	3456	3473
20	·3491	3508	3526	3543	3560	3578	3595	3613	3630	3648
21	·3665	3683	3700	3718	3735	3752	3770	3787	3805	3822
22	·3840	3857	3875	3892	3910	3927	3944	3962	3979	3997
23	·4014	4032	4049	4067	4084	4102	4119	4136	4154	4171
24	·4189	4206	4224	4241	4259	4276	4294	4311	4328	4346
25	·4363	4381	4398	4416	4433	4451	4468	4485	4503	4520
26	·4538	4555	4573	4590	4608	4625	4643	4660	4677	4695
27	·4712	4730	4747	4765	4782	4800	4817	4835	4852	4869
28	·4887	4904	4921	4939	4957	4974	4992	5009	5027	5044
29	·5061	5079	5096	5114	5131	5149	5166	5184	5201	5219
30	·5236	5253	5271	5288	5306	5323	5341	5358	5376	5393
31	·5411	5428	5445	5463	5480	5498	5515	5533	5550	5568
32	·5585	5603	5620	5637	5655	5672	5690	5707	5725	5742
33	·5760	5777	5794	5812	5829	5847	5864	5882	5899	5917
34	·5934	5952	5969	5986	6004	6021	6039	6056	6074	6091
35	·6109	6126	6144	6161	6178	6196	6213	6231	6248	6266
36	·6283	6301	6318	6336	6353	6370	6388	6405	6423	6440
37	·6458	6475	6493	6510	6528	6545	6562	6580	6597	6615
38	·6632	6650	6667	6685	6702	6720	6737	6754	6772	6789
39	·6807	6824	6842	6859	6877	6894	6912	6929	6946	6964
40	·6981	6999	7016	7034	7051	7069	7086	7103	7121	7138
41	·7156	7173	7191	7208	7226	7243	7261	7278	7295	7313
42	·7330	7348	7365	7383	7400	7418	7435	7453	7470	7487
43	·7505	7522	7540	7557	7575	7592	7610	7627	7645	7662
44	·7679	7697	7714	7732	7749	7767	7784	7802	7819	7837

DEGREES TO RADIANS

Differences—	1' 3	2' 6	3' 9	4' 12	5' 15

°	Radians	6'	12'	18'	24'	30'	36'	42'	48'	54'
45	·7854	7871	7889	7906	7924	7941	7959	7976	7994	8011
46	·8029	8046	8063	8081	8098	8116	8133	8151	8168	8186
47	·8203	8221	8238	8255	8273	8290	8308	8325	8343	8360
48	·8378	8395	8412	8430	8447	8465	8482	8500	8517	8535
49	·8552	8570	8587	8604	8622	8639	8657	8674	8692	8709
50	·8727	8744	8762	8779	8796	8814	8831	8849	8866	8884
51	·8901	8919	8936	8954	8971	8988	9006	9023	9041	9058
52	·9076	9093	9111	9128	9146	9163	9180	9198	9215	9233
53	·9250	9268	9285	9303	9320	9338	9355	9372	9390	9407
54	·9425	9442	9460	9477	9495	9512	9529	9547	9564	9582
55	·9599	9617	9634	9652	9669	9687	9704	9721	9739	9756
56	·9774	9791	9809	9826	9844	9861	9879	9896	9913	9931
57	·9948	9966	9983	ō001	ō018	ō036	ō053	ō071	ō088	ō105
58	1·0123	0140	0158	0175	0193	0210	0228	0245	0263	0280
59	1·0297	0315	0332	0350	0367	0385	0402	0420	0437	0455
60	1·0472	0489	0507	0524	0542	0559	0577	0594	0612	0629
61	1·0647	0664	0681	0699	0716	0734	0751	0769	0786	0804
62	1·0821	0838	0856	0873	0891	0908	0926	0943	0961	0978
63	1·0996	1013	1030	1048	1065	1083	1100	1118	1135	1153
64	1·1170	1188	1205	1222	1240	1257	1275	1292	1310	1327
65	1·1345	1362	1380	1397	1414	1432	1449	1467	1484	1502
66	1·1519	1537	1554	1572	1589	1606	1624	1641	1659	1676
67	1·1694	1711	1729	1746	1764	1781	1798	1816	1833	1851
68	1·1868	1886	1903	1921	1938	1956	1973	1990	2008	2025
69	1·2043	2060	2078	2095	2113	2130	2147	2165	2182	2200
70	1·2217	2235	2252	2270	2287	2305	2322	2339	2357	2374
71	1·2392	2409	2427	2444	2462	2479	2497	2514	2531	2549
72	1·2566	2584	2601	2619	2636	2654	2671	2689	2706	2723
73	1·2741	2758	2776	2793	2811	2828	2846	2863	2881	2898
74	1·2915	2933	2950	2968	2985	3003	3020	3038	3055	3073
75	1·3090	3107	3125	3142	3160	3177	3195	3212	3230	3247
76	1·3265	3282	3299	3317	3334	3352	3369	3387	3404	3422
77	1·3439	3456	3474	3491	3509	3526	3544	3561	3579	3596
78	1·3614	3631	3648	3666	3683	3701	3718	3736	3753	3771
79	1·3788	3806	3823	3840	3858	3875	3893	3910	3928	3945
80	1·3963	3980	3998	4015	4032	4050	4067	4085	4102	4120
81	1·4137	4155	4172	4190	4207	4224	4242	4259	4277	4294
82	1·4312	4329	4347	4364	4382	4399	4416	4434	4451	4469
83	1·4486	4504	4521	4539	4556	4573	4591	4608	4626	4643
84	1·4661	4678	4696	4713	4731	4748	4765	4783	4800	4818
85	1·4835	4853	4870	4888	4905	4923	4940	4957	4975	4992
86	1·5010	5027	5045	5062	5080	5097	5115	5132	5149	5167
87	1·5184	5202	5219	5237	5254	5272	5289	5307	5324	5341
88	1·5359	5376	5394	5411	5429	5446	5464	5481	5499	5516
89	1·5533	5551	5568	5586	5603	5621	5638	5656	5673	5691